ANSON SIMS
518 E. GREEN
352-1815

MANUFACTURING PROCESSES

NEW YORK · JOHN WILEY & SONS, INC. · London ·

4 TH
EDITION

MANUFACTURING
PROCESSES

MYRON L. BEGEMAN

Professor of Mechanical Engineering
The University of Texas

FOURTH EDITION

Fourth Printing, January, 1960

Copyright 1942, 1947, 1952, © 1957 by Myron L. Begeman

Library of Congress Catalog Card Number: 57-10801

Printed in the United States of America

Dedicated to
Hazel, Robert, and Jean

PREFACE

The purpose of this book is to provide for students of engineering a text which will give not only a basic knowledge of the materials and processes to be encountered in industry, but also some training in manufacturing operations. While these operations are often taught in large concerns, the necessary training is not always available for the bulk of the graduates entering small industries.

This book provides a comprehensive survey of manufacturing materials and processes. It can be useful to the practicing engineer and will aid the industrial worker who wishes to review some special phase of metal processing. Each topic is dealt with concisely. Line drawings, rather than photographs, have been used for a clearer visualization of each machine process, and the tables have been chosen carefully for the greatest usefulness and for future reference.

New chapters include Manufacturing Processes, Electroforming and Metal Coating Processes, and Metal Cutting. Chapters which have been rewritten to include much new material are those on Foundry Equipment and Procedures, Press Work, Plastic Molding, Inspection, and Drilling and Boring Machines. In all chapters emphasis has been placed on recent developments, and the text has been carefully revised to bring it up to date.

My deep appreciation goes to the many people who have contributed illustrative material, as well as helpful suggestions. I wish to especially acknowledge the assistance of Professor J. R. Holmes in preparing the line diagrams, Dr. John Gross in revising the chapter on Heat Treatment, and of colleagues who reviewed sections of the manuscript for accuracy.

Myron Louis Begeman

Austin, Texas
November 1956

CONTENTS

TABLES

CHAPTER 1

MANUFACTURING
PROCESSES

Since the first use of machine tools there has been a gradual, but steady, trend toward making machines more efficient by combining operations and by transferring more skill to the machine, thus reducing manual labor. To meet these needs, machine tools have become complex both in design and in control. Automatic features have been built into many machines, and some are completely automatic. This technical development has made it possible for industry to attain a high production rate with the accompanying low labor cost which is an essential development for any society wishing to enjoy high living standards.

Along with the development of production machines, the quality in manufacturing has been emphasized. Quality and accuracy in manufacturing operations demand that close dimensional control be maintained to turn out parts which are interchangeable and give the best operating service. For mass production any one of a quantity of parts must fit in a given assembly. A product made of interchangeable parts is quickly assembled, low in cost, and easily serviced. To maintain this dimensional control, appropriate inspection facilities must be provided.

Machine or Process Selection

Product manufacturing requires tools and machines that can produce economically as well as accurately. Economy depends to a large exent on the proper selection of the machine or process for the job that will give a satisfactory finished product. The selection is influenced, in turn, by the quantity of items to be produced. Usually there is one machine best suited for a certain output. In small-lot or jobbing-type manufacture, general-purpose machines such as the lathe, drill press, and planer may prove to be the best type since they are adaptable, have lower initial cost, require less maintenance, and possess the flexibility to meet changing conditions in the shop. However, a special-purpose machine should be considered when large quantities of a standardized product are to be produced. A machine built for one type of work or operation, such as the grinding of a piston or the surfacing of a cylinder head, will do the job well, quickly, and at low cost, requiring only the service of a semi-skilled operator.

Many of the special-purpose machines or tools differ from the usual standard type in that they have built into them some of the skill of the operator. A simple bolt may be produced on either a lathe or an automatic screw machine. The lathe operator must not only know how to make the bolt but must also be sufficiently skilled to operate the machine. On the automatic machine the sequence of operations and movements of tools are controlled by cams and stops, and each item produced is identical with the previous one. This "transfer of skill" into the machine makes possible the use of less skillful operators, but it does require greater skill in supervision and maintenance. Often it is not economical to make a machine completely automatic, as the cost may become prohibitive.

The selection of the best machine or process for a given product requires a knowledge of all possible production methods. Factors that must be considered are volume of production, quality of finished product, and the advantages and limitations of the various types of equipment capable of doing the work. Too much emphasis cannot be given to the fact that production can be by several methods, but usually there is one way that is most economical.

Manufacturing Processes

Most metal products originate as an ingot casting from one of the many ore-reducing or ore-refining processes. Molten metal by these processes is poured into metal or graphite molds to form ingots of convenient size and shape for further processing.

Manufacturing processes used in the working of metals may be classified as follows:

1. Processes used primarily to change the shape of metals:

(a) Casting.
(b) Forging.
(c) Extruding.
(d) Rolling.
(e) Drawing.
(f) Squeezing.
(g) Crushing.
(h) Piercing.
(i) Swaging.
(j) Bending.
(k) Shearing.
(l) Spinning.
(m) Stretch forming.
(n) Roll forming.
(o) Torch cutting.
(p) Electroforming.
(q) Powder metal forming.

In this group of processes material is changed into its primary form for some selected part. In certain cases the parts are suitably finished for commercial use, as in metal spinning, cold rolling of shafting, die casting, stretch forming of sheet metal, and drawing wire. In other cases, neither the dimensions nor the surface finish are satisfactory for the final product, and further work on the part is necessary. It should be noted that the last two processes, electroforming and the forming of powder metal parts, do not originate as a casting. Electroformed parts are produced by electrolytic deposition of metal onto a conductive preformed pattern. Metal is supplied from the electrolyte and a bar of pure metal which acts as an anode. Parts of controlled thickness, having high precision, can be made by this process. The method used in the production of powder metal parts is essentially a pressing operation. Metal powders are placed in a metal mold and compacted under great pressure. Most powder metal products also require a heating operation to assist in bonding the particles together.

2. Processes used for machining parts to planned dimensions:

(a) Turning.
(b) Planing.
(c) Shaping.
(d) Drilling.
(e) Boring.
(f) Reaming.
(g) Sawing.
(h) Broaching.
(i) Milling.
(j) Grinding.
(k) Hobbing.
(l) Routing.

In these secondary operations which are necessary for many products requiring close dimensional accuracy, metal is removed from the parts in small chips. Such operations are performed on machine tools which include the various power-driven machines used for the cutting of metal. All of these operate on either a reciprocating or a rotary-type principle: either the tool or the work reciprocates or rotates, as indicated in Figure 1. The planer is an excellent example of a reciprocating machine since the work reciprocates past the tool, which is held in a stationary position. In other machines, such as

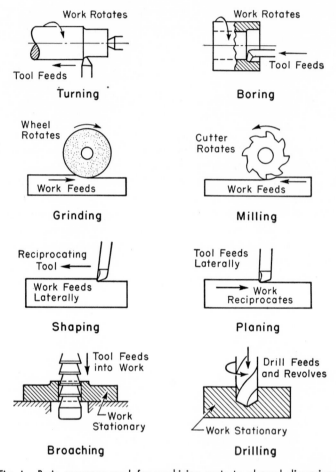

Fig. 1. Basic processes used for machining parts to planned dimensions.

the shaper, the work is stationary and the tool reciprocating. Rotary machines are exemplified by the lathe, which has the work rotating and the tool stationary. In the drill press it is the tool that is rotating.

Many of the machine tools can do a variety of machining operations, and all are capable of producing parts having close dimensional tolerance. The important factor is that the advantages and limitations of each be known so that an intelligent selection of the right machine can be made.

3. Processes used primarily to obtain a surface finish:

(a) Polishing.
(b) Abrasive belt grinding.
(c) Barrel tumbling.
(d) Electroplating.
(e) Honing.
(f) Lapping.
(g) Superfinishing.
(h) Metal spraying.
(i) Inorganic coatings.
(j) Parkerizing.
(k) Anodizing.
(l) Sheradizing.

In this group there are processes that cause little change in dimension and result primarily in giving the surface finish. Other processes, such as grinding, remove some metal and bring the part to a preplanned dimension in addition to giving it a good finish. In the processes such as honing, lapping, and polishing it is a matter of fitting and removing small scratches with little change in dimension. Superfinishing is also a surface-improving process which removes undesirable fragmented metal, leaving a base of solid crystalline metal. Plating and similar processes, used to obtain corrosion-resisting surfaces or just to give a better appearance, do not change dimensions materially.

4. Processes used in joining parts or materials:

(a) Welding.
(b) Soldering.
(c) Brazing.
(d) Sintering.
(e) Pressing.
(f) Riveting.
(g) Screw fastening.
(h) Adhesive joining.

Welding is the fusion or uniting of metal parts by heat. Soldering and brazing operations are similar except that the parts are joined by introducing a different metal between the two in a molten state. Sintering applies to the bonding of metallic particles by the application of heat. Structural adhesives in the form of powders, liquids, solids, and tapes are widely used in the joining of metals, wood, glass, cloth, and plastics.

5. Processes which change the physical properties of metals:

(a) Heat treatment.
(b) Hot working.
(c) Cold working.
(d) Shot peening.

Heat treating includes a number of processes which result in changing the properties and structure of metals. Although both hot and cold working of metals are primarily processes for changing the shape of metals, these processes have considerable influence on both the structure and the properties of the metal being worked upon. Shot peening renders many small parts, such as springs, resistant to fatigue failure.

Engineering Materials

In the design and manufacture of a product it is essential that the material as well as the process be understood. Materials differ widely in physical properties, machinability characteristics, methods of forming, and possible service life. The designer should consider these facts in selecting an economical material and a process which are best suited to the product.

Few metals used in industry exist as elements in nature. The natural compounds used, such as oxides, sulfides, or carbonates, must undergo a separating or refining operation before they can be further processed. Once separated, they must have an atomic structure which is stable at ordinary temperatures over a prolonged period. In metal working, iron is perhaps the most important natural element. Iron has little commercial use in its pure state, but when combined with other elements into various alloys it becomes the leading engineering metal. The nonferrous metals, including copper, tin, zinc, nickel, magnesium, aluminum, lead, and others, all play an important part in our economy, and each has specific properties and uses.

Further descriptions of the common engineering materials and their processing will appear in the following chapters, with particular emphasis given to their advantages and limitations.

Automation

Automation is a word, coined by the automotive industry, to indicate the application of automatic control to the operation of various basic machines. The control may include one machine or a series of machines, whatever is necessary to complete a series of operations in making a product. It may include loading the machines, transferring the product from one machine to another, inspection, and final ejection of the product from the machine. It has been defined in broad terms as ". . . manufacturing, processing or performing of services as automatically as economics permit or demand."[1]

Generally speaking, almost any machine or process can be made automatic. The extent to which this idea is carried out depends entirely on the economics of the situation. In one case a machine

[1] R. W. Bolz, "Automation to Date," address given at Michigan State University.

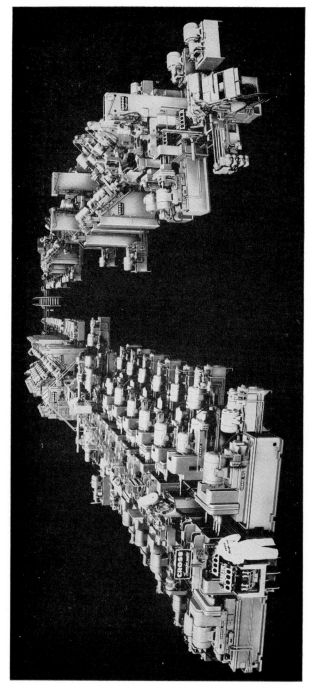

Fig. 2. Automated line, 350 feet long, performing 555 operations on V-8 cylinder blocks. The operations performed in this line include 265 drilling, 6 milling, 21 boring, 56 reaming, 101 countersinking, 106 tapping, and 133 inspection. Of the 104 stations there is one for loading, 53 for machining, 7 for part handling, 6 for mechanical inspection, 36 for visual inspection, and one for unloading. (Courtesy The Cross Company.)

may operate continuously over a long period of time, with the material coming to it automatically, whereas in another case an operator must load and unload the machine, which is automatic only to the extent that it performs a sequence of operations. Automatic screw machines, multiple-spindle automatics, and automatic lathes with magazine or hopper feed illustrate completely automatic machines.

When it is desirable to increase the number of operations above what could be done on a single machine, it becomes necessary to combine two or more machines. Standard machines may then be used with a conveyor or transfer unit between them to handle the part from one machine to the next. The problem of overall control and synchronization becomes very important as soon as it is necessary to mechanize the handling and co-ordinate it with the machine. In Figure 2 is shown an automated line involving a great amount of mechanization and co-ordination. Complete co-ordination, however, is not necessarily automation. Automation also implies self-correction such as the governor controlling the speed of an engine or the simple thermostat controlling the temperature in a house. On a machine doing a turning operation the feedback control would feed the tool in slightly if the diameter became too large. In other words, automation gives to the machine some power of choice or ability to correct itself if certain prescribed limits are exceeded. It is an extension of mechanization which implies complete automatic production of processes. Examples of this new development are found in all phases of manufacturing, but in most cases it is confined to the production of a single part.

CHAPTER 2

FOUNDRY EQUIPMENT

AND

PROCEDURES

With the gradual advancement of civilization to the present industrial age, castings have constituted a basic foundation for the development of mechanical processes. The field for cast parts is increasing constantly because scientific research has brought about applications and adaptations which hitherto were not considered within the scope of the castings industry.

Casting is the process of pouring molten metal into a mold and allowing it to solidify. By this process, intricate parts can be given strength and rigidity frequently not obtainable by any other method. Although all metals can be cast, iron is especially adaptable because of its fluidity, its small shrinkage, and the ease with which its properties can be controlled.

The *mold*, into which the metal is poured, is made of some heat-resisting material. Sand is most often used, as it is easily packed to shape, is somewhat porous, and resists high temperatures. Permanent molds of metal can be used for small castings, particularly those of nonferrous composition. In die casting, metal molds are used exclusively.

Sand molds are filled by pouring the molten metal into an opening at the top of the mold. Properly constructed passages allow the metal to flow to all parts of the mold by gravity. Permanent molds can be filled the same way, but in die casting the practice is to force the metal into the mold under pressure, either by compressed air or by an operating plunger. In centrifugal casting, the metal is introduced into the mold by gravity, additional pressure being obtained by centrifugal force.

Tools and Equipment for Molding

Small or medium-sized castings are made in a *flask*—a box-shaped container without top or bottom. It is made in two parts, held in alignment by dowel pins. The top part is called the *cope* and the lower part the *drag*. If the flask is made in three parts, the center is called a *cheek*. These flasks can be made of either wood or metals. Wood is the cheapest material, and wooden flasks can be quickly made, but they have the disadvantage of wearing out rapidly and of being destroyed by contact with hot metal. Metal flasks of steel, cast iron, magnesium, or aluminum alloys are widely used in production work because of their rigidity and permanence.

One type of flask often used in the production of small castings and in machine molding is the *snap flask*. This flask can be removed from the mold by releasing the latches at one corner and can be immediately used again. A steel slip jacket is placed over the mold to hold it together and to prevent breakage from pressure of the molten metal as it enters the mold. These jackets assist in holding the halves of the mold in proper alignment and eliminate difficulties caused by shifting of the cope. Being of steel, they are not seriously damaged by occasional contact with hot metal.

A *molding board* and a *bottom board* complete the flask. The molding board is a smooth board on which the flask and patterns are placed when the mold is started. It should be perfectly flat and well reinforced with cleats on the bottom. When the mold is turned over, the function of this board is ended; the mold is placed on a similar board, called a bottom board, which acts as a support for the mold until it is poured.

Before any metal is poured into a mold, it is necessary that the flask be clamped in some way to prevent the buoyant effect of the molten metal from lifting up the cope. Small molds are usually held down by flat cast-iron weights, placed on top of the molds. Larger flasks are held together by clamps, placed on the sides or ends—either U-shaped clamps held tight by driving wooden wedges under the end or clamps that can be quickly adjusted to fit the height of the flask.

A *gagger* is a small L-shaped metal accessory used in floor molds to help support hanging bodies of sand in the cope. It is used only in large molds having crossbars. The gagger is first coated with a clay wash and then placed next to one of the crossbars. The lower end should be close to the pattern, and the upper end should extend to the top of the mold.

The hand tools of a molder are few and need little explanation. A brief description of the most important tools is given here.

Riddle. A riddle of a standard mesh screen is used to remove lumps or foreign particles from the sand. Both hand and power riddles are available, the latter being used where large volumes of sand are involved.

Rammer. A hand rammer is used to pack the sand in the mold. One edge of the rammer, called the peen end, is wedge shaped; the other, called the butt end, is flat. Floor rammers are similar in construction but have long handles. Pneumatic rammers are used in large molds, saving considerable labor and time.

Bellows. Standard hand-operated bellows are used for blowing loose sand from the cavities and surface of the mold.

Trowel. Small trowels of various shapes are used for finishing and repairing mold cavities as well as for smoothing over the parting surface of the mold. The usual trowel is rectangular in shape and has either a round or a square end.

Slick. The principal hand tool for repairing molds is called a slick. It is a small double-ended tool having a flat on one end and a spoon on the other. This tool is also made in a variety of other shapes.

Lifter. Lifters are used for smoothing and cleaning out depressions in the mold. They are made of thin sections of steel of various widths and lengths with one end bent at right angles. A combination slick and lifter is known as a Yankee lifter.

Swab. This tool is used for moistening the sand around the edge before the pattern is removed. A simple swab is a small brush having long hemp fibers; a bulb swab has a rubber bulb to hold the water and a soft hair brush at the open end.

Draw spike or screw. The draw spike is a pointed steel rod, with a loop at one end. It is driven into a wood pattern to hold the pattern when it is withdrawn from the sand. The draw screw is similar in shape but threaded on the end to engage metal patterns.

Vent wire. This wire has a sharp point and is used to punch holes through the sand after it has been rammed. In this manner the mold is provided with vents which carry off the steam and gases generated by the hot metal in contact with the sand.

Gate cutter. This tool is a U-shaped piece of thin metal used for cutting a shallow trough in the mold to act as a passage for the hot metal.

Fig. 1. Large pit mold partially completed. (Courtesy Steel Founders' Society of America.)

Molding Processes

Molding practice in the ordinary commercial foundry may be classified according to (1) the *processes* used in making the mold or (2) the *type of material* of which the mold is made. Under the first heading we have the following divisions:

1. Bench molding. This type of molding is for small work, done on a bench of a height convenient to the molder.

2. Floor molding. When castings increase in size (with resultant difficulty in handling), the work is done on the foundry floor. This type of molding is used for practically all medium-sized and large castings.

3. Pit molding. Extremely large castings are frequently molded in a pit instead of a flask. The pit acts as the drag part of the flask, and a separate cope is used above it. The sides of the pit are brick lined, and on the bottom there is a thick layer of cinders with connecting vent pipes to the floor level. Since pit molds can resist pressures developed by the hot gases, this practice saves greatly on pattern expenses. Figure 1 shows a large pit mold partially completed.

4. Machine molding. Machines have been developed to do a number of the operations that the molder ordinarily does by hand. Ramming the sand, rolling the mold over, forming the gate, and drawing the pattern can be done by these machines much better and more efficiently than by hand. So far, no machine has been developed that is completely automatic.

Molds classified as to the materials commonly used are:

1. Green-sand molds. This most common method, consisting of forming the mold from damp molding sand, is used in most of the processes previously described. Figure 2 illustrates the procedure for making this type of mold.

2. Skin-dried molds. Two general methods are used in preparing the skin-dried molds. In one the sand, around the pattern to a depth of about ½ inch, is mixed with a binder so that when it is dried it will leave a hard surface on the mold. The remainder of the mold is made up of ordinary green sand. The other method is to make the entire mold of green sand and then coat its surface with a spray or wash which hardens when heat is applied. Sprays used for this purpose include linseed oil, molasses water, gelatinized starch, and similar liquid solutions. In both methods the mold must be dried either by air or by a torch to harden the surface and drive out excess moisture.

3. Dry-sand molds. These molds are made entirely from fairly coarse molding sand mixed with a binding material similar to those already mentioned. Since they must be oven baked before being used, the flasks are of metal. A dry-sand mold holds its shape when poured and is free from gas troubles due to moisture. Both the skin-dried and dry-sand molds are widely used in steel foundries.

4. Loam molds. Loam molds, like pit molds, are used for large work. The mold is first built up with bricks or large iron parts. These parts are then plastered over with a thick loam mortar, the shape of the mold being obtained with sweeps or skeleton patterns. The mold is then allowed to dry thoroughly so that it can resist the heavy rush of molten metal. Such molds take a long time to make and are not extensively used.

5. Metal molds. Metal molds have their principal use in the die casting of low-melting-temperature alloys. Castings are accurately shaped with a smooth finish, thus eliminating much machine work.

6. Special molds. Plastics, cement, plaster, paper, wood, and rubber are all mold materials used to fit particular applications. These are discussed in more detail in Chapter 5, Special Casting Methods.

Molding Sand

Silica sand (SiO_2), found in many natural deposits, is well suited for molding purposes because it can withstand a high temperature without decomposition. This sand is low in cost, has long life, and is available in a wide range of grain sizes and shapes. On the other hand, it has a high expansion rate when subjected to heat and has some tendency to fuse with the metal. If it contains a high percentage of fine dust, it can constitute a health hazard.

Pure silica sand is not suitable in itself for molding since it lacks binding qualities. The binding qualities can be obtained by adding 8 to 15% of clay. Some natural molding sands are adequately bonded with clay when quarried and need little alteration to make them suitable for use. Clay, when added to the sand and dampened by water, forms a mixture which becomes cohesive and is easily shaped into molds. Synthetic molding sands are made up of washed sharp-grained silica to which bentonite clay is added.

The size of the sand grains will depend on the type of work to be molded. For small and intricate castings the use of a fine sand is desirable so that all the details of the mold will be brought out sharply. As the size of the casting increases, the sand particles likewise should be coarser to permit the ready escape of gases that are generated in the mold.

Sharp, irregular-shaped grains are usually preferred because of their ability to interlock and add strength to the mold.

Good molding sand should be:

1. Refractory—to resist the high temperatures of the molten iron without fusing.

2. Cohesive, when moistened—to provide sufficient bond to hold together.

3. Porous or permeable—to permit the escape of gases and steam formed in the mold.

In addition to silica sand, zircon, olivine, and chamotte sands are coming into general use in foundries. *Zircon* ($ZrSiO_4$) is a cream-colored sand used principally for cores and facing sand. A fine sand with high heat conductivity, good refractory characteristics, and high density, it does not react with the molten metal. *Olivine* 2 (MgFe) $O \cdot SiO_2$, a green-colored sand found in large quantities in the Northwest, does not have high refractory characteristics and contains no free silicon; hence it poses no silicosis hazard. Made from calcined shale or flint clay by crushing and grading the lumps, *chamotte* has low expansion, low heat transfer, and is used satisfactorily with both iron and steel castings.

Molding Procedure

The procedure for molding a cast-iron gear blank is illustrated in Figure 2. The mold for this blank is made in the usual flask, which consists of two parts. The two parts are held in a definite relation to one another by means of pins on either side of the drag which fit into openings in angle clips fastened to the sides of the cope.

The first step in making a mold is to place the pattern on a *molding board,* which fits the flask being used. Next, the drag is placed on the board with the pins down, as shown in section *A* of Figure 2. Molding sand, which has previously been tempered, is then riddled in to cover the pattern. The sand should be pressed around the pattern with the fingers; then the drag should be completely filled. The sand is then firmly packed in the drag by means of a hand rammer. In ramming the sand around the sides of the flask, the peen end should be used first, additional sand being placed into the drag as the sand is packed down. The inside area of the drag is then packed down with the butt end of the rammer. The amount of ramming necessary can be determined only by experience. Obviously, if the mold is not sufficiently rammed, it will not hold together when handled or when the molten iron strikes it. On the other hand, if it is rammed too hard, it will not permit the steam and gas to escape when the molten iron comes into the mold.

After the ramming has been finished, the excess sand is leveled off with a straight bar known as a *strike rod.* In order to insure the escape of the gases when the casting is poured, small vent holes are made through the sand to within a fraction of an inch of the pattern.

The completed lower half of the mold is now ready to be turned over so that the cope may be placed in position and the mold finished. A little sand is sprinkled over the mold, and a bottom board placed on top. This board should be moved back and forth several times to insure an even bearing over the mold. The drag is then rolled over and the molding board removed, exposing the pattern. The surface of the sand is first smoothed over with a trowel

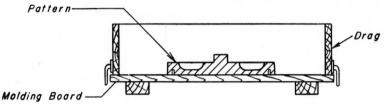

Section A — Pattern on Molding Board. Ready to Ram up Drag.

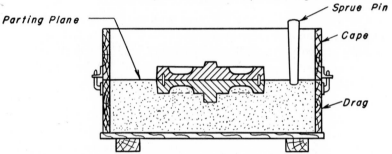

Section B — Drag Rolled over and Pattern Assembled Ready to Ram Cope.

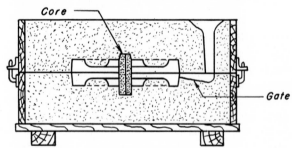

Section C — Mold Complete with Dry Sand Core in Place.

Fig. 2. Procedure for making mold.

and is then covered with a fine coating of dry parting sand. This is done to prevent the sand in the cope from sticking to the sand in the drag when the mold is separated to remove the pattern.

The cope is next placed on the drag, as shown in section *B* of

Figure 2, the pins on either side holding it in proper position. In order to provide a place for the iron to enter the mold, a tapered pin known as a *sprue pin* is placed approximately an inch to one side of the pattern. The operations of filling, ramming, and venting of the cope proceed in the same manner as in the drag.

The mold is now complete except for the removal of the pattern and the sprue pin. The sprue pin is first withdrawn and a funnel-shaped opening is scooped out at the top so that there will be a reasonably large opening in which to pour the iron. Next, the cope half of the flask is carefully lifted off and set to one side. Before the pattern is withdrawn, the sand around the edge of the pattern should be moistened with a swab so that the edges of the mold will hold firmly to-gether when the pattern is withdrawn. To loosen the pattern, a draw spike is driven into it and rapped lightly in all directions. The pattern can then be with-drawn by lifting up on the draw spike.

Finally, before the mold is closed again, a small passage known as a *gate* must be cut from the mold at the bottom of the sprue opening. The completed mold is shown in section *C*, Figure 2. This passage is shallowest at the

Fig. 3. Forming drag part of mold for bell casting. (Courtesy American Foundryman.)

mold, so that, after the iron has been poured, the metal in the gate may be broken off close to the casting. The mold surfaces may be sprayed, swabbed, or dusted with a prepared coating material. Such coatings often contain silica flour and graphite, but their composition varies considerably, depending on the kind of material being cast. The effect of a mold coating is to improve the surface finish of the casting and to reduce possible surface defects. When snap flasks are used, the flask is removed and a metal jacket placed around the mold. This permits the use of the same flask for other molds and eliminates the danger of having the hot iron burn the flask. Before the iron is poured into the mold, a weight should be put on top to keep it in place and to eliminate any tendency of the liquid iron to separate the cope and drag.

Molding procedure varies slightly, depending on the type of pattern used. For example, in Figure 3 is shown the drag part of a mold for a bell casting which is brought to shape by means of a sweep instead of a conventional-type pattern. Such patterns are cheap and well suited for molding symmetrical forms. Molding with match-plate patterns, which is done in most production work, differs in that the operator is relieved of much manual work.

Gates and Risers

The passageway for bringing the molten metal to the mold cavity, which is known as the *gating system,* is usually made up of a *pouring basin,* a downgate or vertical passage known as a *sprue,* and a *gate* through which the metal flows from the sprue base to the mold cavity. In large castings a *runner* may be used which takes the metal from the sprue base and distributes it to several gate passageways around the cavity. The purpose of this system is primarily to get the metal into the cavity. However, the design of the gating system is important and involves a number of factors.

1. Metal should enter the cavity with as little turbulence as possible, at or near the bottom of the mold cavity.

2. Erosion of the passageway or cavity surfaces should be avoided by properly regulating the flow of metal, or by the use of dry-sand cores. Formed gates and runners resist erosion better than those that are cut.

3. Metal should enter the cavity so as to provide directional solidification if possible. The solidification should progress from the mold surfaces to the hottest metal so that there is always hot metal available to compensate for shrinkage. This may be accomplished by pouring the metal into the top of the mold cavity, by the use of risers, or by *step gating.* The last method may be used for large castings and provides several gates at different elevations for bringing metal into the cavity, the hot metal always coming in at the top.

4. Slag or other foreign particles should be prevented from entering the mold cavity. A *pouring basin,* next to the top of the sprue hole, is often provided on large molds to simplify the pouring and to keep slag from entering the mold. Metal should be poured so that the pouring basin and sprue hole are filled all the time. *Skimming gates,* such as the one shown in Figure 4, may be used to trap slag or other light particles into the second sprue hole. The gate to the mold is restricted somewhat to allow time for the float-

ing particles to rise into the skimmer. A *strainer,* made of baked dry sand or ceramic material, can also be used at the pouring basin to control the metal flow and to allow only clean metal to enter.

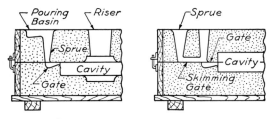

Fig. 4. Methods used in introducing metal to mold cavity.

Risers are often provided in molds to feed molten metal into the main casting cavity to compensate for the shrinkage. They should

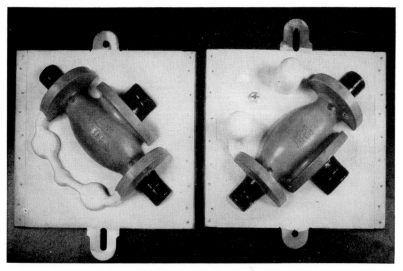

Fig. 5. Pattern with blind risers for supplying hot metal to casting during solidification. (Courtesy American Foundryman.)

be large in section, so as to remain molten as long as possible, and should be located near heavy sections that will be subject to heavy shrinkage. If they are placed at the top of the section, as shown in the figure, gravity will assist in feeding the metal into the casting proper. Risers also serve as a large vent for generated steam and gases and afford a place for collecting loose sand or slag.

Blind risers, as shown on the match plate in Figure 5, are also employed for feeding hot metal to the main casting during solidification. The domelike risers, found in the cope half of the flask, directly on the gate where the metal feeds into the mold cavity, will thus have the hottest metal when the pouring is complete.

Sand-Conditioning Equipment

Properly conditioned sand is an important factor in obtaining good castings. New sand as well as used sand must be properly prepared before it can be used. Proper sand conditioning accomplishes the following results:

1. It distributes the binder uniformly around the sand grains.
2. It controls the moisture content. It is important that all sand particle surfaces be moistened.
3. It eliminates foreign particles from the sand.
4. It aerates the sand so that it is not packed and is in proper condition for molding.
5. It delivers the sand at the proper temperature.

Because conditioning by hand is difficult, appropriate equipment is provided in most foundries for this purpose. A mixer for preparing the sand, shown in Figure 6, consists of a circular pan in which is mounted a combination of plows and mullers driven by a vertical shaft. This arrangement gives a shoveling action to the sand, turning it over on itself and lining it up in front of the mullers, which provide an intensive kneading and rubbing action. The result is a thorough distribution of the sand grains with the bonding material. After the sand is mixed, it is discharged through a door in the bottom of the pan. Both green sand and core sand may be prepared in this manner.

A representative sand-reclamation and conditioning installation is shown in Figure 7. As the molds are shaken out at the ends of the roller conveyor line, the sand falls through a grate onto a belt conveyor which is shown in the figure in phantom view. This conveyor carries the used sand to a smaller belt conveyor equipped with a magnetic separator. The sand is then discharged onto a bucket elevator, from which it goes through an enclosed revolving screen into the storage bin. It is delivered from this bin to one or more mullers, similar to the one shown in the previous figure, and conditioned for re-use. From here it is discharged to an overhead belt conveyor through an aerator which separates the sand grains and improves its flowability for molding. The cycle is complete when the sand is discharged into the several hoppers serving the molding stations.

The advantages of such sand conditioning for all classes of foundries have been demonstrated many times. Some of these advantages are economy of new sand and binder, close control, uniformity of sand condition, and low cost in preparing the sand; likewise, all the sand, or a considerable portion of it, is taken off

Fig. 6. Section view of Simpson intensive mixer for conditioning foundry sand. (Courtesy National Engineering Company.)

the floor, releasing this space for molding and other facilities. Such a system greatly improves the general operating conditions of the foundry. The units with overhead sand storage have high production of uniform high-quality castings, hold closely to tolerances and weights with a minimum of defects, and reduce cleaning labor to a minimum. The fact that all the sand in the system is mulled each time it is used, so that some is maintained virtually at facing grade, eliminates the preparation of special facing sands as such. It also is possible to reduce the number of grades of sand used for different types of work, one grade of sand ordinarily being adequate when properly reconditioned.

Fig. 7. Complete layout for handling molds and recycling the sand. (Courtesy National Engineering Company.)

Sand Testing

Periodic tests are necessary to determine the essential qualities of foundry sand. The properties change by contamination from foreign materials, by washing action in tempering, by the gradual change and distribution of grain size, and by continual subjection to high temperatures. Tests may be either chemical or mechanical; but aside from determining undesirable elements in the sand, the chemical tests are little used. Most mechanical tests are simple and do not require elaborate equipment.

Test for moisture content. Moisture content of foundry sands varies according to the type of molds being made and the kind of metal being poured. For a given condition there is a close range within which the moisture percentage should be held in order to produce satisfactory results. Any system of sand control should include a periodic check on moisture content, and complete records should be kept for future reference.

The most accurate method of moisture determination in molding sand is to dry out the sand and to note weights before and after. The *moisture teller* shown in Figure 8 contains electric-heating units and a blower for forcing warm air through the filter pan containing the sand sample. Fifty grams of tempered sand, accurately weighed, is placed in the pan. The timer for the blower is set for the required time to dry the sand (approximately 5 minutes), and air at 235 F is blown over and through the sand. By weighing the sand after it is dried and noting the difference in the initial and final readings, the percentage of moisture can be determined. The moisture content should vary from 2 to 8%, depending on the type of molding being done.

Permeability test. One of the essential qualities of molding sand is sufficient porosity to permit the escape of gases generated by the hot metal. This depends on several factors, including shape of sand grains, fineness, degree of packing, moisture content, and amount of binder present. Permeability is measured by the quantity of air that will pass through a given sample of sand in a prescribed time and under standard conditions. A permeability meter, meeting AFA Standard Testing Specifications, is shown in Figure 9. Additional pieces of equipment necessary for conducting the test are a sand rammer, a balance, and weights.

The permeability meter consists of an aluminum casting in the form of a water tank and a base. Inside the tank floats a balanced air drum which is sealed at the bottom by the water. The air tube

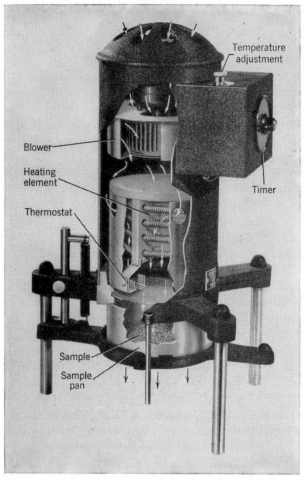

Fig. 8. Moisture teller for quick moisture tests of foundry sands. (Courtesy Harry W. Dietert Company.)

extending down to the specimen opens into the air space of the drum. The sand specimen is placed in the small cup at the base and is sealed with mercury. In taking a permeability reading, the observer may calculate the permeability by obtaining the time in seconds required for 2000 cc of air to pass through the specimen at constant pressure and dividing it into 3007.2. However, if the unit is furnished with an electric timer unit and equipped with a direct-reading dial, permeability values may be obtained by direct reading.

Permeability values are actual volumes of air that the sand will pass for a given pressure and time. The manufacturer of this equipment lists in Table 1 the permeability numbers that are satisfactory for various types of castings.

Fig. 9. Direct-reading meter for measuring green- and dry-AFA permeability of molding and core sands. (Courtesy Harry W. Dietert Company.)

TABLE I. Permeability Numbers

Castings	Permeability Number
Aluminum (light and medium)	8– 15
Brass (light)	8– 12
Brass (medium)	8– 20
Cast iron (light)	15– 65
Cast iron (medium)	65–100
Cast iron (heavy)	75–150
Malleable iron (light)	20– 50
Malleable iron (medium)	50–100
Steel (light)	100–150
Steel (medium)	125–200

Mold and core hardness test. The mold hardness tester shown in Figure 10 operates on the same principle as a Brinell hardness tester.[1] A spring-loaded (237 grams) steel ball 0.2 inch in diameter is pressed into the surface of the mold, and the depth of penetration is indicated on the dial in thousandths of an inch. The reading will not change, even with excessive pressure on the tester. Medium-rammed molds give a value around 50. Such a quick method of checking mold hardness is particularly useful in investigating mold uniformity and different machine settings. Mold hardness readings to be expected for the molding conditions listed are:

Fig. 10. Mold-hardness tester for measuring the surface hardness of green-sand molds. (Courtesy Harry W. Dietert Company.)

Soft-rammed molds	40
Medium-rammed molds	50
Hard-rammed molds	70

Clay-content test. The equipment necessary for determining the percentage of clay in molding sands consists of a drying oven, a balance and weights, and a sand washer. A small quantity of sand is thoroughly dried out, and a sample of 50 grams is selected and placed in a wash bottle. To this sand is added 475 cc of distilled water and 25 cc of a 3% caustic soda solution. This mixture is then stirred 5 minutes in a rapid sand stirrer or 1 hour if a rotating sand washer is used. Sufficient water is then added to fill the bottle up to a level line marked on the bottle, and, after settling for about 10 minutes, the liquid is siphoned off. The bottle is then refilled twice more and the siphoning operation repeated, time being allowed for the sand to settle. The bottle is finally placed in the oven; and, after the sand is dried out, a sample is weighed. The percentage of clay is determined by the difference in the initial and final weights of the sample.

Fineness test. This test, to determine the percentage distribution of grain sizes in the sand, is performed on a dried-sand sample from which all clay substance has been removed. A set of standard testing sieves is used having U. S. Bureau of Standard meshes 6, 12, 20, 30, 40, 50, 70, 100, 140, 200, and 270. These sieves are stacked and

[1] The Brinell test consists of indenting the surface of a metal specimen with a 10-mm hardened-steel ball by means of a predetermined load.

placed in one of the several types of motor-driven shakers. The sand is placed on the coarsest sieve at the top; and, after 15 minutes of vibration, the weight of the sand retained on each sieve is obtained and converted to a percentage basis.

To obtain the AFA fineness number, each percentage is multiplied by a factor as given in the following example. The fineness number is obtained by adding all the resulting products and dividing the total by the percentage of sand grain.

Example of AFA Fineness Calculation

Mesh	Percent Retained	Multiplier	Product
6	0	3	0
12	0	5	0
20	0	10	0
30	2.0	20	40.0
40	2.5	30	75.0
50	3.0	40	120.0
70	6.0	50	300.0
100	20.0	70	1400.0
140	32.0	100	3200.0
200	12.0	140	1680.0
270	9.0	200	1800.0
Pan	4.0	300	1200.0
Totals	90.5		9815.0

$$\text{Grain fineness number} = \frac{9815}{90.5} = 104$$

This number is a useful means of comparing different sands for uses in the foundry. A fineness check of sands should be made every month.

Sand-strength test. Several strength tests have been devised to test the holding power of various bonding materials in green and dry sand. Compression tests are the most common, although tension, shear, and transverse tests are sometimes used in strength investigations. Procedure varies according to the type of equipment used, but, in general, the tests are similar to those used for other materials. The fragile nature of sand requires special consideration in the handling and loading of test specimens.

A universal sand-strength machine is shown in Figure 11. This machine, consisting of a frame, on which is mounted a pendulum weight and a pusher arm, is motor driven, although hand operation may be used if desired. In testing green strength under compression, a cylindrical specimen of sand is placed between the pusher arm and the compression head of the pendulum weight. The compression load is applied by the motor at the rate of 7.5 pounds per 15 seconds. Pressure is continued until the specimen fails, at which time the compression value (indicated by a small magnetic bar) is read directly on the curved scale.

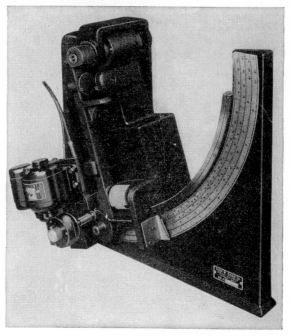

Fig. 11. Universal sand-strength machine. (Courtesy Harry W. Dietert Company.)

The tests just described are the ones most commonly used in sand control. In addition to these, there are several others used to check various properties. New sand may be given a sintering test to determine whether or not it has a tendency to burn onto the metal at high temperatures. Chemical analysis is frequently necessary in order to check the composition of sand grains, since some elements greatly reduce the refractory qualities of the sand. Strength at high temperatures and expansion coefficients of different sands can be determined to check the action of the sand in contact with hot metal.

Molding Machines

Machines can eliminate much of the hard work of molding and at the same time produce better molds. Molding machines, varying

considerably in design and method of operation, are named according
to the manner in which the ramming operation is performed. In
Figure 12 the various principles used in packing a mold are illustrated diagrammatically. The shading indicates the density or
uniformity of sand packing for each process involved. Machines
utilizing these principles are listed below.

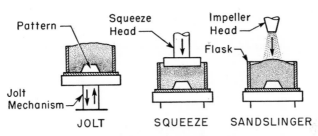

Fig. 12. Machine molding principles.

Jolt machine. The plain jolt molding machine, shown in
Figure 13, is equipped with adjustable flask-lifting pins to permit the
use of flasks of various sizes within the capacity of the machine. In
the operation of this machine the flask is raised a short distance by
the machine table and then dropped. This sudden action causes the
sand to be packed evenly about the pattern. The density of the sand
is greatest around the pattern and at the parting line and varies
according to the height of the drop or the depth of the sand in the
flask. The uniform ramming about the pattern gives added strength
to the mold and reduces the possibility of swells, scabs, or runouts.
Castings produced under such conditions will not vary in size or
weight. The lifting pins on the machine engage the flask and raise
it from the match plate after the mold is complete. Jolt machines
quite obviously can take care of only one part of a flask at a time
and are especially adapted to large work.

Squeezer machine. Squeezer machines press the sand in the flask
between the machine table and an overhead platen. Greatest mold
density is obtained at the side of the mold from which the pressure
is applied. Because it is impossible to obtain uniform mold density
by this method, squeezing machines are limited to molds only a few
inches in thickness.

Jolt-squeeze machine. Many machines, such as the one shown
in Figure 14, have used both the jolt and the squeeze principle.
To produce a mold on this machine, the flask is assembled with
the match plate between the cope and drag, and the assembly is

Fig. 13. Plain jolt flask lift-molding machine. (Courtesy The Tabor Manufacturing Company.)

placed upside down on the machine table. Sand is shoveled into the drag and leveled off, and a bottom board is placed on top. The jolting action then rams the sand in the drag. The assembly is turned over and the cope filled with sand and leveled off. A pressure board is placed on top of the flask, and the top platen of the machine is brought into position. By the application of pressure, the flask is squeezed between the platen and table, packing the sand in the cope to the proper density. After the pressure is released, the platen is swung out of the way. The cope is then lifted from the match plate while the plate is vibrated, after which the plate is removed from the drag. This machine eliminates six separate hand operations: ramming, smoothing the parting surface, applying parting sand, swabbing around the patterns, rapping the pattern, and cutting the gate.

Diaphragm molding machine. A recent development in molding machines utilizes a pure gum rubber diaphragm for packing the sand over the pattern contour as illustrated in Figure 15. The

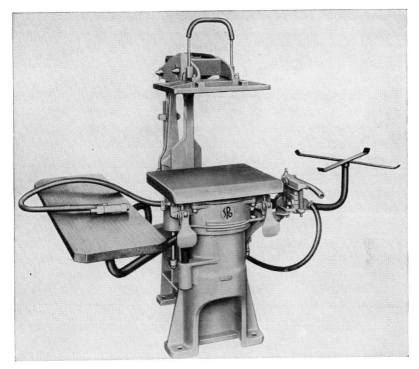

Fig. 14. Jolt squeeze molding machine. (Courtesy Spo, Incorporated.)

process uses the same air pressure to force the rubber diaphragm over the entire surface of the pattern, regardless of the pattern con-

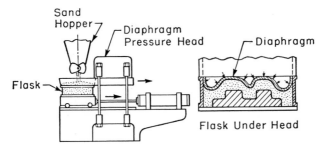

Fig. 15. Contour-diaphragm molding machine. (Courtesy Taccone Pneumatic Foundry Equipment Corporation.)

tour. This procedure results in a mold of uniform hardness throughout.

In the figure the flask is shown at the filling position. The flask and sand chute are then moved to the right under the diaphragm pressure head. Air is admitted to the pressure head and the diaphragm is forced against the molding sand in the flask with equal pressure over the entire area. The flask is then returned to its original position, striking off any sand above the flask. A pin lift removes the match plate from the flask. The entire process is very rapid, and close tolerances can be maintained due to the uniform packing of the sand.

Stripper-plate machine. Some patterns are difficult to withdraw without cracking or otherwise damaging the mold. To eliminate this trouble, stripper-plate machines may be used. One type of this machine is identical with the pin-type stripping machine except that a stripper plate, having the same outline as the pattern, supports the sand in the flask during the drawing operation. When the pins rise, they contact the stripper plate, which is lifted with the mold. In some machines the mold remains stationary, and the patterns are lowered through the stripper plate.

Jolt rollover pattern-draw machine. For large molds that are difficult to handle, machines (as shown in Figure 16) have been developed which roll the mold over and draw the pattern. The sand is first packed by jolting as shown in *a* of the figure. After the sand is leveled off, a bottom board is placed on the mold and clamped in position; then the assembly is rolled over. Part *b* of the figure shows the match-plate pattern withdrawn from the mold. This machine is used for separate cope or drag molding; in most cases the cavity is in the drag only.

Jolt-squeeze rollover machine. This machine is similar to the conventional jolt-squeeze molding machine, but has two arms which engage the flask after jolting and lift it a sufficient height so that it may be rolled over. The cope is then filled with sand and rammed by squeezing action, after which it is clamped by the two air clamps on the upper platen and drawn from the match plate. This lifting device handles the cope while the match plate is manually removed from the drag. When the mold is ready to be closed, the cope is swung back into position and the drag raised until the mold halves are together. This machine is designed to handle larger flasks than can be conveniently handled on the usual jolt-squeeze machine.

Sandslinger. Uniform packing of the sand in molds is an important operation in the production of castings. To accomplish this operation in a satisfactory manner, particularly for large molds, a mechanical device known as the sandslinger has been developed. Figure 17 shows a motive-type sandslinger, which is a self-propelled unit operating on a narrow-gage track. The supply of sand is carried

a   Flask and pattern in jolt position.

b   Pattern withdrawn from mold in rollover position.

Fig. 16.   Jolt rollover pattern draw machine.   (Courtesy Beardsley & Piper.)

Fig. 17. Motive-type sandslinger in operation. (Courtesy The Beardsley & Piper Company.)

in a large tank of about 300 cubic feet capacity, which may be re-filled at intervals by overhead handling equipment. A delivery belt, feeding out of a hopper on the frame at the fixed end, conveys the sand to the rotating impeller head. The impeller head, which is enclosed, contains a single, rotating, cup-shaped part which slings the sand into the mold. This part, rotating at high speed, slings over a thousand small buckets of sand a minute. The ramming capacity of this machine is 7 to 10 cubic feet, or 1000 pounds of sand per minute. The density of the packing can be controlled by the speed of the impeller head. For high production, machines of this type are available, having a capacity of 4000 pounds of sand per minute.

Similar machines can also be obtained either wih a tractor mounting or as a stationary unit. Tractor-type sandslingers travel along the sand piled on the floor and are used in foundries having no auxiliary sand-handling equipment. In addition to the ramming operation, these machines cut, riddle, and magnetically separate the sand from the scrap. The stationary machine is adapted to production work and must be served by sand preparation and conditioning equipment, as well as conveyors for removing the molds. Sand-slinger machines greatly increase foundry production and insure the uniform ramming of molds.

Cores

When a casting is to have a cavity or recess in it, such as a hole for a bolt, some form of *core* must be introduced into the mold. A core is sometimes defined as "any projection of the sand into the mold." This projection may be formed by the pattern itself or made elsewhere and introduced into the mold after the pattern is withdrawn. Either internal or external surfaces of a casting can be formed by a core.

Types of cores. Cores may be classified under two headings: *green-sand cores* and *dry-sand cores.* Figure 18 shows various types of cores. Green-sand cores, as shown in Figure 18*A,* are those formed by the pattern itself and made from the same sand as the rest of the mold. This drawing shows how a flanged casting can be molded with the hole through the center "cored out" with green sand.

Dry-sand cores are those formed separately to be inserted after the pattern is withdrawn but before the mold is closed. They are usually made of clear river sand, which is mixed with a binder and then baked to give the desired strength. The box in which they are formed to proper shape is called a *core box.*

Several types of dry-sand cores are also illustrated in Figure 18. At *B* is the usual arrangement for supporting a core when molding a cylindrical bushing. The projections on each end of the cylindrical pattern are known as *core prints* and form the seats which support and hold the core in place. A *vertical core* is shown at *C,* the upper end of which requires considerable taper so as not to tear the sand in the cope when the flask is assembled. Cores which have to be supported only at one end must have the core print of sufficient length to prevent the core from falling into the mold. Such a core, shown at *D,* is known as a *balanced core.* A core supported above and hanging into the mold is shown at *E.* This type usually requires a hole through the upper part to permit the metal to reach the mold. A *drop core,* shown at *F,* is required when hole is not in line with the parting surface and must be formed at a lower level.

In general, green-sand cores should be used where possible to keep the pattern and casting cost to a minimum. Separate cores naturally increase the production cost. *Core boxes* must be made, and the cores must be formed separately, baked, and properly placed in the

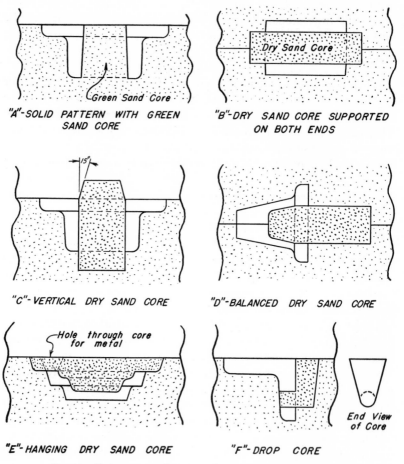

"A"-SOLID PATTERN WITH GREEN SAND CORE

"B"-DRY SAND CORE SUPPORTED ON BOTH ENDS

"C"-VERTICAL DRY SAND CORE

"D"-BALANCED DRY SAND CORE

"E"-HANGING DRY SAND CORE

"F"-DROP CORE

Fig. 18. Various types of cores used in connection with patterns.

molds. All of this adds to the molding cost. However, more accurate holes can be made with dry-sand cores, for they give a better surface and are less likely to be washed away by the molten metal.

In setting dry-sand cores into molds, adequate supports must be provided. Ordinarily, these supports are formed into the mold by the pattern; but, for large or intricate cores, additional supports in the form of *chaplets* (small metal shapes made of low-melting alloy) are placed in the mold to give additional support to the core until the molten metal enters the mold and fuses the chaplets into the casting. The use of chaplets should be limited as much as possible because of the difficulty in securing proper fusion of the chaplet with the metal.

Essential qualities for dry-sand cores. A core must have sufficient *strength* to support itself. Naturally this strength depends on the kind of sand and binding material used. Sharper grains of sand will bond together better and form a stronger core.

Porosity or permeability is also important consideration in the making of cores. As the hot metal pours over the cores, gases are generated by the heat's being in contact with the binding material, and provision must be made to carry away these gases. The size of the sand grain and its freedom from fines in between the grains largely determine its permeability. In addition to the natural porosity of the sand, it is usually advisable to vent the core as well. This may be done with an ordinary vent wire or, where two pieces go together to make up a core, the vent may be scraped out with the sharp corner of a trowel.

To insure a smooth casting, the core must have a *smooth surface*. This smoothness depends largely on the grain size of the sand, although the surface may be improved by coating the core with a thin mixture of water and plumbago. In the attempt to produce a smooth surface, care must be exercised not to go too far since permeability is lost as the fineness of the sand increases.

All cores must have sufficient *refractory* property to resist the action of the heat until the hot metal has found its place in the mold. Because sand naturally is very refractory, a binder must be selected that will stand the temperature required of the core. A thin coating of graphite or similar material adds considerably to its ability to withstand the intense heat momentarily. It must be kept in mind that it is not desirable to have the core remain hard after the metal has cooled; the binding material used should disintegrate or be burned out by the prolonged contact with the hot metal so that the core may be removed easily from the finished casting. This is also important from the standpoint of preventing shrinkage cracks during cooling.

Core making. The first consideration in making dry-sand cores is to mix and prepare the sand properly. If the binder is dry, it should be thoroughly mixed with the sand before any moisture is added. The mixture must be homogeneous so that the core will be of uniform strength throughout. All ingredients should be measured out exactly, and care should be taken not to get the mixture too wet. Wet material sticks to the tools and core box, causes the cores to sag before they are baked, and tends to produce a hard core. Large foundries generally use some sort of mechanical mixer.

The core is formed by being rammed into a core box or by the use of sweeps. Fragile and medium-sized cores should be reinforced with wires to give added strength to withstand deflection and the floating action of the metal. In large cores perforated pipes or arbors are used. In addition to giving the core strength, they also serve as a large vent.

When the cores are properly formed, they are placed on small metal plates which support them during the baking period. These plates are placed in the core oven and heated to a temperature ranging from 350 to 450 F, depending on the type of binder used. The actual process of baking consists of driving off the volatile matter and moisture that is in the core and then allowing sufficient time for the binder to become oxidized and hard. The color of the cores on emerging from the oven is a good index of their condition. The usual color for oil binders is a nut brown, whereas flour or similar binding materials produce a light brown. A burnt core is very dark and crumbles when handled.

One of the most critical stages in core making is the fitting of the cores after baking since many mistakes can be corrected at this point. If made in two parts, the fitting consists of procuring the halves of a core, scraping or filing the contact surfaces so that a perfect fit is obtained, venting by cutting a trough in each half, and finally gluing them together. A graphite or silica wash can be applied to the surface of the core to improve surface smoothness and to add to its refractory property. After the drying process, cores should again be inspected to insure a proper fit into the mold.

Binders and core mixtures. Among several types of binders used in making cores are those classified as oil binders. One of these, linseed oil, is frequently used in the making of small cores. The oil forms a film around the sand grain, which hardens when oxidized by the action of the heat. Such cores should be baked for 2 hours at a temperature between 350 and 425 F. A common mixture uses 40 parts of river sand and 1 part of linseed oil. An advantage of this core is that it does not absorb water readily and retains its strength in the mold for some time. A similar core oil having the following analysis has proved very successful: raw linseed oil, 42.5 to 45%; gum rosin, 27.5 to 30%, with the remainder, kerosene, water-white and acid-free. The gum rosin is also used to prevent the thinned oil from draining to the bottom of the core on standing. About a pint of this oil is required for 100 pounds of core sand.

In another group of binders, soluble in water, are found wheat flour, dextrin, gelatinized starch, and many commercial preparations. The ratio of binder to sand in these mixtures is rather high, being 1 to 8 or more parts of sand. Frequently a small percentage of old sand is used in place of new sand. Such mixtures are all moistened with water to the proper dampness for working, a temperature of about 350 F being sufficient to harden the cores. One mixture using wheat flour contains 1 part of flour, 6 parts of clean river sand, and 2 parts of molding sand. This should be mixed thoroughly and wet with a thin clay wash after baking. Another cereal binder, obtained from the corn-products industry, contains about 90% starch and 6% glucose. It is available in powdered form and, when used in the same proportions as an oil binder, produces a weaker and softer core.

In addition, pulverized pitch or rosin may be used. During the baking, these products melt and flow between the sand grains and, when cooled, form a very hard core. Both these binders melt at a temperature below 350 F. Such cores are not very refractory because of the rapid melting and consequent softening of the core when it comes in contact with the hot metal.

Several types of thermosetting plastics, including urea and phenol formaldehyde, are being successfully used as core binders. Binders of this type are made in both the liquid and powder form and are mixed with such other ingredients as silica flour, cereal binder, water, kerosene, and a parting liquid. Urea resin binders are baked at 325 to 375 F; and the phenolic binders, at 400 to 450 F. Both respond to dielectric heating and are completely combustible under the heat of the metal. Their success as core binders is based on their high adhesive strength, moisture resistance, burnout characteristic, and ability to provide a smooth surface to the core.

There are many other commercial binder preparations, the analyses of which are difficult to obtain, but most of them contain one or more of the afore-mentioned materials. No single binder can answer all the requirements in a diversified foundry.

Core-making machines. Cores can be made not only in hand-filled boxes, but also on a variety of molding machines, including many of the conventional types such as the jolt, squeeze, rollover, jolt-squeeze, and sandslinger machines. Pneumatic core-blowing machines also offer a rapid means of producing small and medium-sized cores in quantity production work. In this method sand is blown under pressure and at high velocity from the machine hopper into the core box. A machine of this type, together with a unit for rolling over core box and drawing core, is shown in Figure 19. When

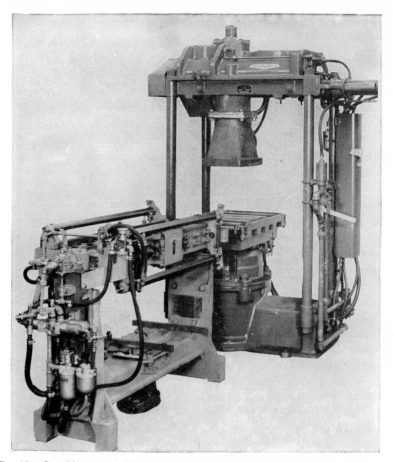

Fig. 19. Core-blowing machine with core rollover and draw machine. (Courtesy Osborn Manufacturing Company.)

set up for use, the blowing machine has a sand hopper above it, not shown in figure, which feeds sand to the reservoir and blow plate beneath.

In operation, the core box is placed on the table and clamped in position. The table and box are then raised, sealing the space between the blow plate and top of the core box. Compressed air, at pressures ranging from 100 to 120 pounds per square inch (psi), is introduced into the reservoir, forcing the sand through the small holes in the blow plate to the mold cavity. Suitable vents are built into the core box or blow plate to permit the air to escape. These vents must be small enough to resist any flow of sand through them, as their sole purpose is to relieve the air from the box. Their location plays an important part in successful core making, since they are used to direct the flow of sand to the desired parts of the core. A core box, filled in a few seconds, is then rolled from the machine onto the rollover draw machine. Here a drier plate is positioned and clamped over the core box. This assembly is then rolled over and the box automatically drawn from the core. During this operation, and while the operator places the drier plate with core on a rack, a second core can be made if a duplicate core box is available.

The holes in the blow plate are countersunk and vary in size from $\frac{3}{16}$ inch to $\frac{1}{2}$ inch in diameter. The larger holes are placed opposite the larger portions of the core; and the smaller ones, opposite small or restricted pockets that would not tend to fill from the main openings. Thus their size and position offer a means of controlling the flow of sand into the core-box cavities. No definite rule can be given concerning the number and size of holes, each installation being worked out in accordance with past experience.

Core boxes for this process should be made of metal. Cast iron, aluminum, and magnesium are the metals most commonly used. For medium-sized and large boxes it is economical to use the lighter alloys. All boxes must fit properly to avoid excess air leakage at parting lines. In addition, the outer surfaces should be machined to fit squarely in the clamping fixture.

Sand used in this process need not differ from that used in regular core making. It should, however, have good flowability and a minimum of moisture content. Sharp silica sand which has been thoroughly cleaned is recommended.

This type of equipment is especially adapted to production work and is limited to applications where the expense of metal core boxes is justified. It is rapid in its operation, and the cores produced are true to form, with excellent permeability.

Stock cores of uniform cross section may be produced continuously by an extrusion process. The machine consists of a hopper in which the sand is mixed. Below it in a horizontal position is a spiral screw conveyor which forces the prepared sand through a die tube at uniform speed and pressure. These machines require little skill in their operation and have an output of about 10 feet of core per minute.

Core baking. The purpose of baking a core is to harden the organic binder mixed with the sand and thus give it strength. In the baking operation the moisture is first driven off; then, as the temperature is increased, the binder surrounding the sand grains is chemically changed from a liquid to a solid. Temperature control is

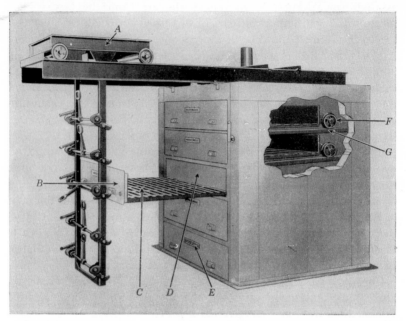

Fig. 20. Coleman drawer-type core oven. *A.* Trolley or drawer-puller. *B.* Insulated drawer front with lifting lugs. *C.* Place for cores. *D.* Rear plate to close opening. *E.* Time indicator. *F.* Drawer rollers. *G.* Rails to carry drawer. (Courtesy The Foundry Equipment Company.)

important, since overbaking causes loss in core strength and underbaking causes gases to be formed when the metal enters the mold.

The choice of a *core* oven depends upon the core size, type of binder used, and the quantity involved. Core ovens may be classified either as to their general design or as to the type of fuel used. From the design point of view, there are the shelf, drawer, rack, car, and continuous types. The last type may be further subdivided into vertical and horizontal arrangements. Gas has proved to be an excellent fuel because it is clean, easily controlled, and low in cost. An objection to its use is that it gives off some moisture. Other fuels, such as oil, coal, coke, and electric power, are all used and prove satisfactory under certain conditions. Dielectric heating, the placing of cores between electrodes charged with high-frequency current, has a limited use in the baking of cores with plastic binders.

The shelf-type oven is the simplest design. Cores are placed on core plates, which in turn are placed on the oven shelves. Temperature control is difficult, because much heat is lost each time the door is opened. The drawer type, as shown in Figure 20, is a better arrangement for conserving heat, as only one drawer is opened at a time during loading and unloading periods. Both kinds are used for small and medium-sized cores. The rack-type oven is similar except that the rack on which the cores are placed is portable. It may be conveniently loaded, adjacent to the coremaker's bench, and moved about with hand-lift trucks. This arrangement permits easy loading of the racks and saves much walking between the work station and oven. For very large cores and molds the car-type oven is best. Work of this type is placed on the cars by hoists and cranes, and the car is rolled into the oven.

Continuous ovens are those in which the cores are placed on some sort of a conveyor that moves them slowly through the ovens. They are especially adapted to drying out cores of approximately the same size since the time through the oven is constant for a given run. Loading and unloading is a continuous operation, and high production can be obtained from these furnaces. Vertical ovens of this type are widely used since they conserve floor space. A suspended tray-type elevator which holds the tray in a horizontal position at all times is the usual means of conveying the cores. Single-strand, horizontal designs are very flexible in that the overhead chain carrying the racks can be installed to pass the coremakers' benches, and it is not restricted to movements in either the horizontal or the vertical direction.

REVIEW QUESTIONS

1. What materials may be used for molds?
2. How do zircon and olivine sand differ from silica sand?
3. Under what conditions are snap flasks used?
4. List the hand tools of a molder, and give a brief description of each.
5. What are the various processes used in making molds?
6. How are skin-dried molds made, and for what type of work are they used?
7. What are the essential qualities of a good molding sand?
8. Briefly describe how a simple gear blank would be molded.
9. Show by sketch how a skimming gate is constructed.
10. Why are risers used on some molds?
11. Explain how pressure feeding of metal to the casting is obtained by the use of blind risers.

12. What is the usual procedure followed in a representative sand-reclamation-and-conditioning installation?

13. Describe the procedure for determining moisture and clay contents of molding sand.

14. How is the permeability of molding sand measured?

15. What factors must be considered in designing the gating system for a mold?

16. What are the various types of machines used for packing sand into molds?

17. Describe the operation of a jolt-squeeze molding machine.

18. What is a stripper-plate machine, and why is it used?

19. What is a sandslinger, and how does it operate?

20. What results are accomplished by properly conditioning the sand?

21. Name and sketch five kinds of cores.

22. What are the qualities that a dry-sand core should possess?

23. What type of plastics are used for core binders?

24. List and briefly describe the different types of core ovens.

REFERENCES

Barnett, C. A., "Modern Foundry Core and Mold Ovens," *American Foundryman,* May 1949.

Campbell, H. L., *Metal Castings,* John Wiley and Sons, 1936.

Cast Metals Handbook, 3rd edition, American Foundrymen's Association, 1944.

Dietert, H. W., "Processing Molding Sand," Charles E. Hoyt Annual Lecture, AFS, May 12, 1954.

Heine, R. W., and P. C. Rosenthal, *Principles of Metal Casting,* McGraw-Hill Book Company, 1955.

Laing, J., and R. T. Rolfe, *A Manual of Foundry Practice,* Sherwood Press, 1934.

Lincoln, R. F., "Fundamentals of Core Blowing," *Foundry,* February-March 1940.

Marek, C. T., *Fundamentals in the Production and Design of Castings,* John Wiley and Sons, 1950.

Steel Castings Handbook, Steel Founders' Society of America, 1950.

Wendt, R. E., *Foundry Work,* 4th edition, McGraw-Hill Book Company, 1942.

CHAPTER 3

PATTERNS
FOR CASTINGS

The first step in making a casting is to prepare a model, known as a pattern, which differs in a number of respects from the resulting casting. These differences, known as pattern allowances, compensate for metal shrinkage, provide sufficient metal for machined surfaces, and facilitate molding. A thorough understanding of these allowances is necessary for successful pattern design and construction.

Most patterns are made of wood because of its cheapness and ability to be worked easily; and since only a small percentage of patterns go into quantity production work, the majority do not need to be made of material that will stand hard usage in the foundry. Where durability and strength are required, patterns are made from metal, usually aluminum alloy, brass, or magnesium alloy. In large work, steel or cast-iron patterns may be preferred. A wooden master pattern must first be made from which the metal pattern is cast.

Before a pattern is made, the pattern maker must visualize from the blueprint what the casting will look like when completed and how it can best be molded. This preliminary estimate is important, since the molding expense in the foundry depends to a great extent on proper pattern construction. After the molding procedure and

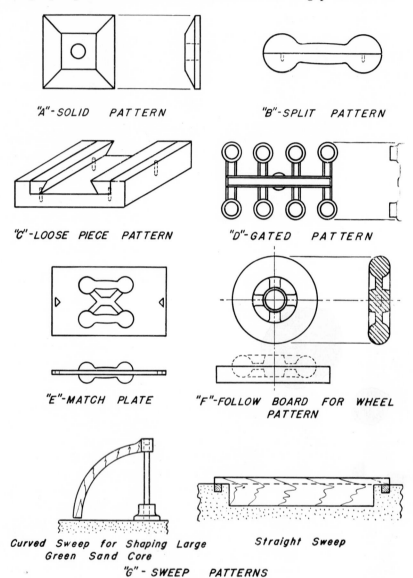

"A"- SOLID PATTERN   "B"-SPLIT PATTERN

"C"-LOOSE PIECE PATTERN   "D"-GATED PATTERN

"E"-MATCH PLATE   "F"-FOLLOW BOARD FOR WHEEL
                                                      PATTERN

Curved Sweep for Shaping Large   Straight Sweep
      Green Sand Core
                       "G" - SWEEP   PATTERNS
                    Fig. I. Types of patterns.

the general form the pattern will take have been decided upon, a layout of the pattern as it will be built is made. Such layouts are, in general, reproductions of the detail on the drawings submitted, laid out to full-size scale.

Types of Patterns

In Figure 1 are shown seven types of pattern construction. The simplest form is the solid or single-piece pattern shown at *A*. Many patterns cannot be made in a single piece because of the difficulties encountered in molding them. To eliminate this difficulty, some patterns are made in two parts, as shown in the figure at *B*, so that half of the pattern will rest in the lower part of the mold and half in the upper part. The split in the pattern occurs at the parting line of the mold. At *C* is shown a pattern with two loose pieces which are necessary to facilitate withdrawing it from the mold. The method of constructing this pattern is discussed later in connection with Figure 2. In production work where many castings are required, *gated* patterns, as shown in *D*, may be used. Such patterns are made of metal to give them strength and to eliminate any warping tendency. The gates or runners for the molten metal are formed by the connecting parts between the individual patterns. *Match plates* provide a substantial mounting for patterns and are widely used with machine molding. At *E* is shown such a plate, upon which are mounted the patterns for two small dumbbells. It consists of a flat metal or wooden plate, to which the patterns and gate are permanently fastened. On either end of such plates are holes to fit onto a standard flask. The *follow board,* which is shown at *F*, may be used with either single- or multiple-gated patterns. Patterns requiring follow boards are usually somewhat difficult to make as a split pattern. The board is routed out so that the pattern rests in it up to the parting line, and this board then acts as a molding board for the first molding operation. Many molds of regular shape may be constructed by the use of *sweep* patterns as illustrated at *G* in the figure. The curved sweep might be used to form part of the mold for a large cast-iron kettle and the straight sweep, for any type of groove or ridge. The principal advantage of this pattern is that it eliminates expensive pattern construction.

The pattern to be made for a given part depends largely on the judgment and experience of the pattern maker and is governed by the pattern cost and the number of castings to be made. When only a few castings are to be made, it is quite obvious that the pattern should be constructed in the cheapest manner possible. A single pattern, of wood construction, would best serve the purpose. Single wood patterns may also be used with economy in the production of large castings. Wood is a light material, and the pattern is easy to handle. Large castings are usually cast singly in a mold, and a multiple or gated pattern would only increase molding and casting difficulties. In large castings having a uniform symmetrical section there is a distinct saving in pattern cost if the sweep or skeleton type of pattern can be used. Practically all high-production work on molding machines uses the match-plate pattern. Aside from the fact that several castings may be molded simultaneously with the pattern of this type, there are also numerous savings effected by the machine molding. Although expensive to make, such patterns will last a long time under severe use.

Pattern Allowances

In pattern work one sometimes asks why a finished gear blank or any other object could not be used for making molds without the trouble and expense of making a pattern. In some cases they might be used, but, in general, this procedure is not practical.

Shrinkage. When any metal cools, it naturally shrinks in size. Hence, if the object or model itself were used for the pattern, the resulting casting would be slightly smaller than desired. To compensate for this possibility, a *shrink rule* must be used in laying out the measurements for the pattern. A shrink rule for cast iron is $\frac{1}{8}$ inch longer per foot than a standard rule, the average shrinkage for cast iron. If the gear blank was planned to have an outside diameter of 6 inches when finished, the shrink rule in measuring it 6 inches would actually make it $6\frac{1}{16}$ inches in diameter, thus compensating for the shrinkage. The shrinkage for brass varies with its composition but is usually close to $\frac{3}{16}$ inch per foot. For steel the shrinkage is $\frac{1}{4}$ inch per foot, and for aluminum and magnesium, $\frac{5}{32}$ inch per foot. These shrinkage allowance figures are only approximate and vary slightly, depending on the casting design, section thickness, and metal analysis.

When metal patterns are to be cast from original patterns, double shrinkage must be allowed. For example, if the metal pattern is to be made of aluminum and the resulting castings of cast iron, the shrinkage on the original wood pattern would have to be $\frac{5}{32}$ inch plus $\frac{1}{8}$, or $\frac{9}{32}$ inch per foot.

Draft. When a pattern is drawn from a mold, the tendency to tear away the edges of the mold in contact with the pattern is greatly decreased if the surfaces of the pattern, parallel to the direction it is being withdrawn, are given a slight taper. This tapering of the sides of the pattern, known as *draft*, is done to provide a slight clearance for the pattern as it is lifted up.

The amount of draft on exterior surfaces is about ⅛ to ¼ inch per foot. On interior holes which are fairly small the draft should be around ¾ inch per foot. These figures are influenced considerably by the size of the pattern and the method to be used in molding it. In allowing for draft, the usual practice is to add it to the pattern; that is, the top dimensions would be slightly larger than they would be if no draft were allowed.

Finish. When a draftsman draws up the details of a part to be made, each surface to be machined is indicated by a finish mark. This mark indicates to the pattern maker that additional metal must be provided at this point so that there will be some metal to machine. Surfaces of parts that have to be machined must be made thicker. The amount that is to be added to the pattern depends on the size and shape of the casting, but, in general, the allowance for small and average-sized castings is ⅛ inch. When patterns are several feet long, this allowance must be increased because of the tendency of castings to warp in cooling. It must be kept in mind that the term "finish" does not in any way apply to the sanding or finishing of the pattern itself.

Distortion. This allowance applies only to those castings of irregular shape which are distorted in the process of cooling as a result of metal shrinkage. A casting in the form of a letter U will contract at the closed end on cooling, while the open end will be held by the sand in fixed position. Hence, the legs of the U pattern should converge slightly so that, when the casting is made, the sides will be parallel. Such an allowance depends on the judgment and experience of the pattern maker, who knows the shrinkage characteristics of the metal.

Shake. When a pattern is rapped in the mold before it is withdrawn, the cavity in the mold is slightly increased. In an average-sized casting, this increase in the size can be ignored. In large castings or in ones that must fit together without machining, however, shake allowance should be considered by making the pattern slightly smaller to compensate for the rapping of the mold.

Method of Constructing a Solid Pattern

The details of a cast-iron V block are shown in Figure 2A. The first step in constructing this pattern is to make a layout of the part, taking into account the various allowances. Such a layout is shown in part B of the figure, where the end view is drawn first, using a shrink rule. As the detail calls for "finish" all over, an additional amount of metal must be provided which is shown by the second outline of the V block on the layout. In providing for the draft, consideration must be given to the method of molding the pattern. A slight tape, as shown at *D*, is provided on all vertical surfaces

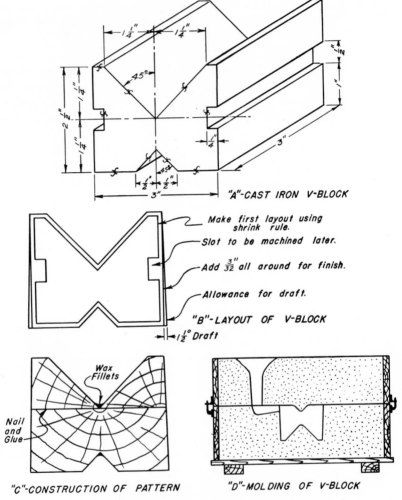

Fig. 2. Method of constructing and molding a cast-iron V block.

of the pattern to facilitate its removal from the sand. The final outline on the layout board represents the actual size and shape which is used for constructing the pattern.

The method of constructing the V-block pattern is shown at *C*. The three parts are nailed and glued together, and sharp interior corners are filleted to eliminate the tendency for metal shrinkage cracks to develop.

Pattern Construction Details

Fillets. A fillet is a concave connecting surface or the rounding out of a corner at two intersecting planes. In all castings sharp corners should be avoided. Rounded corners and fillets assist materially in molding, since there is less tendency for the sand to break out when the pattern is drawn. The metal flows into the mold more easily, and there is less danger of sand washing into the mold. The appearance of the casting is improved, and it is generally stronger, having fewer internal or shrinkage strains.

A casting in a mold cools on the outside first. As the cooling progresses to the center, the grains of the metal arrange themselves normal to the surface in a dendritic structure. In patterns that have sharp corners there is a tendency for the metal at the corners to open up because of shrinkage. In patterns with rounded corners this tendency is eliminated, and a sound casting is the result.

Fillets are made of wood, leather, metal, or wax. In lathe work the fillets can usually be taken care of in the turning. Wood fillets may also be used in other shapes; but, if they are made with a feather edge, they are quite fragile. For irregular shapes and patterns which are to be subject to considerable use, leather fillets have been found to be very satisfactory. They are cut to the desired length, laid face down on a flat surface, and brushed over with glue. They are then put on the pattern and rubbed into place, a fillet tool of the proper curvature being used. Wax fillets, in strips which have been extruded to proper shape, are often used on small work, because they are cheap and easy to apply. A strip is laid in a corner and formed into place by means of a fillet tool, the end of which has previously been heated. This heat melts the wax and forms it to the curve of the tool being used.

Section thickness. So far as service and design factors permit, all sections should be as uniform as possible. When light sections must be adjacent to heavy sections, the transition should be as gradual as possible since abrupt changes in thickness always result in strains which are likely to cause cracks in the casting. Solidification should normally progress from the points farthest from where the metal enters the gate and risers, and should be as uniform as possible.

Sanding and shellacking patterns. Because the best possible finish is desired on a casting, it is important that the pattern itself be carefully finished so as to produce a smooth mold. No special allowance is made for the sanding that is required prior to shellacking or varnishing. All that is necessary is to remove the tool marks and other slight irregularities on the wood surface. The sanding operation should always be the last. No tool work should be done later, because the cutting edge would be spoiled by the small particles of sand imbedded in the wood.

Shellac seems to be the best material for finishing patterns. It fills the pores of the wood, gives a smooth finish, and leaves a surface that is impervious to moisture. Three coats are usually required to give a good surface.

Pattern colors. Many foundries have a color scheme of their own for indicating the kind of metal to be cast, core prints, and the like. The following color scheme for all foundry patterns and core boxes of wood construction is recommended by the American Standards Association and is in general use:

1. Surfaces to be left unfinished are to be painted black.

2. Surfaces to be machined are to be painted red.

3. Seats of and for loose pieces are to be marked by red stripes on a yellow background.

4. Core prints and seats for loose core prints are to be painted yellow.

5. Stop-offs[1] are to be indicated by diagonal black stripes on a yellow base.

Material Used for Patterns

Wood. Although patterns are made from a variety of woods, white pine is a favorite because it is straight grained, light, and easy to work, and has little tendency to warp or check. When a more durable wood is necessary for fragile patterns or hard use, mahogany is preferred. Other woods suitable for patterns are cherry, beech, poplar, basswood, and maple, the last being especially desirable for work on the lathe. Lumber from mature trees is best for pattern work because the structure is more compact and less susceptible to shrinkage.

Before lumber can be used commercially, it must be dried or seasoned. This may be done by either natural or artificial means. Frequently both methods are used, the lumber being air-seasoned for a period of time and then kiln-dried. Kiln drying, which requires only a short time, reduces the moisture to a minimum, drives off

---

[1] A *stop-off* is a reinforcing portion of a pattern. It indicates that the cavity formed by that portion of the pattern is to be filled with sand or a core.

volatile matter in the wood, hardens the resin, and, to some extent, makes the wood less susceptible to future absorption of moisture. A minimum moisture content in wood is an advantage in pattern work, because the wood is in better condition for taking glue and shellac and is less likely to change in shape.

Metal. Many of the patterns used in production work are made of metal because of its ability to withstand hard use. Furthermore metal patterns do not change their shape when subjected to moist conditions and require a minimum of maintenance work to keep them in operating condition. Where limited production is desired, metal patterns are sometimes assembled on gates. The most important application of metal for pattern use is the making of production match plates. Small metal patterns are either mounted on or cast integrally with the plate.

Metals used for patterns include brass, white metal, cast iron, and aluminum. Aluminum is probably the best all-round metal because it is easy to work, light in weight, and resistant to corrosion. Pattern shops making principally metal patterns must of necessity use standard metal-working machines, described in later chapters.

Plastics. Plastics are especially well adapted for pattern materials because they do not absorb moisture, are strong and dimensionally stable, and have a very smooth surface. They can be produced economically by casting in a fashion similar to metal casting. Duplicate patterns can be made quickly, and the process of finishing them is rapid. Wood-working tools are used, and no protective coating is necessary on the pattern.

In the process of making a plastic pattern it is necessary first to make a master pattern which forms the mold into which the plastic resin is poured. These molds may be made of a variety of materials, including wood, rubber, plastics, metal, or plaster of Paris, the last two being the ones most commonly used. Plaster, although somewhat fragile, is simple to prepare. To facilitate parting, the mold should be coated with acid-resisting paint, followed by a light coating of wax. Upon completion, a phenol formaldehyde-type casting resin is poured into the mold.[2] It is then necessary to bake the mold at a temperature of about 140 F in order to cure and harden the resin.

The process[3] employed in making the plastic match plate shown in Figure 3 is somewhat different in that a bismuth-lead alloy (melting point 158 F) is sprayed onto the master pattern so as to form a

[2] C. R. Simmons, "Liquid Phenolic Resins for Casting," *American Foundryman*, May 1947.

[3] E. J. McAfee, "Making Plastic Patterns," *American Foundryman*, July 1947.

rigid shell mold about ⅛ inch thick. After both shell halves are complete, they are assembled in the flask and held in place either by ramming sand behind them or using plaster of Paris. After it has

been coated with a parting agent and necessary gates and risers provided, the mold is ready for casting the phenolic resins. If a match plate is desired, it is placed between the cope and drag with holes provided so the resins can flow through the plate as well as anchor the patterns to the plate.

Plaster. Gypsum cements are now available for patterns and core boxes. They have a high compressive strength and can be readily worked with wood tools. The cement is a high-expansion setting type and can be controlled to have setting expansions up to 0.02 inch per inch; thus the shrinkage

Fig. 3. Plastic match plate. (Courtesy
E. J. McAfee, Puget Sound Naval Shipyard.)

allowance of the metal can be provided for by this expansion. When the cement is mixed with water, it forms a plastic mass capable of being cast into a mold or formed to shape by sweeps or by template.

Wax or mercury. Both these pattern materials, used for precision castings, are described in Chapter 5, "Special Casting Methods."

Tools Used in Pattern Work

Although much of the work in making patterns is done with machine tools, skill in the use of hand tools is an essential accomplishment for a pattern maker. Most patterns of medium and large size are built up from small pieces of wood, necessitating considerable fitting and assembly work. In general, it can be stated that pattern work requires more skill and accuracy in the use of hand tools than other types of woodwork.

Indispensable also to the pattern maker are a number of machine tools which are great time savers and especially valuable in preparing stock and working large patterns. Chief among these are the band saw, circular saw, sander, jointer, planer, wood milling machine, combination tool grinder, and wood lathe. Care in the operation of all such equipment must be exercised because of the high speed involved.

Workability of Woods

The workability of wood depends upon such characteristics as specific gravity (hardness), moisture content, and the directional arrangement of the grains. It is difficult to rate one wood over another as far as machinability is concerned since the type of operation has considerable influence on the quality of the work. A wood excellent for turning may not be very good for planing. The moisture content is probably the most important factor to control; low moisture content (around 6%) results in better machining than a high moisture content.

The cutting speeds and feeds for the different woods, as well as the cutting angle of the tools, are also affected by these characteristics. In general the cutting speed of wood-working machines ranges from 4000 to 10,000 fpm. Since most wood-working machine cutters operate at a fixed speed, there is no opportunity for changing cutting speeds other than by changing cutter diameters. The amount of material removed and the finish are governed entirely by the feed

TABLE 2. Wood Cutting Speeds and Feeds

Machine	Spindle Speed or Cutting Speed	Range of Feed
Planers	3600–7200 rpm	20–90 fpm
Jointers	3600–5400 rpm	Hand
Lathes	Up to 4000 rpm	Hand or automatic
Borers	1200–3600 rpm	2–35 strokes per minute
Band saws	4000–9000 fpm	50–225 fpm
Circular saws (9 to 18 in. diameter)	2000–3600 rpm	50–300 fpm

and the depth of the cut. Cutting angles used in wood machining range from 5 to 30 degrees; most cutting angles, however, fall in the range of 15 to 25 degrees. There is little relation between wood hardness and the cutting angle used.

Cutting speeds and feeds for various wood-working machines are shown in Table 2.

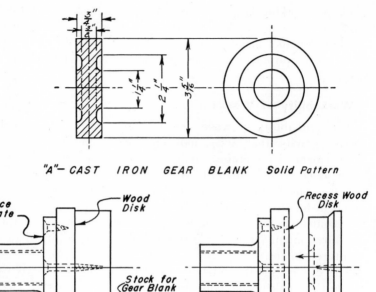

"A"— CAST   IRON   GEAR   BLANK   Solid Pattern

"B"—METHOD OF HOLDING   "C"—MOUNTING BLANK ON FACE
    STOCK ON FACE PLATE   PLATE FOR LAST OPERATION

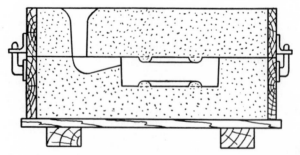

"D"— METHOD   OF MAKING AND MOLDING A SOLID
              PATTERN GEAR BLANK

Fig. 4. Construction and method of molding pattern for solid gear blank.

Construction of Typical Patterns

Solid gear pattern. Assume that a pattern for the gear blank shown in Figure 4 is to be turned. A face plate, as shown at *B*, is used for a pattern of this size. The pattern stock should be cut out slightly larger than the finished diameter on a band saw, and should be smoothed off, on one side, on the sander. The work should then be screwed to the wood face plate by one or more screws. With this mounting, most of the outside diameter and one side can be finished. A template should be provided to check the size of the recess in the pattern.

After this much of the pattern is made, it should be removed from the face plate. The face plate should then be recessed, as shown at C, so that the finished diameter of the gear blank fits in closely. This insures that the pattern will be fastened perfectly true, and concentric with the previous turning. The gear blank may now be completed in the same manner as the first half. The method of molding the gear blank in the foundry is shown at D.

Patterns with loose pieces. In some cases patterns have to be made with projections or overhanging parts so that it is impossible to remove them from the sand, even though they are parted. In such patterns the projections have to be fastened loosely to the main pattern by means of wooden or wire dowel pins. When the mold is being made, such loose pieces remain in the mold until after the pattern is withdrawn and are then drawn out separately through the cavity formed by the main pattern.

The use of loose pieces is illustrated in the pattern for a gib casting which fits over a dovetailed slide, a detail of which is shown in Figure 5.

In beginning this pattern it is necessary first to make a layout, with all allowances for draft, finish, and shrinkage. Next it should be decided how the pattern is to be molded. Two methods are possible, as illustrated at D and E of the figure. In the first method two loose pieces facilitate the withdrawal of the pattern from the sand. The main pattern is first withdrawn, leaving the two loose pieces in the sand. These pieces may then be withdrawn from the sand, owing to the additional space occupied by the main part of the pattern. The pattern constructed in this manner is made up of five pieces, as shown in the figure at B.

The loose pieces may be eliminated by using a dry-sand core. If such construction is desired, the pattern would then be made as shown at C. In addition, a core box would be necessary. This latter method is less economical because of the expense involved in making the core box and core.

Pattern and core box for jackscrew base. The detail for a jackscrew base is shown in Figure 6A. Such a pattern requires a rather long core print in order to balance and hold the dry-sand

core in place. A layout is first made to plan for the various allowances and to provide a working detail for the pattern and core box.
The completed pattern is illustrated at *B*. The body of the pattern
is made up of two pieces of stock assembled as shown at *C*. Dowel

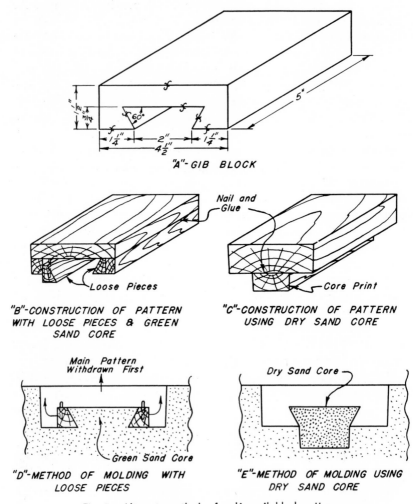

Fig. 5. Alternate methods of making gib-block patterns.

pins are located and drilled before the turning starts. At the completion of the turning, the two ends held by corrugated fasteners are
sawed off and the necessary draft sanded on the ends of the pattern.

The core box, shown at *D* and *E*, is designed to mold half the
core at a time. After being baked, the halves are assembled and

glued together. They are then ready for use in a mold. The two blocks which make up the main part of the box must have square

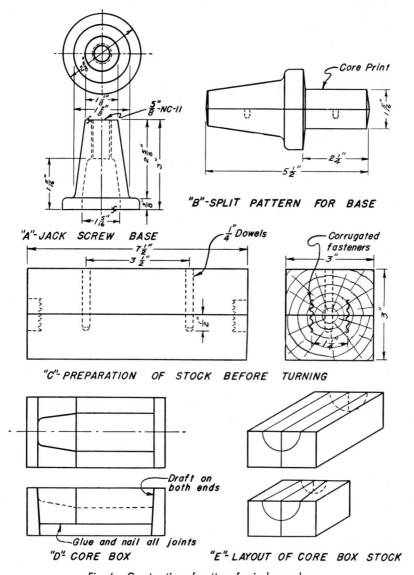

Fig. 6. Construction of pattern for jackscrew base.

sides and be carefully laid out as shown in the figure. The layout lines on each block represent the outline of the wood that is to be cut out. When this is done, the two blocks are assembled on a bottom board, and draft is provided at each end of the box by sanding. Any corner that becomes an inside corner in the casting should be filleted. The box is completed when both end pieces are put on.

REVIEW QUESTIONS

1. Why should a finished casting not be used as a pattern in making a mold?
2. Why are some patterns made in two parts?
3. What is a match plate, and for what type of work is it used?
4. What is the purpose of a follow board?
5. List and define the various allowances that must be considered in making a pattern.
6. How does a shrink rule differ from a standard rule?
7. What is meant by draft as applied to pattern work? Must all surfaces on a pattern have draft?
8. Why should fillets be used at connecting surfaces of a pattern?
9. Upon what characteristics does the workability of wood depend?
10. What is the accepted color scheme for use on wood patterns?
11. Why is wood seasoned, and how is it done?
12. How are plastic patterns made?
13. List the various materials used for making patterns.
14. List the essential wood-working machines for a pattern shop.
15. Briefly describe how a solid gear blank pattern is made.
16. Why are some patterns made with loose pieces?

REFERENCES

Benedict, O. Jr., *Manual of Foundry and Pattern Shop Practice,* McGraw-Hill Book Company, 1947.

Hanley, E. C., *Wood Pattern Making,* Bruce Publishing Company, 1924.

Harbison, C. B., "Designers Should Cooperate with Foundrymen," *Steel,* June 22, 1936, pp. 54, 56.

Holland, Kiley, *Pattern Design,* 1st edition, International Text Book Company, 1939.

McCaslin, H. J., *Wood Pattern Making,* 4th edition, McGraw-Hill Book Company, 1946.

Richards, W. H., *Principles of Pattern and Foundry Practice,* McGraw-Hill Book Company, 1930.

Ritchey, Monroe, Hall, Beese, *Pattern Making,* American Technical Society, 1946.

Tool Engineers Handbook, The American Society of Tool Engineers, McGraw-Hill Book Company, 1949.

CHAPTER 4

MELTING
AND
CASTING METALS

The principal raw material for all ferrous products is *pig iron,* the product of the *blast furnace.* Pig iron is obtained by smelting iron ore with coke and limestone, the final analysis depending primarily on the kind of ore used. The principal iron ores used in the production of pig iron are listed in Table 3.

TABLE 3. Iron Ores

Name	Symbol	Color	% Metallic Iron	Location
Hematite	Fe_2O_3	Red	70	Lake Superior District
Magnetite	Fe_3O_4	Black	72.4	N. Y., Ala., Sweden
Siderite	$FeCO_3$	Brown	48.3	N. Y., Ohio, Germany, England
Limonite	$Fe_2O_3X (H_2O)$	Brown	60–65	Eastern U. S., Tex., Mo., Colo., France

The metallic contents listed are those of pure ores. Most ore, however, contains impurities, and the metallic content is much less. Hematite is by far the most important ore used in the United States.

Vast quantities of *iron pyrite* (FeS_2) are available but are not used because of the sulfur content, which must be eliminated by an additional roasting process.

Blast Furnace

Figure 1 is a diagrammatic view of a blast furnace for producing pig iron. The average blast furnace is about 20 feet in diameter and around 100 feet in height. Daily capacities of such furnaces range from 600 to 1000 tons of pig iron per 24 hours. The raw materials—ore, coke, and limestone—are brought to the top of the furnace with a skip hoist and dumped into the double-valve hopper. The hot blast of air enters the furnace through *tuyères* placed around the furnace just above the hearth. As the coke burns, the ore is reduced by contact with the hot carbon monoxide gas. The limestone added with the charge combines with the gangue materials of the ore to render it into a fluid slag. Slag floats over the molten iron and is withdrawn at frequent periods; the iron is tapped at intervals of 4 to 6 hours. In addition to the equipment shown in the figure, there are three or four *stoves*—large cylindrical towers for preheating the air blown into the furnace. These stoves are heated by gas taken from the top of the blast furnace and passed through suitable cleaners to remove ashes. The remainder of the gas is washed and used for generating power and as fuel in other furnaces in the plant.

By regulation of operation conditions and proper selection of ore mixtures, the composition of the pig iron can be controlled. Common grades of pig iron produced in the United States are shown in Table 4.

TABLE 4. Classification of Pig Iron

Grade of Iron	Silicon	Sulfur	Phosphorus	Manganese
No. 1 Foundry	2.5 –3.0	Under 0.035	0.05–1.0	Under 1.0
No. 2 Foundry	2.0 –2.5	Under 0.045	0.05–1.0	Under 1.0
No. 3 Foundry	1.5 –2.0	Under 0.055	0.05–1.0	Under 1.0
Malleable	0.75–1.5	Under 0.050	Under 0.2	Under 1.0
Bessemer	1.0 –2.0	Under 0.050	Under 0.1	Under 1.0
Basic	Under 1.0	Under 0.050	Under 1.0	Under 1.0

Refining Process

As the pig iron comes from the blast furnace, some of it is poured into large hot-metal cars, with an approximate capacity of 100 tons,

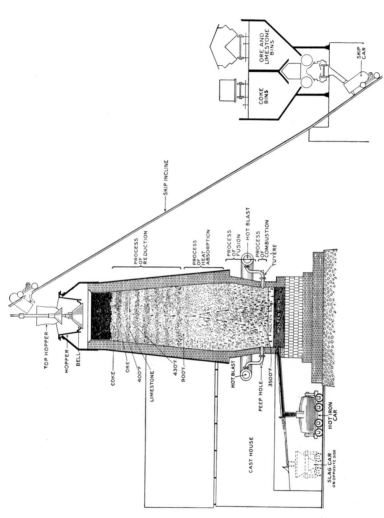

ORE AND
LIMESTONE
BINS

COKE
BINS

SKIP
CAR

SKIP INCLINE

PROCESS
OF
REDUCTION

PROCESS
OF
HEAT
ABSORPTION

PROCESS
OF
FUSION

HOT BLAST

PROCESS
OF
COMBUSTION

TUYÈRE

TOP HOPPER

HOPPER

BELL

COKE

ORE

400°F

LIMESTONE

430°F

900°F

HOT BLAST

PEEP HOLE

MOLTEN IRON

3500°F

CAST HOUSE

HOT IRON
CAR

SLAG CAR
ON OPPOSITE SIDE

Fig. I. Sectional view of a blast furnace. (Courtesy Bethlehem Steel Company.)

and transferred to steel-refining furnaces as indicated in Figure 2. Since much of it is to be used in remelting processes for the production of castings, it is cast into convenient sizes (around 100 pounds) on a pig casting machine. Whether remelting or refining, the operation is principally one of controlling or partially eliminating the

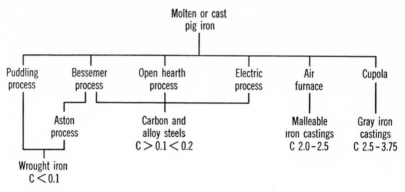

Fig. 2. Principal processes used for remelting or refining pig iron.

undesirable elements in the pig iron. In some cases more than one process is used to obtain the final product. The principal difference between cast iron, steel, and wrought iron is the carbon content. The approximate carbon limits for each are:

Cast iron	$C > 2.0\%$
Steel	$C < 2.0\%$, but $> 0.1\%$
Wrought iron	$C < 0.1\%$

Cast Iron

Cast iron is a general term applied to a wide range of iron-carbon-silicon alloys in combination with smaller percentages of several other elements. It is an iron containing so much carbon, or its equivalent, that it is not malleable. Quite obviously, cast iron has a wide range of properties, since small percentage variations of its elements may cause considerable change. Cast iron should not be thought of as a metal containing a single element, but rather as one having in its composition at least six elements. All cast irons contain iron, carbon, silicon, manganese, phosphorus, and sulfur. Alloy cast iron has still other elements which should not be thought of as impurities, for they all have important effects on the physical properties. Pure iron, known as ferrite, is very soft and has few uses in industrial work. All desirable properties, such as strength, hardness, and machinability, are controlled by regulating the elements other than ferrite in the cast iron.

Kinds of Cast Iron

1. Direct-iron castings. This iron, a product of the blast furnace, is usually known as pig iron. It is not suitable for most commerical castings until it has been remelted in a cupola or furnace of some other type. The output of iron from a blast furnace is so large that it would be difficult to provide sufficient commercial molds to take care of the output.

2. Gray iron. Gray iron is ordinary commercial iron, which is so called because of the grayish color of the fracture. This color is due to the carbon being principally in the form of flake graphite. Gray iron is easily machined and has a high compression strength, a low tension strength, and no ductility. The percentages of the several elements may vary considerably, but are usually within the following limits:

Carbon	3.00–3.50
Silicon	1.00–2.75
Manganese	0.40–1.00
Phosphorus	0.15–1.00
Sulfur	0.02–0.15
Iron	Remainder

Figures 3 and 4 are micrographs showing the structure of gray cast iron. If a specimen is polished and examined under the microscope, the appearance is as shown in Figure 3. The dark lines are small flakes of graphite which greatly impair the strength of the iron. The strength of cast iron is greater if these flakes are small, and uniformly distributed throughout the metal. Etching a specimen with a dilute solution of nitric acid results in the structure shown in Figure 4. The light-colored constituent appears to be steadite, a structural component in cast iron that contains phosphorus; the other new constituent is known as pearlite. *Steadite* can be identified by its white dendritic formation and is a eutectic structure of alpha iron and iron phosphide. Ferrite, or pure iron, also appears as a constituent of gray irons having a high silicon content, or irons that have been slowly cooled. *Pearlite* (composed of alternate lamellae of ferrite and iron carbide) is found in most irons and is similar to the pearlite found in carbon steels. This constituent adds to the strength and wear resistance of the iron. The dark graphite flakes may also be seen in this photomicrograph.

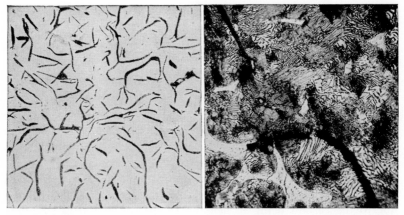

Fig. 3. Structure of gray cast iron (ASTM Class 40). Graphite flakes in unetched matrix. Magnification ×125.

Fig. 4. Structure of gray cast iron (ASTM Class 40). Etched in 5% nital showing graphite, pearlite, and steadite. Magnification ×562.

3. White iron. This iron shows a white fracture, which is due to the fact that the carbon is in the form of a carbide, Fe_3C. The carbide, known as *cementite,* is the hardest constituent of iron.

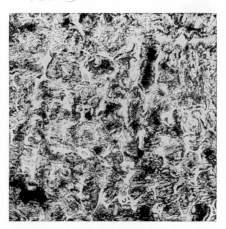

Fig. 5. Structure of white cast iron as cast. Etched in 5% nital showing pearlite and cementite. Magnification ×125.

White iron with a large percentage of carbide cannot be machined. The principal constituents shown in the micrograph (Figure 5) are cementite and pearlite. The dark area is the pearlite and the light area the cementite.

White cast iron may be produced by casting against metal chills or by regulating the analysis. Chills are used when a hard, wear-resisting surface is wanted for such products as car wheels, rolls for crushing grain, and jaw-crusher plates. The first step in the production of malleable iron is to produce a white-iron casting by controlling the analysis of the metal. One specification[1] for the production of these castings is as follows:

Carbon	1.75–2.30
Silicon	0.85–1.20
Manganese	Less than 0.40
Phosphorus	Less than 0.20
Sulfur	Less than 0.12
Iron	Remainder

4. Mottled cast iron. This is a product, intermediary between gray and white cast iron, the name again being derived from the appearance of the fracture. It is obtained in castings where certain wearing surfaces have been chilled.

5. Malleable cast iron. As in the production of white iron, malleable iron castings, when first cast, have all the carbon in the carbide form. Several types of furnaces, including the cupola, air furnace, and electric furnace, are utilized for producing malleable cast iron. Often two furnaces, such as the cupola and air furnace, are used together. This arrangement, known as duplexing, permits continuous pouring as well as more accurate control of the pouring temperatures and analysis of the metal. The castings obtained are packed in pots and placed in an annealing oven so arranged as to allow free circulation of heat around each unit. The annealing time lasts 3 to 4 days at temperatures varying from 1500 to 1850 F. In this process, the hard iron carbides are changed into nodules of *temper* or *graphitic carbon* in a matrix of comparatively pure iron, as shown in the micrograph in Figure 6. Malleable iron has a tensile strength of around 55,000 psi and an elongation of 18%. Malleable castings which have considerable shock resistance and good machinability are used principally by the railroad, automotive, pipe-fitting, and agricultural-implement industries.

6. Nodular iron. A high-strength high-ductility iron (Figure 7), having the carbon in the form of graphite nodules, is now being produced by adding a small amount of a magnesium-containing agent such as magnesium-nickel or magnesium-copper-ferrosilicon alloy to gray iron. The magnesium required to produce graphite depends on the amount of sulfur present. Sulfur is first eliminated by being converted to magnesium sulfide, additional magnesium present

[1] ASTM Specification A47–33, Grade 35018.

changing the graphite to the nodular form.   This type of iron is usually obtained in the as-cast condition; however, casting, followed by a short annealing period, is often employed to obtain certain required properties.   In this process, the time for annealing is much shorter than that used in the manufacture of malleable iron.   With

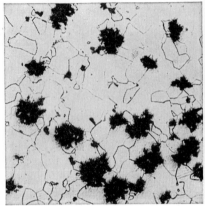

Fig. 6. Structure of malleable iron. Etched in 5% nital showing temper carbon in ferrite matrix. Magnification × 125.

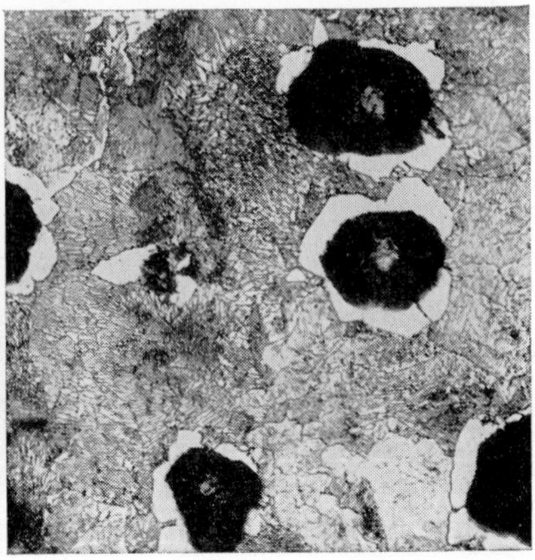

Fig. 7. Structure of nodular or ductile cast iron. Magnification × 250. (Courtesy The International Nickel Company, Inc.)

improved physical properties, this iron may be used for the casting of crankshafts and for miscellaneous parts in a wide variety of machines.

Effect of Chemical Elements on Cast Iron

Carbon.   Although any iron containing over 2.0% carbon is in the cast-iron range, gray cast iron has a carbon content of 3 to 4%. The amount depends on the carbon content in the pig iron and scrap used and that absorbed from the coke during the melting process. The final properties of the iron depend not only on the amount of carbon but also on the form in which it exists.   The formation of graphitic carbon depends on slow cooling and on the silicon content. High silicon promotes the formation of graphitic carbon.   Carbon in this state acts as a softener for the iron, reduces the shrinkage, and gives the iron machinability.   The strength of the iron increases with the percentage of carbon in the combined form.

Silicon.   Silicon up to 3.25% is a softener in iron and is the predominating element in determining the amounts of combined and graphitic carbon. It combines with iron that otherwise would combine with carbon, thus allowing the carbon to change to the graphitic state. After an equilibrium is reached, additional silicon unites with the ferrite to form a hard compound. Hence, silicon above 3.25% acts as a hardener. In melting, the average loss of silicon is about 10% of the total silicon charged into the cupola. High silicon content is recommended for small castings and low for large castings. When it is used in percentages from 13 to 17, an alloy having acid and corrosion resistance is formed.

Manganese. Manganese in small amounts does not have an appreciable effect, but in amounts over 0.5% it combines with sulfur to form a manganese sulfide. The mixture has a low specific gravity and is eliminated from the metal with the slag. It acts as a deoxidizer as well as a purifier and increases the fluidity, strength, and hardness of the iron. If the percentage is increased appreciably over the usual amounts, it will promote the formation of combined carbon and rapidly increase the hardness of the iron. Of the manganese originally charged, 10 to 20% is lost in the melting process.

Sulfur. There is nothing good to be said for sulfur in cast iron. It promotes the formation of combined carbon, with accompanying hardness, and causes the iron to lose fluidity, with resultant blow holes. Sulfur gets into the iron from the ore and also from the coke during the melting process. Each time the iron is remelted there is a slight pickup in sulfur, frequently as much as 0.03%. To counteract this increase, manganese should be added to the charge in the form of ferromanganese briquettes and spiegeleisen.

Phosphorus. Phosphorus increases the fluidity of the molten metal and lowers the melting temperature. For this reason phosphorus up to 1% is used both in small castings and in those having thin sections. Large castings should have low phosphorus content since additional fluidity in the iron is not required. There is a slight increase in strength and shock resistance as the percentage increases with little change in the phosphorus content during the melting process, although in some calculations it is assumed that there is a pickup of about 0.02%. The action of any remelting process upon phosphorus is principally one of concentration, because this element does not oxidize readily except under special conditions. In order to control this element, care should be exercised in selecting the grade of scrap to be used.

Phosphorus also forms a constituent known as *steadite,* a mixture of iron and phosphide, which is hard, brittle, and of rather low melting point. It contains about 10% phosphorus, so that an iron with

0.50% phosphorus would have 5% steadite by volume. Steadite appears as a light, structureless area under the microscope but may appear as a network if sufficient phosphorus is present.

Cupola

Description. Iron castings are made by remelting scrap along with pig iron in a furnace called a cupola. The construction of this furnace is simple, consisting of a vertical stack lined with a refractory material, with provisions for introducing an air blast near the bottom. A cross section of a cupola is shown in Figure 8, with the principal parts labeled.

The entire cupola rests on a circular plate, which is supported above the floor by four columns, suitably spaced so that the hinged bottom doors can swing freely. In operation, these doors are swung into horizontal position and held in place by a vertical prop. The charging door is located about halfway up the vertical shell, and the top of the cupola is open except for a metal shield or spark arrester.

The openings for introducing the air to the coke bed are known as *tuyères*. Usual practice is to have a single row around the circumference of the wall, although some large cupolas have two rows. The tuyères, flaring in shape, with the large end on the inside to cause the air to spread evenly, are placed fairly close together to obtain as nearly uniform air distribution as possible. The number of tuyères varies with the cupola diameter, ranging from four, on small cupolas, to eight or more on large installations, the combined area of the inlets being roughly one fourth of the cross-sectional area of the cupola. Normally, the bottom plate of the iron tuyère casting is about 20 inches above the bed of the cupola, although this height will vary according to whether the type of operation is intermittent or continuous. A shallow hearth is satisfactory for long heats, since less coke is required.

Surrounding the cupola at the tuyères is a wind box or jacket for the air supply. Small windows covered with mica are located opposite each tuyère so that conditions in the cupola can be inspected. The air blast, furnished by a positive displacement or centrifugal type of blower, enters the side of the wind jacket.

The opening through which the metal flows to the spout is called the tap hole. Opposite the pouring spout at the rear of the cupola is another spout for slag disposal. This opening is a few inches below the tuyères to prevent slag running into them and also to prevent possible chilling of the slag by the air blast.

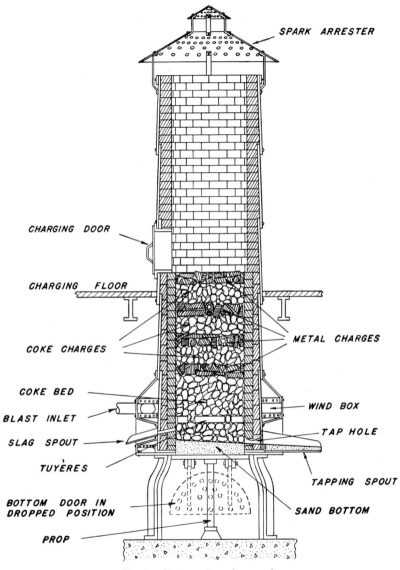

SPARK ARRESTER

CHARGING DOOR

CHARGING FLOOR

METAL CHARGES

COKE CHARGES

COKE BED

BLAST INLET

WIND BOX

TAP HOLE

SLAG SPOUT

TUYÈRES

BOTTOM DOOR IN
DROPPED POSITION

TAPPING SPOUT

SAND BOTTOM

PROP

Fig. 8.   Cross section of a cupola.

Preparing and charging. The first operation in preparing a
cupola is to clean out the slag and refuse on the lining and around
the tuyères from the previous run.   Care must be exercised in doing
this so as not to damage the refractory lining.   Any bad spots or
broken bricks are repaired with a daubing mixture of fire clay and

silica sand or ganister. Brick and clay in the breast are removed preparatory to rebuilding it with new materials. After the lining is repaired, the bottom doors are swung into position and the prop placed under them. All cracks are closed with fire clay, and a layer of black molding sand is placed on the bottom. This sand is rammed down and given a slope towards the spout, the depth being not less than 4 inches at the lowest point. The breast opening at the spout is made up of a mixture of fire clay and sand, or a separate breast brick can be used. A small tap hole about $\frac{3}{4}$ to 1 inch in diameter is provided.

The firing of a cupola is started $2\frac{1}{2}$ to 3 hours before the first metal is to be tapped. Kindling wood is thrown in the charging door after a few flat pieces are placed on the bottom to protect the packed sand. A sufficient amount of wood should be used to ignite a bed of coke. All the tuyères are open when the fire is started, and only a natural draft is used. Coke is added from time to time until the bed is built up to its proper height above the tuyères. The height of the bed coke is important, as it determines the height of the melting zone and affects both the temperature and oxidation of the metal. Another controlling factor is the pressure of the air blast, as with increased pressure a higher bed is necessary. Depending on the afore-mentioned conditions, the bed height may range from 20 to 50 inches above the top of the tuyères. The height of the bed should be gaged by dropping a gage bar from the charging door to coke level.

As soon as the coke bed is thoroughly ignited, the pig iron and scrap may be charged. The alternate charges of coke and iron are made in a ratio of 1 part of coke to 8 or 10 parts of iron, measured by weight. The ratio depends on the heating value of the coke, the size of the iron pieces making up the charge, and metal temperature desired. A ratio of 1 to 8 probably represents average practice. The size of the charge depends on the diameter of the cupola and also on the amount of coke that is necessary to provide sufficient heat for the charge. In general, a uniform layer thickness of 6 to 8 inches is used between each charge. By calculating the weight of the coke necessary for this layer and knowing the coke—iron ratio, the weight of the iron charge may be obtained. If the coke layer in a small cupola weighs 60 pounds, the iron charge will be 480 pounds.

In addition to charging iron and coke, a fluxing material should be used if the runs are to be long. The object of adding a flux is to remove impurities in the iron, protect the iron from oxidation, and render the slag more fluid for easy removal from the cupola.

Limestone ($CaCO_3$) is the principal fluxing material, although fluorspar (CaF_2) and soda ash (Na_2CO_3) are also used. This material is applied over the coke charges in small lumps not exceeding 2 inches in diameter. Although limestone is cheaper, fluorspar gives the slag more fluidity. Experience has proved that about 75 pounds of limestone should be used per ton of iron. Frequently fluorspar is added in a ratio of 1 to 2 or 3, replacing part of the limestone. The amount of fluxing materials is subject to considerable variation, depending on the amount of coke ash formed and the cleanness of the metal. Slag that is formed floats on the metal accumulated on the hearth and flows continuously from the slag hole at the rear of the cupola during the heat.

After the cupola is fully charged up to the charging door, the iron should soak in the heat about three-fourths of an hour or longer. No forced draft is used during this period, the only draft coming from the tuyère peep holes and the spout opening. Before turning on the blast, the tuyère openings should be closed. After the blast has been on a few minutes, molten metal starts accumulating in the hearth. The tap hole is then stopped up until a sufficient amount of molten metal is accumulated in the cupola to warrant pouring operations. During operation the cupola should be kept filled to the charging door by addition of successive charges, as rapidly as room is provided by the settling of the material. This is important, for the settling of the charges permits a rapid escape of the gases, and the iron that is charged loses the advantage of this heat. The length of a heat may be as much as 16 hours, although most runs last only a few hours.

Intermittently the tap hole of the cupola is opened, allowing the metal to flow into a large ladle. It is then closed again with a conical clay plug called a *bot*. This procedure is repeated until all the metal is melted and poured. At the end of the run, the blast is shut off and the prop under the bottom doors knocked down, allowing the remains in the cupola to drop to the floor. The bed of hot iron, slag, and coke is quenched with water as quickly as possible and removed from beneath the cupola. Any coke or iron in the remains is salvaged and taken into account in the cupola calculations for the heat.

Cupola air supply. The amount of air required to melt a ton of iron depends on the quality of coke and the coke—iron ratio. Theoretically, 113 cubic feet of air at 14.7 psi and at 60 F is required for one pound of carbon. For other operating conditions some correction should be made to get the correct volume of air. For coke, the previous figure should be reduced slightly to compensate for the ash content. Assuming a 1 to 8 ratio, we find that 250 pounds of coke is required to melt one ton of iron. Multiplying 250 by 105 gives 26,250 cubic feet of air, required to melt one ton. Actually, in practice perfect combustion is not obtained, and a larger volume of air is required. A value of 30,000 cubic feet of air per ton of iron is frequently used in estimating the capacity of a blower.

The pressure of the blast to be maintained will depend on the size of the cupola, compactness of the charge, kind of iron being melted, and the temperature. Small cupolas may require a pressure of only 5 to 8 ounces; large cupolas may operate as high as 28 ounces. No definite rule for pressure can be laid down; the proper value can be obtained only by actual operating experience.

The best type of blower for cupola operation is the positive-displacement type, because it delivers a constant volume of air to the cupola, irrespective of changing furnace conditions. In making calculations a small air-slippage loss should be taken into account. This loss is a known value for a given blower. Variations in capacity are obtained by speed regulation. With centrifugal blowers the volume to the cupola varies according to the pressure in the wind jacket, which in turn is affected by the height of charge and other conditions in the cupola. Volume may be controlled by a gate in the blast line connected with suitable electric controls. The regulation is obtained by changing the power input of the motor driving the blower.

Hot-blast type. Combustion in the cupola may be appreciably improved by preheating the air as is done in regenerative-type melting furnaces. One method removes the stack gases from the cupola just below the charging door and completes their combustion in a furnace adjacent to the cupola. Incoming air goes through a preheater in this furnace and then into the wind box of the cupola at a temperature around 600 F. The other method preheats the air in a separate external furnace and does not attempt to reclaim any heat from the cupola operation. One advantage of this method is that the hot blast is ready as soon as the cupola is started. Both methods improve the melting rate and save appreciably on the amount of fuel required.

Calculation of cupola charge. Careful consideration must be given to the materials charged into a cupola if a uniform product is desired from day to day. Raw materials vary in composition, and there are also changes that take place during the melting operation. For some elements (silicon and manganese) there is a definite percentage loss due to oxidation. Carbon also has a loss due to oxidation, but this is compensated for by absorption from the coke. Sulfur does not suffer any loss from oxidation and actually picks up additional amounts from the coke. There is little change in the phosphorus content. Most cupolas operate on a fairly large percentage of return scrap, which is close to the desired analysis. In computing a charge, however, both return and new scrap must be included as well as the various grades of pig iron. The following problem illustrates the procedure involved in calculating a charge.

Problem. Given the following materials to work with, what would the final iron analysis be, using cupola melting? Assume a 3000-pound charge made up of metals of the following composition:

Iron	Carbon	Silicon	Manganese	Phosphorus	Sulfur
No. 1 pig iron	3.5	2.50	0.72	0.180	0.016
No. 2 pig iron	3.5	3.00	0.63	0.120	0.018
New cast-iron scrap	3.4	2.30	0.50	0.200	0.030
Returns from foundry	3.3	2.50	0.65	0.170	0.035

The material is to be used in the following proportions: no. 1 pig—10%; no. 2 pig—20%; returns—40%; new scrap—30%.

(*a*) Carbon content; oxidation loss = gain from coke

No. 1 pig	$3000 \times 0.10 \times 0.035 =$	10.5 lb
No. 2 pig	$3000 \times 0.20 \times 0.035 =$	21.0 lb
New scrap	$3000 \times 0.30 \times 0.034 =$	30.6 lb
Returns	$3000 \times 0.40 \times 0.033 =$	39.6 lb
		101.7 lb

$$\text{Per cent carbon} = \frac{101.7}{3000} \times 100 = 3.39$$

(*b*) Silicon content; oxidation loss = 10%

No. 1 pig	$3000 \times 0.10 \times 0.025 =$	7.5 lb
No. 2 pig	$3000 \times 0.20 \times 0.030 =$	18.0 lb
New scrap	$3000 \times 0.30 \times 0.023 =$	20.7 lb
Returns	$3000 \times 0.40 \times 0.025 =$	30.0 lb
		76.2 lb

$$\text{Per cent silicon} = \frac{76.2 - (76.2 \times 0.10)}{3000} \times 100 = 2.28$$

(*c*) Manganese content; oxidation loss = 20%

No. 1 pig	$3000 \times 0.10 \times 0.0072 =$	2.16 lb
No. 2 pig	$3000 \times 0.20 \times 0.0063 =$	3.78 lb
New scrap	$3000 \times 0.30 \times 0.0050 =$	4.50 lb
Returns	$3000 \times 0.40 \times 0.0065 =$	7.80 lb
		18.24 lb

$$\text{Per cent manganese} = \frac{18.24 - (18.24 \times 0.2)}{3000} \times 100 = 0.49$$

(d) Phosphorus; oxidation loss = 0

No. 1 pig	3000 × 0.10 × 0.0018 =	0.54 lb
No. 2 pig	3000 × 0.20 × 0.0012 =	0.72 lb
New scrap	3000 × 0.30 × 0.0020 =	1.80 lb
Returns	3000 × 0.40 × 0.0017 =	2.04 lb
		5.10 lb

$$\text{Per cent phosphorus} = \frac{5.10}{3000} \times 100 = 0.17$$

(e) Sulfur; oxidation loss = 0. Gain from coke is approximately 4% of sulfur in coke.

No. 1 pig	3000 × 0.10 × 0.00016 =	0.048 lb
No. 2 pig	3000 × 0.20 × 0.00018 =	0.108 lb
New scrap	3000 × 0.30 × 0.00030 =	0.270 lb
Returns	3000 × 0.40 × 0.00035 =	0.420 lb
		0.846 lb

Assuming a coke to iron melting ratio of 1 to 8 and a coke with a sulfur content of 0.50%, we have

$$375 \times 0.005 = 1.875 \text{ lb of sulfur}$$
$$\text{Pickup } 4\% = 0.075 \text{ lb}$$

$$\text{Then per cent sulfur} = \frac{0.846 + 0.075}{3000} \times 100 = 0.0307$$

Advantages and limitations. The cupola has been used extensively for many years because of its simplicity of construction and economy in operation. It melts iron continuously at a high production rate, requiring a minimum of maintenance.

However, when metal is melted in contact with the fuel, some elements are picked up while others are lost. This affects the final analysis of the metal and necessitates close regulation of the cupola. Also, close temperature control is difficult to maintain.

Air Furnace

The air or reverberatory furnace shown in Figure 9 has been widely used for the production of malleable-iron and high-test gray-iron castings. Early furnaces were hand-fired with bituminous coal, but most furnaces of today use pulverized coal or oil. Charging is done through the roof of the furnace by removing sections of the arch called *bungs*. This furnace lends itself to close control, since the metal can be tested at intervals. Furthermore, the metal is not in contact with the fuel as it is in the cupola furnace; and the analysis, particularly the carbon content, can be held to close limits. Since the initial and operating costs of this furnace are higher than those of a cupola, the air furnace does not have wide application except for malleable-iron castings. Capacities of these furnaces range from 5 to 50 tons per heat.

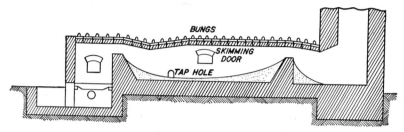

Fig. 9. Air furnace.

Wrought Iron

Wrought iron is a ferrous metal containing less than 0.1% of carbon with 1 to 3% of finely divided slag, distributed uniformly throughout the metal. It has been produced for many centuries by a variety of processes, the two in use today being the *puddling process* and the *Aston process*. The latter came into prominence in the nineteen-twenties and today accounts for most of the tonnage of wrought iron.

In the hand puddling process, pig iron and iron scrap were melted in a small, reverberatory, 500-pound capacity *puddling furnace* fired with coal, oil, or gas. Most of the elements were removed by oxidation, since they came in contact with the basic refractory lining of the furnace. This process was subsequently improved by using mechanical puddling furnaces of greatly increased capacities and by eliminating much of the hand labor of stirring and gathering the metal into large balls. Freed from impurities, the product was removed from the furnace as a pasty mass of iron and slag, and then mechanically worked both to squeeze out the slag and to form it into some commercial shape.

The Aston process melts the pig iron in a cupola and refines it in a Bessemer converter. The blown metal is then poured into a ladle (known as a *shotting*) containing a required amount of slag previously prepared in a small open-hearth furnace. Since the slag is at a lower temperature, the mass solidifies rapidly, liberating the dissolved gases with sufficient force to blow the metal into small pieces. These pieces settle to the bottom of the ladle and weld together as sponge iron. Each ball of iron collected in the ladle weighs 3 to 4 tons, and the rate of production is about one every

5 minutes. A chemical analysis[2] of wrought iron produced by this process is as follows:

Element	Per cent
Carbon	0.02
Silicon	0.15
Manganese	0.03
Phosphorus	0.12
Sulfur	0.02
Slag	3.00 (by weight)
Iron	Remainder

The grain structure of a piece of polished and etched wrought iron is shown in Figure 10. The particles of slag may be seen as dark streaks running through the metal.

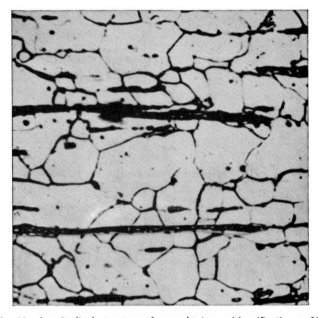

Fig. 10. Longitudinal structure of wrought iron. Magnification × 200.

The principal use of this metal is in the production of pipe and other products subjected to deterioration by rusting, such as those used in shipyards, railroads, farms, and oil companies. Advantages other than its resistance to corrosion include ease of welding, high ductility, and ability to hold protective coatings.

[2] J. Aston and E. B. Storey, *Wrought Iron*, A. M. Byers Company, Pittsburgh, Pa., 2nd edition, 1950.

Steel Castings

Steel is a crystalline alloy of iron, carbon, and several other elements, which hardens when quenched above its critcal temperature. It contains no slag and may be cast, rolled, or forged. Carbon is an important constituent because of its ability to increase the hardness and strength of the steel. Steel castings may be classified as follows:

STEEL CASTINGS*

1. Carbon steel
   (a) Low carbon (less than 0.20%).
   (b) Medium carbon (0.20 to 0.40%).
   (c) High carbon (over 0.40%).

2. Alloy steel
   (a) Low alloys (special alloying elements totaling less than 8.0%).
   (b) High alloys (special alloying elements totaling over 8.0%).

* Cast Metals Handbook, American Foundrymen's Association.

Medium-carbon-steel castings are used most frequently in the carbon-steel range. They have ductility and good tensile strength in a normalized condition, ranging from 60,000 to 80,000 psi. The range of chemical composition is as follows:

MEDIUM-CARBON—STEEL CASTINGS

Carbon	0.20–0.40
Manganese	0.50–1.00
Silicon	0.20–0.75
Phosphorus	0.05–maximum
Sulfur	0.06–maximum
Ferrite	Remainder

Alloy castings may contain special elements in addition to those already listed, or they may have more than the usual percentage of some normal element. Special elements frequently added to foundry steel are aluminum, nickel, chromium, cobalt, molybdenum, vanadium, and copper. Steels alloyed with silicon and manganese, both normal constituents, are also frequently used. A great variety of steels is possible in this range, differing widely in strength, resistance to corrosion, high temperatures, and abrasion.

A microstructure of a medium-carbon cast steel is shown in Figure 11. The light areas are ferrite and the dark areas, pearlite. The grain structure of most cast steels is large because of the high casting temperature of the metal combined with relatively slow cooling.

Fig. II. Structure of medium-carbon cast steel. Magnification ×200.

This defect can be remedied by subsequent heat treatment. For the production of steel castings, four types of furnaces are used:

1. Open hearth (both acid and basic).
2. Electric (arc and induction).
3. Crucible.
4. Converter (acid).

The largest tonnage is produced in basic open-hearth furnaces illustrated in Figure 12. Because of the large capacities of these furnaces, ranging from 25 to 100 tons, this process is used principally for large castings. The basic process is preferred to the acid process, because phosphorus can be controlled and sulfur can be partially eliminated.

Although electric-arc furnaces are used principally for the production of steel and alloy-steel castings, they are also used, to a limited extent, for high-test iron castings. Both *direct-arc* and *indirect-arc* furnaces are used. In the direct-arc furnace, shown in Figure 13, the current passes from the electrode to the metal, through the metal, and back to the electrodes or the hearth. Indirect-arc furnaces have horizontal electrodes above the metal which heat by radiation. Heating costs for electric furnaces are higher than for other furnaces, but this increase may be counteracted to some extent by using low-priced materials in the furnace charges. Electric furnaces lend themselves to close temperature control, and the analysis of the metal may be held to accurate limits. The direct-arc electric furnace is primarily a remelting furnace, using steel scrap as the raw material. The acid type of furnace is used when the raw material

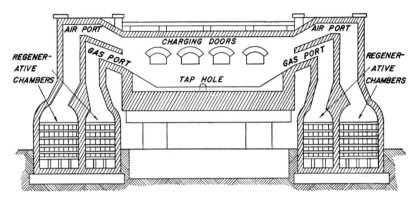

Fig. 12. Open-hearth furnace.

does not contain high phosphorus or sulfur. Foundry furnaces of this type, ranging in capacity from $\frac{1}{2}$ ton to 10 tons per heat, are used for medium-sized and small steel castings.

The crucible process is the oldest process for making steel castings, but it is little used today. Wrought iron, washed metal, steel scrap, charcoal, and ferro-alloys constitute the raw materials for this process. These materials are placed in crucibles having a capacity of about 100 pounds and are melted in a regenerative furnace.

In making steel castings from a converter, liquid metal or cupola iron is poured into the converter, and the heat for the

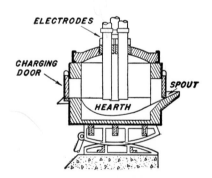

Fig. 13. Direct-arc furnace.

refining operation is produced by blowing air through the molten metal. The result is the oxidation of the silicon, manganese, and carbon. Side-blower converters, as shown in Figure 14, are used in foundry work and have a capacity of about 2 tons. Both the converter and the crucible process have largely been replaced by electric-arc and induction furnaces.

Electric induction furnaces, as shown diagrammatically in Figure 15, are used primarily in the production of alloy-steel castings because of the accurate control of melting conditions and composition. These furnaces, invented by Mr. E. F. Northrup in 1916, are of the coreless, induction type. High-frequency current is supplied to the primary water-cooled coil surrounding the crucible, inducing a heavy secondary current in the charge. The resistance of this current soon melts the charged metal and brings it to a pouring temperature. Current

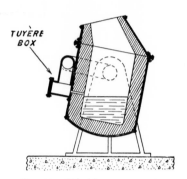

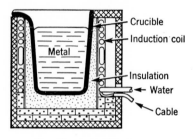

Fig. 14. Side-blower converter.   Fig. 15. Induction furnace.

may be supplied to the furnace from spark gap converters having a frequency range from 20,000 to 80,000 cycles or from motor-generator sets operating up to 25,000 cycles. Induction furnaces range in capacity from a few pounds to 4 tons and are capable of melting either ferrous or nonferrous metals.

Since the pouring temperature for steel castings is 2900 to 3200 F, it is necessary to use a highly refractory and permeable sand. Most molds for large and medium castings are either baked or skin-dried to eliminate gas troubles in the mold, but green sand may be used for light and intricate castings. Green sand has the advantage of offering less resistance to the normal contraction of the castings. Large risers must always be used on steel castings to compensate for the large amount of shrinkage.

Nonferrous Casting

The foundry method for making nonferrous castings in sand differs little from that used for iron castings. Molds are made in the same way and with the same kind of tools and equipment. The molding sand is usually of finer grain size, since most castings are very small and a smooth surface is desired. The sand need not be so refractory as sand for iron and steel castings, because the melting temperature for nonferrous alloys is lower.

The crucible furnace shown in Figure 16 is frequently used for this work. It may be either the stationary or the tilting type. Coke is commonly used as the fuel for the stationary-pit furnaces, although oil or gas can be used equally well if available. Oil and gas have the advantage of heating more quickly than coke. Electrical-resistance, indirect-arc, and induction furnaces having accurate temperature

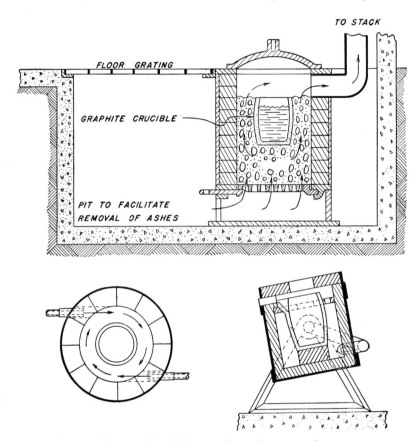

Fig. 16. Crucible furnace for nonferrous metals.

control, and low melting losses may be used under certain conditions. Electric furnaces are widely used for laboratory work as well as for installations requiring large production.

Crucibles used in nonferrous melting are made of a mixture of graphite and clay. New crucibles contain a small percentage of moisture and should be dried out slowly and uniformly before use. Although these crucibles are quite fragile when cold and must be handled with care, they possess considerable strength when heated.

To remove the crucible from the furnace, special tongs are required which conform to the outside. When heated, a crucible becomes somewhat plastic, and serious strains are imposed upon it if the tongs do not fit properly.

Nonferrous Metals and Alloys

The common elements used in nonferrous castings are copper, aluminum, zinc, tin, and lead. Many alloys, however, have small amounts of other elements, such as antimony, phosphorus, manganese, nickel, and silicon.

Two of the most common alloys using copper are brass and bronze. *Brass* is essentially an alloy of copper and zinc. The percentages of each element may vary considerably, but in most cases the zinc percentage ranges from 10 to 40. The strength, hardness and ductility of the alloy are increased as the percentage of zinc is raised up to 40. Percentages of zinc over 40 are not desirable, owing to a rapid decrease in strength and the tendency for the zinc to volatilize in melting. An addition of a small percentage of lead (0.5 to 5%) increases machinability. Brass is used extensively in industry because of its strength, appearance, resistance to corrosion, and ability to be rolled, cast, or extruded.

Bronze is a copper-base alloy containing tin, manganese, and several other elements. If zinc is present, these elements are the predominating ones so far as the properties are concerned. Most elements used as alloys with copper add to the hardness, strength, or corrosion resistance of the metal. Table 5 lists several typical analyses of commercial copper-base alloys.

TABLE 5.   Copper-Zinc-Tin Casting Alloys*

Name	Cu	Sn	Zn	Pb	Ni	Si	Mn	Al	Fe	Use
Red brass	90		10							Hardware
Yellow brass	70		30							Cartridges, tubes
Leaded red brass	85	5	5	5						Castings, machinery
Leaded yellow brass	72	1	24	3						Plumbing fixtures
Tin bronze	88	8	4							Bearings, ship hardware
Bell metal	80	20								Bells
Bearing bronze	83	7	3	7						Machine bearings
Silicon bronze	95					4	1			Machinery castings
Manganese bronze	62	1.5	31	1			1.5	1.5	1.5	High-strength parts
Aluminum bronze	78				5		3	10	4	Corrosion-resisting parts
Nickel silver	65	4	6	5	20					Dairy and laundry equipment

* *Cast Metals Handbook,* 3rd edition, American Foundrymen's Association.

Because of light weight and ability to resist many forms of corrosion, aluminum alloys have a wide application in industry today. Many of them respond to heat treatment and are suitable where high strength is needed. Copper has always been one of the principal alloying elements and, in amounts up to 8%, adds to strength and hardness. Aluminum alloys containing silicon have excellent casting characteristics and increased resistance to corrosion. Magnesium as an alloying element improves machining, makes the castings lighter, and also assists in resisting corrosion. Table 6 shows some of the typical analyses of aluminum alloys suitable for sand casting.

TABLE 6. Aluminum-Base Sand Casting Alloys*

Name	Al	Cu	Fe	Si	Mg	Mn	Ni	Use
Al-Cu (heat-treatable)	93	5	1	1				Engine castings
Al-Cu	92	8						Miscellaneous
Al-Si	95			5				Marine castings
Al-Si (heat treatable)	93	1	0.5	5	0.5			Leakproof castings
Al-Cu-Si	92	4	1	3				Good strength
Al-Mg	95	0.15	0.2	0.2	4	0.5		Cooking utensils
Al-Cu-Mg-Ni	93	3.5			1.5		2	Pistons, bearings

* *Cast Metals Handbook,* 3rd edition, American Foundrymen's Association.

Magnesium alloys are useful where light weight is essential since they are about two-thirds the weight of aluminum and one-fourth the weight of cast ferrous metals. They have excellent machinability and respond to certain treatments which improve their physical properties. Aluminum, the principal alloying element, increases hardness and strength. Manganese in small amounts increases the resistance of the metal to salt water. Sand castings made from magnesium alloys find use in portable tools, aircraft, and other constructions where weight saving is important. The approximate analysis for some of the sand casting alloys is listed in Table 7.

TABLE 7. Magnesium-Base Sand Casting Alloys*

Name	Mg	Al	Zn	Mn	Use
Mg-Al-Mn	95	4		0.2 minimum	Low-stress castings
Mg-Al-Mn	91	8		0.2 minimum	Tough, leakproof casting
Mg-Al-Zn	90	6	3	0.2 minimum	General castings

* *Metals Handbook,* American Society for Metals, 1948.

A list of the numerous alloys available for casting purposes and complete information as to the analysis and physical properties of both ferrous and nonferrous metals can be found in handbooks.

Pouring and Cleaning Castings

In jobbing and small production foundries, the molds are lined up
on the floor as they are made, and the metal is brought to them in
small ladles. Figure 17 illustrates the use of a hand ladle in the pouring of aluminum into the molds. When more metal is required or if

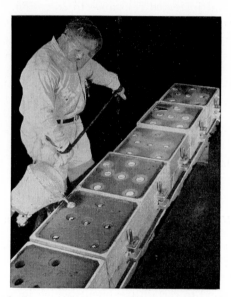

Fig. 17. Pouring aluminum sand castings with hand ladle. (Courtesy Aluminum
Company of America.)

heavier metal is poured, ladle tongs designed for two men are used.
In large foundries, engaged in the mass production of castings, the
problem of handling molds and molten metal is solved by placing the
molds on conveyors and passing them slowly by a pouring station.
The pouring station may be located permanently next to the furnace,
or metal may be brought to certain points by overhead handling
equipment. The conveyor serves as a storage place for the molds
while they are being transported to the cleaning room.

After a casting has solidified and cooled to a suitable temperature
for handling, it is shaken from the mold. Very often this is done at
a ventilated mold shakeout, the dust being collected by a cyclone dust
collector while the sand is collected underneath and transported to
the conditioning station. All castings are retained on grate bars of
the shakeout.

Nonferrous castings do not present much of a cleaning problem, since they are poured at lower temperatures than iron or steel, and the sand has little tendency to adhere to the surface. Gates and sprues are cut off, either in a sprue press or with a metal band saw. Hand or rotary machine brushing is usually sufficient to prepare the casting for machining operations.

Fig. 18. Phantom view of Wheelabrator Tumblast. (Courtesy American Foundry Equipment Company.)

Iron and steel castings are covered with a layer of sand and scale which is somewhat difficult to remove. The gates and risers on iron castings may be broken off, but to remove them from steel castings, a cutting torch or a high-speed cutting-off wheel is necessary.

To clean castings, several methods may be used, depending on the size, kind, and shape of the castings. The most common piece of equipment used is the rotating, cylindrical *tumbling mill*. The cleaning is accomplished by the tumbling action of the castings upon one another as the mill rotates. A similar piece of equipment, known as Wheelabrator Tumblast, is shown in Figure 18. This is one of the smaller machines and is recommended for small shops. It will clean 65 to 100 pounds of gray iron or malleable castings in 5 to 8 minutes. Larger machines of this type have capacities of over a ton per charge. The machine consists of a cleaning barrel formed by an endless apron conveyor. The work is tumbled beneath a blasting unit located just above the load, and metallic shot is blasted onto the castings. After striking the load, the shot falls through holes in the conveyor and is carried overhead to a separator and storage hopper. From there it is fed by gravity to the blasting unit. The unit is unloaded by reversing the apron conveyor. A dust collector is installed with the machine to eliminate dust hazards.

Sand-blasting units may be used separately for cleaning castings. Sharp sand is blown against castings inside a blasting cabinet, removing all foreign matter completely and giving the casting a clean surface appearance. Castings that are to be plated or galvanized are frequently pickled in a weak acid solution and then rinsed in hot water. Large castings, which are difficult to handle, are often cleaned by hydraulic means. The casting is placed on a rotating table, and streams of water under considerable pressure wash away the sand.

In addition to these cleaning processes, many castings require a certain amount of chipping or grinding to remove surface and edge defects. Stand, portable, and swing-frame grinders are used for this work. Fast free-cutting abrasive wheels, operating at a cutting speed of around 9500 feet per minute, are also recommended for this type of grinding.

REVIEW QUESTIONS

1. What is the difference between cast iron, steel, and wrought iron?
2. What are the raw materials and products of a blast furnace?
3. List the principal iron ores, and give the chemical symbol for each.
4. Sketch a cupola, and label the essential parts.
5. Describe the procedure of charging a cupola.
6. Why is a fluxing material added to the charge of a cupola?
7. How much air is required to melt a ton of iron?
8. For what purpose is an air furnace used?
9. What different kinds of iron are produced?
10. How are malleable-iron castings made?
11. How is nodular cast iron made?
12. List the elements in gray cast iron, and state the influence of each.
13. How is wrought iron made?
14. What is steel? How are steel castings classified?
15. What furnaces are used in the production of steel castings?
16. How is steel produced in a converter?
17. Describe the operation of a Wheelabrator Tumblast.

18. What various methods are used in cleaning castings?

19. What is the difference between brass and bronze?

20. What furnaces are used for nonferrous casting?

21. What alloying elements are found in aluminum casting metals? What influence does each have on the properties of the metal?

22. List the principal elements used in magnesium casting alloys, and state the effects of each.

REFERENCES

J. Aston, and E. B. Story, *Wrought Iron*, A. M. Byers and Company, Pittsburgh, Pa.

Bennett, J. S., "Essentials in the Production of Sound Steel Castings," *Foundry Trade Journal*, April 11, 1935, pp. 253, 256.

Briggs, C. W., and R. A. Gezelius, "Studies on Solidification and Contraction in Steel Castings," *Transactions AFA*, Vol. 43, pp. 274–302, 1935.

Campbell, H. L., *Metal Castings*, John Wiley and Sons, 1936.

Campbell, J. S., Jr., *Casting and Forging Processes in Manufacturing*, McGraw Hill Book Company, 1950.

Cast Metals Handbook, 3rd edition, American Foundrymen's Association, 1944.

Heine, R. W., and P. C. Rosenthal, *Principles of Metal Casting*, McGraw-Hill Book Company, 1955.

Marek, C. T., *Fundamentals in the Production and Design of Castings*, John Wiley and Sons, 1950.

Massari, S. C., "The Properties and Uses of Chilled Iron," *ASTM Transactions*, Vol. 38, part 2, pp. 217–234, 1938.

Metals Handbook, American Society for Metals, 1948.

Steel Castings Handbook, Steel Founders' Society of America, 1950.

Wendt, R. E., *Foundry Work*, 4th edition, McGraw-Hill Book Company, 1942.

CHAPTER 5

SPECIAL CASTING METHODS

Casting from various types of sand molds probably have fewer limitations than those produced by any other processes. All metals may be cast in sand molds, and there is no restriction as to size. However, sand molds are single-purpose molds, being completely destroyed after the metal has solidified. Quite obviously, the use of a *permanent mold* would effect considerable saving in labor cost. Great strides have been made in this field, particularly in the die casting of nonferrous alloys. A summary of the various, special casting methods which will be discussed in this chapter is as follows:

1. Casting in metallic molds
   (a) Gravity or permanent-mold casting
   (b) Slush casting
   (c) Pressed or Corthias casting
   (d) Die casting
      (1) Hot-chamber machines
      (2) Cold-chamber machines

2. Casting in nonmetallic molds
   (a) Centrifugal casting
      (1) True centrifugal
      (2) Semicentrifugal
      (3) Centrifugal

   (b) Precision casting
      (1) "Lost-wax" method
      (2) Plaster molds
      (3) Mercast process
      (4) Shell molding
   (c) CO_2 Mold-hardening process
   (d) Molds of wood, paper, rubber, and the like

3. Continuous casting
   (a) Reciprocating molds
   (b) Draw casting
   (c) Stationary molds
   (d) Direct sheet casting

Methods of Casting in Metallic Molds

Permanent molds must be made of metals capable of withstanding high temperatures. Because of their high cost they are recommended only when many castings are to be produced. Although permanent molds would be impractical for large castings and alloys of high melting temperatures, they can be used advantageously for small and medium-sized nonferrous castings that are manufactured in large quantities.

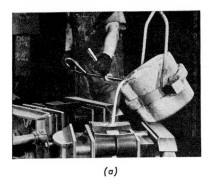 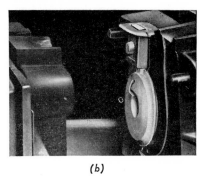

(a)   (b)

Fig. I. Multi-station machine for permanent mold casting. (a) Pouring into metal mold. (b) Mold opening for removal of casting. (Courtesy Eaton Manufacturing Company.)

Gravity or permanent-mold casting. This method consists of filling a metal mold as in sand casting. No pressure is used except that obtained from the head of metal in the mold. The process is used successfully for both ferrous and nonferrous casting, although the latter type does not present so many problems as ferrous castings because of the lower pouring temperatures. The simplest type of permanent mold hinges at one end of the mold with provision for clamping the halves together at the other. Some production machines, as illustrated in Figure 1, are circular in arrangement and have molds placed at a number of stations. The cycle of events consists of pouring, cooling, and ejecting the casting, blowing out the molds, coating them, and, in some cases, setting the cores. Both metal and dry-sand cores can be used in molds of this type. If metal cores are used, they are withdrawn as soon as the metal starts to solidify.

Molds are made of either cast iron or steel and should be of such composition as to resist the high temperature of the metal. They are usually coated with a refractory wash and then lampblack, which reduces the chilling effect on the metal and facilitates the removal of the casting. At the start of a run, the molds should be heated to the proper temperature by being filled with hot metal several times. As the proper temperature is obtained, surface defects disappear, and there is no longer any evidence of excessive chilling. Further control is obtained by regulating the rate at which castings are produced or by cooling the molds with air or water. Castings are frequently removed before they are completely solidified to prevent cracks from developing as a result of shrinkage strains.

Permanent molds produce castings free from sand and with good finish and surface detail. They are especially adapted to the quantity production of small and medium-sized castings and are capable of maintaining tolerances ranging from 0.0025 to 0.010 inch. The high initial cost of equipment and the cost of mold maintenance might be listed as disadvantages of this process, which turns out such products as aluminum pistons, cooking utensils, refrigerator parts, electric irons, and small gear blanks.

Slush casting. Slush casting is a method of producing hollow castings in metal molds without the use of cores. Molten metal is poured into the mold, which is turned over immediately so that the metal, remaining liquid, can run out. A thin-walled casting results, the thickness depending on the chilling effect from the mold and the time of the operation. The casting is removed by opening the halves of the mold. This method of casting is used only for ornamental objects, statuettes, toys, and other novelties. The metals used for these objects are lead, zinc, and various low-melting alloys. Parts cast in this fashion are either painted or finished to represent bronze, silver, or other more expensive metals.

Pressed or Corthias casting. This method of casting resembles both the gravity and the slush processes but differs somewhat in the manner in which the operation is performed. A definite amount of metal is poured into an open-ended mold, and a close-fitting core is forced into the cavity, causing the metal to be forced into the mold cavities with some pressure. The core is removed as soon as the metal sets, leaving a hollow thin-walled casting. This process, developed in France by Corthias, is limited in use mainly to ornamental casting of open design.

Die casting. Die casting, as practiced in the United States, refers to the forcing, by pressure, of molten metal into a metal die or mold. The term *die* used in this process implies a metallic mold which is filled under pressure. The pressures, which range from 80 to 40,000 psi, are maintained until solidification is completed.

The most widely used of any of the permanent-mold processes, die casting, is done by the *hot-chamber method* or the *cold-chamber method*. In the former, a melting pot is included with the machine, and the injection cylinder is immersed in the molten metal at all times, the injection cylinder being actuated either by air or hydraulic pressure which forces the metal into the dies to complete the casting. Machines using the cold-chamber process have a separate melting furnace, and metal is introduced into the injection cylinder by hand or mechanical means. Hydraulic pressure then forces the metal into the die.

The essential parts of a die-casting machine using the hot-chamber method are the container for molten metal, a heating chamber, means for forcing the metal into the die, stationary and movable dies, a mechanism for opening and closing dies, an ejector mechanism for removing the casting, and the necessary framework for the machine. Metal is forced into the mold and pressure maintained during solidification, either by a *plunger* or by *compressed air*. Both methods are shown diagrammatically in Figure 2. The plunger-type machine, shown in the upper part of the figure, is hydraulically operated for both the metal plunger and the mechanism for opening and closing the die. In this machine the plunger operates in one end of a gooseneck casting which is submerged in the molten metal. With the plunger in the upper position, metal flows by gravity into this casting through several holes just below the plunger. On the down stroke these holes are closed by the plunger, and pressure is applied on the entrapped metal, causing it to be forced into the die cavity. Pressures over 5000 psi are used in some machines of this type, resulting in castings of dense structure. As soon as the casting is solidified the pressure is relieved, the dies are forced open, and the casting is ejected by means of knockout pins. The sprue is removed with the runner and the castings.

Air-operated machines, such as the one shown in the lower part of Figure 2, have a gooseneck casting that is operated by a lifting mechanism. In the starting position the casting is submerged in the molten metal and is filled by gravity. It is then raised, so that the nozzle is in contact with the die opening, and locked in position. Compressed air, at pressures ranging from 80 to 600 psi, is applied directly on the metal, thus forcing it into the die. When solidification is about complete, the air pressure is turned off and the gooseneck lowered into position to receive more metal. The operation of opening the dies, withdrawing cores, and ejecting the castings is the same as for the plunger-type machine.

A plunger-type hot-chamber machine is shown in Figure 3. This machine is primarily used for zinc, and has a capacity of 9½ pounds per shot, with an injection pressure of 2000 psi. In operation it is similar to the plunger machine shown in the top half of Figure 2. Molten metal enters the gooseneck casting in the melting pot and is

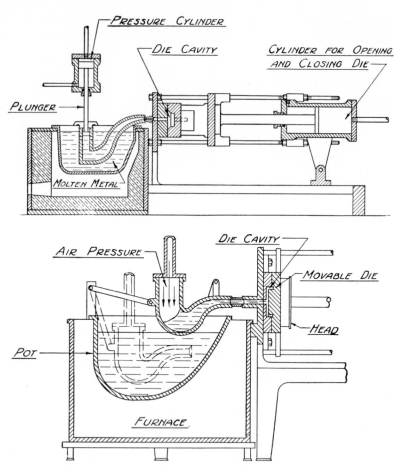

Fig. 2. Diagrammatic view of plunger and pneumatic die-casting machine.

forced into the dies by pressure exerted from the plunger. As the dies open, the castings are automatically ejected.

Hot-chamber machines are used with low-melting alloys because of machine difficulties encountered at high temperatures and the increased corrosion of the machine parts. Since many metals have an affinity for iron, only those casting alloys that do not attack the im-

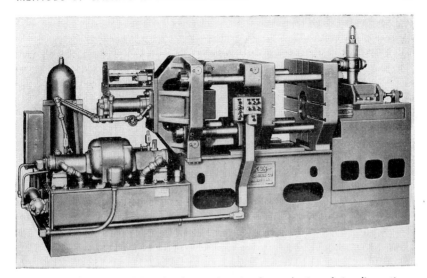

Fig. 3. Plunger gooseneck hot-chamber machine for the production of zinc die castings. (Courtesy Kux Machine Company.)

mersed metal parts are used. Alloys of zinc, tin, and lead are particularly recommended for these machines.

The die casting of brass, aluminum, and magnesium requires higher pressures and melting temperatures and necessitates a change in the melting procedure from that previously described. These metals are not melted in a self-contained pot, since the life of the pot would be very short. The usual procedure is to heat the metal in an auxiliary furnace and ladle it to the plunger cavity next to the dies. It is then forced into the dies under hydraulic pressure. Machines operating by this method are built very strong and rigid to withstand the heavy pressures exerted on the metal as it is forced into the dies. Of the two machines in general use, one has the plunger in a vertical position, the other, in a horizontal position.

A diagrammatic sketch illustrating the operation of horizontal-plunger cold-chamber machines is shown in Figure 4. In the first figure the dies are shown closed, with cores in position, and the molten metal ready to be ladled in. As soon as the ladle is emptied, the plunger moves to the left and forces the metal into the two, cup-shaped molds. After the metal solidifies, the cores are withdrawn, and then the dies are opened. In the third figure the dies are opening, and the casting is shown as ejected from the stationary half. To complete the process of opening, an ejector rod comes into operation and ejects the casting from the movable half of the die.

This operating cycle is used in a variety of machines which operate
at pressures ranging from 5600 to 22,000 psi. These machines are
fully hydraulic and semiautomatic. After the metal is ladled in, the

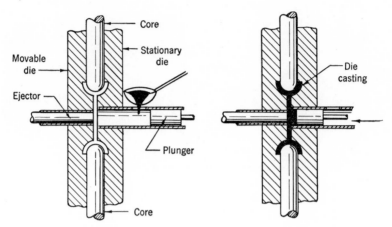

Pouring the molten metal. Cores in
position.

Molten metal forced into the dies by
the plunger.

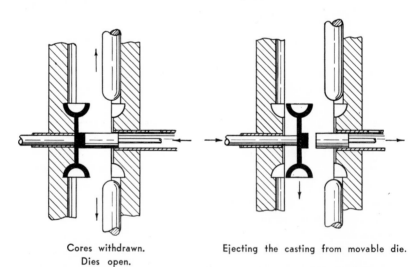

Cores withdrawn.
Dies open.

Ejecting the casting from movable die.

Fig. 4. The die casting of brass, aluminum, or magnesium in horizontal plunger Cold-
chamber machine. (Courtesy Reed-Prentice Corporation.)

rest of the operations are automatic. Aside from the ladling procedure, the operation of the machine is the same for hot-chamber
machines.

The manufacture of brass die castings is a comparatively recent achievement. The difficulties of the high temperatures involved and the resulting rapid oxidation of the steel dies have been largely overcome by improvements in die metals and by casting at as low a temperature as possible. A machine developed in Czechoslovakia, known as the Polak machine, is used successfully for the production of these castings by the Titan Metal Manufacturing Company of the United States. This machine is designed to use metal in a semiliquid or plastic state to permit operation at lower temperatures than those used for liquid metal. To protect the dies further from overheating, water is circulated through plates adjacent to the dies. Metal is maintained under close temperature control and is ladled by hand to the compression chamber. The pressure used in this machine is 9800 psi; 100 to 200 shots per hour can be made, depending on the size of the machine.

Two variations of this process, each with the injection plunger in a vertical position, are diagrammatically illustrated in Figure 5. In the lower figure the compression chamber, into which the plastic metal is ladled, is separate from the dies. The metal is poured into this cavity onto a spring-backed plunger. As the ram descends, this plunger is forced down until the gate opening is exposed, permitting the metal to be forced into the die cavity. As the ram returns to its upper position, the ejector plunger also moves upward, carrying with it any surplus metal. As the die opens the casting is ejected.

A variation of this machine, with the compression chamber a part of the die, is shown in the upper part of the figure. Metal is poured into this chamber at the upper part of the die and forced by pressure into the die cavity as the ram descends. As soon as the ram moves up, the dies open, and the casting is ejected by means of the ejector pins. The sprue and excess metal are trimmed off in the finishing operation.

Dies. Dies for both the hot- and cold-chamber machines are similar in construction because there is little difference in the method of holding and operating them. They are made in two sections, to provide means of removing the castings, and are usually equipped with heavy dowel pins to keep the halves in proper alignment. Metal enters the stationary side when the die is locked in closed position. As the die opens, the ejector plate in the movable half of the die is advanced so that pins project through the die half and force the casting from the cavity of fixed cores. The dies are provided with a separate mechanism for moving the ejector plate or movable cores. The life of these molds depends on the metal cast and may range

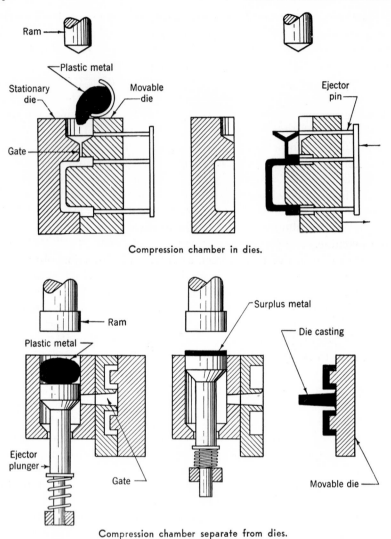

Compression chamber in dies.

Compression chamber separate from dies.

Fig. 5. Die construction for pressing brass castings. (Courtesy Titan Metal Manufacturing Company.)

from 10,000 fillings, if brass castings are made, to several million if zinc is used.

It is always desirable to provide vents and small overflow wells (see Figure 7) on one side of a die to facilitate the escape of air and to catch surplus metal that has passed through the die cavity. In spite of this provision, there is a certain amount of flash metal which must be trimmed off in the finishing operation.

For large or complex castings a single-cavity mold is used. The casting and gate from such a mold are shown in Figure 6. If the quantity of castings to be produced is large and they are relatively small in size, a multiple-cavity die can be used. Figure 7 shows a number of castings with the flask, gates, and sprue from such a die.

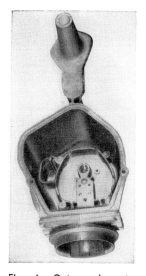

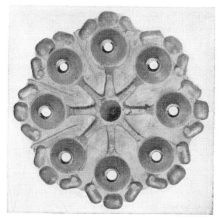

Fig. 6. Gate and casting from single-cavity die. (Courtesy The New Jersey Zinc Company.)

Fig. 7. Gate, flash metal, and reflector castings from multiple-cavity die. (Courtesy The New Jersey Zinc Company.)

A combination die is one that has two or more cavities, each of which is different. They are frequently made up of insert blocks that can be removed so that other die blocks can be substituted. Most dies are provided with channels for water cooling to keep the die at correct temperature for rapid production.

Advantages and disadvantages of die casting. One of the main advantages of die casting over sand castings is the rapidity of the process, since both molds and cores are permanent. This feature warrants its consideration in the mass production of castings. Also, the metal molds give die castings a smooth surface which not only greatly improves appearance but also minimizes the work required to prepare them for plating or other finishing operations. By this method, size is so accurately controlled that little or no machining is necessary. Because of the uniformity in wall thickness, less material is required in die castings than in sand castings. There are no possibilities for sand inclusions, and a strong dense metal structure is obtained. Finally, because of the accurate tolerance that can be maintained, the process eliminates such machining operations as drilling and certain types of threading. Die-casting tolerances vary according to the size of the casting and the kind of metal used. For small castings the tolerance ranges from ± 0.002 to 0.010 inch. The closest tolerances are obtained when zinc alloys are die-cast.

One of the limitations of die casting is the high cost of the equipment and dies. This is not an important factor in mass production, but it does eliminate its use in short-run jobs. There is also a rapid decrease in the life of the dies as the metal temperature increases. In some cases there is an undesirable chilling effect on the metal unless high temperatures are maintained. Metals having a high coefficient of contraction must be removed from the mold as soon as possible because of the inability of the mold to contract with the casting. There are certain limitations in the shape of die castings, and the process is not adapted to the production of large castings. For these reasons, die casting has, to a large extent, been limited to low-melting alloys, but, with a gradual improvement of heat-resisting metals for dies, this process can now be used for numerous alloys.

Die-Casting Alloys

A relatively wide range of nonferrous alloys can be die-cast. The principal base metals used, in order of commercial importance, are zinc, aluminum, copper, magnesium, lead, and tin. The alloys may be further classified as low-temperature alloys and high-temperature alloys; those having a casting temperature below 1000 F, such as zinc, tin, and lead, are in the low-temperature class. The low-temperature alloys have the advantages of lower cost of production and lower die-maintenance costs. As the casting temperature increases, alloy and other special steels in the best treated condition are required to resist the erosion and heat checking of die surfaces. The destructive effect of high temperatures on the dies has been the principal factor in retarding the development of high-temperature die castings.

Another factor governing the choice of alloy is the erosive or solvent action of the molten metal on the respective machine parts and dies. This action increases with temperature, although it is more pronounced with some alloys than with others. Aluminum, in particular, has a destructive action on ferrous metals and, for this reason, is seldom melted in the machine, whereas the copper-base alloys are never melted in the machine.

Other considerations that influence alloy selection are the mechanical properties required, weight, machinability, resistance to corrosion, surface finish, and, of course, cost. Obviously, the least expensive alloy that will give satisfactory service should be selected.

- **Zinc-base alloys.** Over 75% of die castings produced are the zinc-base type. This alloy casts easily with a good finish at fairly low temperatures. It also has considerable strength and is low in cost. The purest grades of commercial zinc, $99.99 + \%$ zinc, known as Special High Grade, should be used, since such elements as lead, cadmium and tin are impurities that cause serious casting and aging defects unless properly alloyed for a specific purpose. The usual elements alloyed with zinc are aluminum, copper, and magnesium; all are held within close limits.

Nominal compositions of the two standard zinc die-casting alloys are indicated in the following table.

TABLE 8. Zinc-Base Die-Casting Alloys

ASTM No.	Al	Cu	Mg	Zn
XXIII	4.1	0.1 max.	0.04	Remainder
XXV	4.1	1.0	0.04	Remainder

These alloys are much alike in composition except for the copper content and in most cases can be used interchangeably. Aluminum, in amounts around 4%, greatly improves the mechanical properties of the alloys and, in addition, reduces the tendency of the metal to dissolve iron. Copper increases the tensile strength, ductility, and hardness. Magnesium, which is usually held to an optimum of 0.04%, is used because of the beneficial effect it has in making the castings permanently stable.

Zinc alloys are widely used in the automotive industry and for other high-production markets such as washing machines, oil burners, refrigerators, radios, phonographs, television, business machines, parking meters, small machine tools, and literally hundreds of other kindred products.

Aluminum-base alloys. Many die castings are made of aluminum alloys because of their lightness in weight and resistance to corrosion. Compared to zinc alloys, however, they are slightly lower in physical properties and more difficult to die-cast.

Since molten alloys of aluminum will attach steel if kept in continuous contact with it, the cold-chamber process generally is used in casting. Although more expensive to operate than the air-injection type of machine formerly used, it has the advantage of producing sounder castings. The melting temperature of aluminum alloys is around 1185 F.

The principal elements used as alloys with aluminum are silicon, copper, and magnesium. Silicon increases the hardness and corrosion-resisting properties; copper improves the mechanical properties slightly; and magnesium increases the lightness and resistance to impact. In Table 9 is shown the nominal composition of the principal aluminum die-casting alloys.

TABLE 9.   Aluminum-Base Die-Casting Alloys*

ALCOA No.	Cu	Si	Mg	Al	Uses
13		12		Remainder	Large intricate castings with thin sections, resists corrosion
43		5		Remainder	General purpose and for permanent mold casting
218	3		8	Remainder	Castings requiring high strength, ductility, and resistance to corrosion
360		9.5	0.5	Remainder	General purpose castings, good properties and excellent casting characteristics
380	3.5	9		Remainder	Good machinability, physical properties, and casting characteristics

* *Casting Alcoa Alloys,* Aluminum Company of America, 1954.

In addition to being light in weight, these alloys have a wide range of helpful properties, including resistance to corrosion, high electrical conductivity, ease of applying surface finishes, and good machinability. Figure 8 shows a few castings made from aluminum-base alloys.

Copper-base alloys.   Die castings of brass and bronze have presented more of a problem in pressure casting because of their high casting temperatures. These temperatures range from 1600 F to 1900 F and make it necessary to use heat-resisting alloy steel for the dies to reduce their rapid deterioration. Because of these high temperatures copper-base alloys are melted in an auxiliary furnace and ladled to the machine in either a liquid or a plastic state. The latter method is used a great deal, as it permits operating at temperatures considerably lower than the melting temperatures of the molten metal. A plunger-type cold-chamber machine is used in this work.

The nominal composition of the most common copper-base die-casting alloys is shown in Table 10.

Copper-base alloys have extensive use in miscellaneous hardware, electric-machinery parts, small gears, marine aircraft and automotive fittings, chemical apparatus, and numerous other small parts. Since the high casting temperatures and pressures cause the die life to be

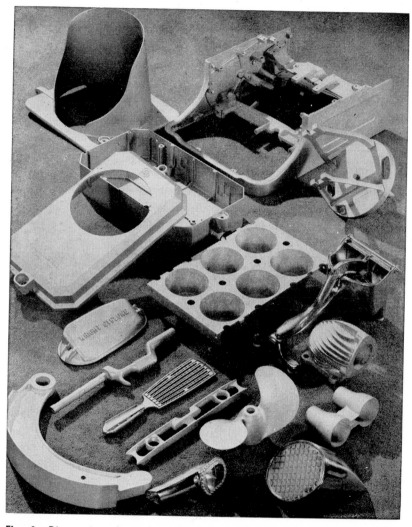

Fig. 8. Die castings from aluminum alloys. (Courtesy Aluminum Company of America.)

short, the cost of brass die castings is higher than that of other metals. However, these alloys are useful where high strength, resistance to corrosion, or wear resistance is considered important.

TABLE 10. Copper-Base Die-Casting Alloys*

ASTM No.	Cu	Si	Sn	Pb	Zn	Uses
Z30A	57		1.5	1.5	40	Yellow brass alloy having good machinability and casting qualities.
ZS331A	65	1			34	General-purpose casting. Good properties, corrosion resistance and castability.
ZS144A	81	4			15	High strength, hardness and wear resistance—but most difficult to make.

* Composition and Properties of Copper-Base Alloy Die-Castings ADC1—M5-56T. American Die Casting Institute, Inc., 1956.

Magnesium-base alloys. Magnesium is alloyed principally with aluminum but may contain small amounts of silicon, manganese, zinc, copper, and nickel. Its alloys are the lightest in weight of all die-cast metals, being about two-thirds the weight of alloys of aluminum. Although the price per pound is slightly higher than for aluminum, the extra cost is compensated for by light weight and improved machinability.

The corrosion resistance of magnesium alloys is inferior to that of the other die-casting alloys, especially in moist or sea atmospheres, and usually necessitates a chemical treatment as well as the subsequent application of a special priming coat shortly after the casting is produced. These treatments render the casting suitable for a wide range of applications.

ASTM Specification B94, alloy AZ91B, is the principal die-casting alloy, having good casting characteristics and fairly high mechanical properties. This alloy contains 9% aluminum, 0.5% zinc, 0.13% manganese, 0.5% maximum silicon, 0.3% copper, 0.03% nickel, and the remainder magnesium. It is desirable that copper and nickel be kept very low to minimize corrosion.

Magnesium alloys are cast in much the same manner as aluminum alloys and require a casting temperature between 1200 and 1300 F. Best results are obtained in so-called cold-chamber machines, and it is necessary to ladle the alloy from a crucible which is hooded, keeping the metal covered by a nonoxidizing atmosphere. The lightness of these alloys, combined with good mechanical properties and excellent machinability, fits them admirably for aircraft, motor and instrument parts, portable tools, textile machinery, household appliances, and many other similar applications.

Lead-base alloys. Pure lead, which melts at 621.3 F, will melt at around 470 F when alloyed with about 16% antimony. This element is the principal one used with lead, and its percentage ranges from 9.25 to 16. Antimony hardens lead and reduces its shrinkage value. Lead alloys have low mechanical properties but are inexpensive and easily cast. They are used principally for light-duty bearings, weights, battery parts, X-ray shields, and applications requiring a noncorrosive metal.

Alloy ASTM B23-46T, grade 8, contains 80% lead, 15% antimony, 5% tin, and 0.5% copper, and is used principally as a bearing material for moderate loads. The tin increases the fluidity, hardness, and strength of the alloy, thus improving its use for bearing purposes. The use of lead compounds for die casting is limited due to its toxic effect upon workers.

Tin-base alloys. Die-casting alloys based on tin are in about the same category as the lead alloys, as far as mechanical properties are concerned, but are high in price. On the other hand, the tin alloys are high in corrosion resistance, and some of them are well suited for use in contact with foods and beverages. Also, tin alloys have excellent bearing properties and can be cast within remarkable close dimensional tolerances. This fact, together with high corrosion resistance, accounts for their use in small parts such as number wheels, especially where contact with corrosive inks may be involved. Bearings were once die-cast in large quantities from tin alloys, but cheaper as well as better methods of making bearings have resulted in substantial, if not complete, elimination of die-cast bearings. Tin alloys can also be used for low-cost jewelry, and certain grades are classed as pewter.

Several tin alloys that can be die-cast are covered by ASTM Specifications B-102. Antimony is used in most tin alloys, usually in amounts of 4 to 16%; and up to 19% lead is common, although it should be eliminated where the die casting remains in contact with foods or beverages. The low melting point and low solidification shrinkage of the tin alloys favor their use in die casting and promote long die life. Because the use for tin-alloy die castings is very limited and because die casters cannot afford the risk of contaminating zinc alloys with tin, applications are so restricted that the total output has become of little significance to the industry.

Methods of Casting in Nonmetallic Molds

Nonmetallic molds are restricted neither to high nor to low temperatures. Each mold material has its own temperature limitations as to the kind of metal for which it is suitable. In many cases non-metallic molds are used in precision casting, as the dimensional accuracy obtained with accompanying smooth-surface finish tends to offset the higher costs. Centrifugal casting is included under this heading although castings are made by this process in both metal and nonmetallic molds.

Centrifugal casting.[1] Centrifugal casting is the process of rotating a mold while the metal solidifies, so as to utilize centrifugal force to position the metal in the mold. The metal is forced against the walls of the mold with much greater pressure than that obtained by static pressure in ordinary sand casting. Greater detail on the surface of the casting is obtained, and the dense metal structure has superior physical properties. Castings of symmetrical shape lend themselves particularly to this method, although many other types of castings can be produced. The methods of centrifugal casting may be classified as follows:[2]

1. True centrifugal casting
2. Semicentrifugal casting
3. Centrifuging

True centrifugal casting is used for pipe, liners, and symmetrical objects which are cast by rotating the mold about its horizontal or vertical axis. The metal is held against the wall of the mold by centrifugal force, and no core is required to form a cylindrical cavity on the inside. This method is illustrated by the casting machine shown in Figure 9, designed for the production of steel or cast-iron pipe. The wall thickness of the pipe produced is controlled by the amount of metal poured into the mold.

Another example of true centrifugal casting is shown in Figure 10, which illustrates two methods that may be used for casting radial-engine cylinder barrels. The horizontal method of casting is similar to the process followed in casting pipe lengths, and the inside diameter is a true cylinder requiring a minimum amount of machining. In vertical castings the inside cavity takes the form of a paraboloid as illustrated by the figure. The slope of the sides of the paraboloid depends on the speed of rotation, the dotted lines at *A* representing a higher rotational speed than shown by the paraboloid *B*. In order to reduce the inside diameter differences between the top and bottom

[1] Acknowledgement is given to the Centrifugal Casting Company for supplying certain illustrations used in this discussion.

[2] S. D. Moxley, "Centrifugal Casting of Steel," *Mechanical Engineering*, October 1944.

of the cylinder, spinning speeds are higher for vertical than for horizontal casting.

As the name implies, *semicentrifugal* casting is the rotating of the mold about its vertical axis. In this method the center of the

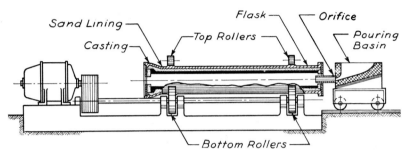

Fig. 9. Centrifugal casting machine for casting steel or cast-iron pipe. (Courtesy American Cast Iron Pipe Company.)

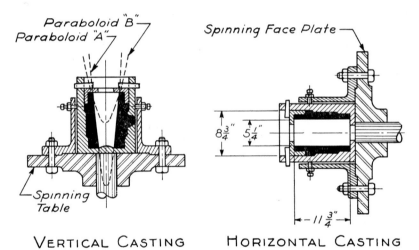

VERTICAL CASTING   HORIZONTAL CASTING

Fig. 10. True centrifugal method of casting radial-engine cylinder barrels. (Courtesy American Cast Iron Pipe Company.)

casting is usually solid, and the center cavity is machined out later or is formed by the metal passing down around the outside of a core. This method, often used in stack molding, is illustrated in Figure 11, where five track wheels are cast solid in one mold. The number of castings made in a mold depends on the size of the casting and the convenience in handling and assembling the molds. Rotational speeds for this form of centrifugal casting are not so great as for the true centrifugal process. The process produces a dense structure at the outer circumference where it is needed, while the center metal is machined out.

In the *centrifuge* method several casting cavities are located around the outer portion of a mold, and metal is fed to these cavities by radial gates from the center of the mold. Either single or stack molds can be used. The mold cavities are filled under pressure

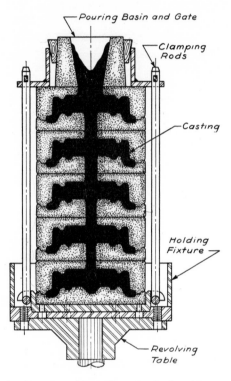

Fig. 11. Semicentrifugal stack molding of track wheels. (Courtesy American Cast Iron Pipe Company.)

from the centrifugal force of the metal as the mold is rotated. In Figure 12 are shown five castings made in one mold by this process. The internal cavities of these castings are irregular in shape and are formed by dry-sand cores. The centrifuge method, not limited to symmetrical objects, can produce castings of irregular shape, such as bearing caps or small brackets. For many years the dental profession has used this process for the casting of gold inlays.

The average rotational speed for miscellaneous centrifugal castings approximates 600 surface feet per minute (sfpm), although for cast-iron pipe the speeds may be as high as 1250 sfpm. Too great a speed may result in surface cracks caused by high stresses set up in the mold. The rotational speed[3] depends on the kind of mold used (whether sand or metal), the manner of rotation (whether horizontal or vertical), the size of casting, and the kind of metal being cast.

Centrifugal casting is more economical than other methods. Cores in cylindrical shapes and risers or feedheads are both eliminated.

Fig. 12. Centrifuged castings with internal cavities of irregular shape.

The castings have a dense metal structure with all impurities forced back to the center where frequently they can be machined out. Because of the pressure exerted on the metal, thinner sections can be cast than would be possible in static casting. Finally, any metal can be cast by this process. All castings, however, cannot be made centrifugally, since there are definite size and shape limitations.

"Lost-wax" precision casting process. This process[4] derives its name from the fact that the wax pattern used in the process is subsequently melted from the mold, leaving a cavity having all the details of the original pattern. The process as originally practiced by artisans in the sixteenth century consisted of forming the object in wax by hand. The wax object or pattern was then covered by a plaster investment. When this plaster became hard, the mold was heated in an oven, melting the wax and at the same time further drying and hardening the mold. The remaining cavity, having all

[3] G. E. Stedman, "Unique Centrifugal Steel Casting Method," *Metals & Alloys,* August 1944.

[4] J. D. Wolfe, "Precision Castings for Ordnance and Aircraft," *Metals & Alloys,* Vol. 18, October 1943.

the intricate details of the original wax form, was then filled with metal. Upon cooling, the plaster investment was broken away, leaving the casting. In large castings, such as statuary,[5] plaster cores were used to provide relatively thin walls in the casting.

The procedure followed in the lost-wax process is first to prepare one or more master patterns of steel or brass which are replicas of the

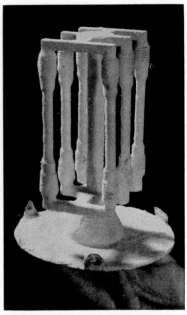

Fig. 13. Split lead-alloy mold shown with a wax pattern being lifted from it.

Fig. 14. Wax-pattern assembly is shown precoated with silica flour suspended in suitable binder. (Courtesy General Electric Company.)

part to be cast. Using these patterns, a bismuth- or lead-alloy split mold is cast, similar to the one shown in Figure 13. The mold is properly finished and gated and is then ready for use in forming the wax patterns. In the forming operation, the mold is held in a water-cooled vise, and the heated wax is injected into it under considerable pressure. Thermoplastic-polystyrene resin is sometimes used in place of wax. Upon solidification, the wax patterns are removed from the mold and are ready for final assembly.

[5] Benvenuto Cellini's famous chapter on the casting of his bronze statue, Perseus, contains much interesting information on methods of molding used during the Renaissance. Cellini used a form of "lost-wax" process.

In this operation several patterns are usually assembled with necessary gates and risers and by heating the contact surfaces (wax welding) with a hot wire held to correct temperature by electrical resistance. The patterns are then ready to be placed in a metal flask and surrounded by a refractory plaster. This is done by pouring into the flask a finely ground refractory material, thinned by some mixing agent as alcohol or water. The general procedure is to dip or spray the pattern first with a fine silica-flour mixture to insure having a smooth surface on the castings (see Figure 14), and then to fill the flask with a coarser plaster mixture. After the plaster sets, the mold is placed upside down and heated in an oven for several hours to melt out the wax and to dry the mold. The final casting can be produced by gravity, vacuum, pressure, or centrifugal casting. Pressures ranging from 3 to 30 psi are generally used in the casting operation. When the mold has cooled, the plaster is broken away. After gates and feeders are cut off, the castings are finally cleaned by grinding, sand blasting, or other finishing operations.

Advantages of precision casting are: (1) Intricate forms having undercuts can be cast. (2) A very smooth surface on casting is obtained with no parting line. (3) Dimensional accuracy is good. (4) Certain unmachinable parts can be cast to preplanned shape. (5) It may be used to replace die casting where short runs are involved. On the other hand, the process is expensive, is limited to small castings, and presents some difficulties where cores are involved.

Plaster-mold casting. The use of plaster as a casting investment has had limited use for many years, but recent improvement in its ability to dry quickly with sufficient porosity has greatly accelerated its use as a modern casting material. The molds are not permanent and are destroyed when the castings are removed.

Patterns are made of a free-machining brass and are held to a close tolerance. They are assembled on bottom plates of standard-size flasks (usually 10 by 18 by 3 inches and 12 by 18 by 4 inches), as shown in Figure 15. Before receiving the plaster, they are sprayed with a parting compound. The plaster, which is made of gypsum with added strengtheners and settling agents, is dry-mixed, and water is added. It is then poured over the patterns, and the mold is vibrated slightly to insure the plaster's filling all small cavities. The plaster sets in a few minutes and is removed from the flask by a vacuum head. All moisture is driven from the molds by baking them in an oven conveyor at a temperature around 1500 F. These molds are shown in Figure 16 as they are emerging from the drying oven.

After pouring, the castings are removed by breaking up the mold, any surplus plaster being removed by a washing operation.

Mold porosity, for the removal of any gases developed in the mold, is controlled by the water content of the plaster. When the mold is

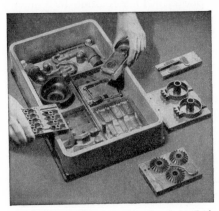

dried, the water driven out leaves numerous fine passageways which act as vents. The amount of water added originally is in excess of what is needed for setting of the plaster and provides the excess of voids needed for venting. In addition to having adequate porosity, plaster molds have the necessary structural strength for casting, plus enough elasticity to allow some contraction of the metal during its cooling.

Fig. 15. Assembling metal patterns in flask. (Courtesy Universal Castings Corporation.)

Plaster molds are suitable only for nonferrous alloys having casting temperatures not much over 2100 F. Although plaster has proved to be an excellent mold material for yellow brass, certain bronzes and aluminum alloys may also be used. The wide variety of small castings made by this process includes miscellaneous airplane parts, small gears, cams, handles, pump parts, small housings, and numerous other intricate castings.

One of the principal advantages of plaster-mold casting is the resulting high degree of dimensional accuracy. This, coupled with the smooth surface obtained, enables the process to compete favorably

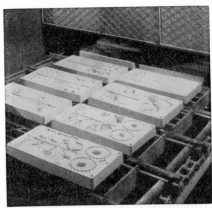

Fig. 16. Finished plaster molds coming from drying oven. (Courtesy Universal Castings Corporation.)

with sand casting in producing parts requiring a considerable amount of machining. Because of the low thermal conductivity of plaster, the metal does not chill rapidly, and very thin sections may be cast. There is little tendency towards internal porosity in plaster-mold castings, and no difficulty is experienced with sand or other inclusions. In general, the process competes more successfully with die casting using the high-temperature alloys such as brass rather than metals such as zinc and aluminum. At high temperatures, metal molds have a relatively short life; with plaster molds, which are used only once, the temperature is no problem.

A tolerance of ±0.005 inch can be maintained for simple castings: slightly more is required if the dimension crosses the parting line. The process can be used for both small and quantity production runs.

Molds from mercury patterns. A casting process utilizing frozen mercury and known as the Mercast process[6] has been developed for the production of precision castings. A metal mold or die is first made of the part to be cast with the necessary gates and sprue hole. When assembled and ready for pouring, it is partially immersed in a cold bath and filled with acetone, which acts as a lubricant. As the mercury is poured into the mold, the acetone is displaced. Freezing takes place in a liquid bath held at around -76 F and is complete in about 10 minutes.

The patterns are then removed from the mold and invested in a cold ceramic slurry by repeated dippings until a shell about $\frac{1}{8}$ inch thick is built up. Mercury is melted and removed from the shell at room temperature, and, after a short drying period, is fired at a high temperature resulting in a hard permeable form. The shell is then placed in a flask, surrounded by sand, preheated, and filled with metal. Casting is usually done by the centrifugal method.

Castings produced by this method are accurate in detail, have a smooth surface, and, for small castings, maintain a tolerance of ±0.002 inch per inch. Both ferrous and nonferrous metals can be cast by this process, the maximum pouring temperature being around 3000 F. Wide commercial use of this process is limited by the high cost of the castings.

Shell molding process.[7] The mold in this process is made up of a mixture of dried silica sand and phenolic resin, formed into thin, half-mold shells which are clamped together for pouring, as illustrated by the series of sketches in Figure 17. The sand, free from clay, is first mixed with either urea or phenol formaldehyde resin (thermoplastic) and the mix then put into a dump box or blowing machine. A metal pattern must be used since it is preheated to a temperature around 450 F and sprayed with a silicone release

[6] Process controlled by the Mercast Corporation, New York.
[7] Process originally developed by Johannes Croning of Hamburg, Germany.

agent before being placed on top of the dump box. The box is then inverted, causing the sand mix to drop on the pattern, and is held there for 15 to 30 seconds before it is returned to its original posi-

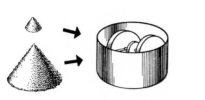

Mulling the sand and resin.

Curing the shells on pattern.

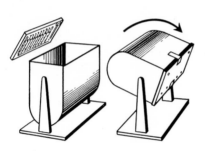

Resin-sand mixture applied to pattern.

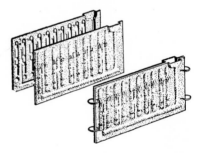

Mold halves are aligned and joined.

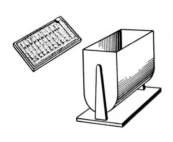

Excess resin-sand material falls back in dump box.

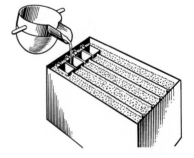

Molds are supported and poured.

Fig. 17. Schematic diagram of shell molding process. (Courtesy The Borden Company.)

tion. The pattern, with a thin shell of sand, $\frac{1}{8}$ to $\frac{3}{16}$ inch thick, adhering to it, is then placed in an oven and the shell cured $\frac{1}{2}$ to 1 minute until it is rigid. The shell is finally removed from the pattern by ejector pins and the mold halves assembled with clamps, resin adhesives, or other devices. They may then be put in a flask, supported against one another, or by some backing material such as shot or gravel. Some are poured while they are resting flat on the floor with a weight on top.

Advantages claimed for this process include close tolerances (0.002 to 0.005 inch per inch), low cleaning costs, and smooth surfaces. Little molding skill is necessary and the sand requirements are low. Shell molding also can be readily adapted to automatic mechanization. Disadvantages are that the process requires metal patterns and fairly expensive equipment for making and heating the molds. Resin is an expensive binder, and little of the sand can be economically reclaimed. Most metals can be cast by this process, but the castings are usually small, seldom exceeding 25 pounds.

CO_2 **mold hardening process.** The process of hardening molds and cores using CO_2 and a sodium-silicate liquid base binder has been widely used in Europe for some time. Because of its inherent advantages and the rapid speed with which it hardens the sand, it is now being used in many foundries in this country. Briefly, the process consists of thoroughly mixing clean, dry silica or other conventional sand (AFS fineness number around 75) with $3\frac{1}{2}$ to 5% sodium-silicate liquid base binder in a muller. It is then ready for use and may be packed in flasks and core boxes by standard molding machines, core blowers, or by hand. The sand should be free from moisture and clay, but in some cases other ingredients such as coal dust, pitch, graphite, or wood flour may be added to improve certain properties like collapsibility.

When the packing is complete, CO_2 is forced into the mold or core at a pressure of around 20 psi. The reaction is quite involved, but is usually represented by the following simple chemical equation:

$$Na_2SiO_3 + CO_2 = SiO_2 \text{ aq} + Na_2CO_3$$

The silica gel, which is formed, hardens and acts as a cement to bond the sand grains together. The method of introducing the gas, important to the success of the process, must be simple, rapid, and uniform throughout the sand body, and not be cumbersome to apply. The time to harden a small or medium-size body of sand will range from 15–30 seconds. Overgassing is wasteful and results in deteriorating the sand. For small cores a gasketed, funnel-shaped head may be placed over the core box. Larger molds may be hardened by placing a hood over the mold, by running small tubes into the mold (as illustrated in Figure 18), or by introducing the gas into a hollow, vented pattern.

Figure 18 shows diagrammatically the steps followed in preparing a mold. In some cases the sprue is at the ends of the cope and

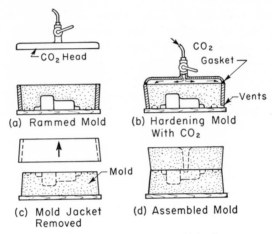

Fig. 18.   Schematic diagram of CO_2 mold hardening process.

drag, and a number of molds may be book-stacked between end braces for pouring.

Advantages claimed for this process include:

1. Operation is speedy.
2. No core baking equipment is involved.
3. Core plates are unnecessary.
4. Semiskilled labor can be used.
5. Cores may be stored for long periods of time.
6. A uniform sand may be used for both molds and core production.

Factors which limit the use of this process are the difficulty in reclaiming used sand and the tendency of sand with a silica-base binder to air-harden to some extent if kept a long time. Poor collapsibility of molds and cores will sometimes give trouble, but with proper additives this can be eliminated. This process may be used for both ferrous and nonferrous castings.

Molds of other materials.   Various materials such as rubber, paper, and wood can be used for molds of low-melting-temperature metals. Costume jewelry and similar small items are successfully cast in rubber molds.[8]   A two-piece rubber casing is vulcanized over a

   [8] Lupke, Paul, Jr., "Making Cast Models in Rubber Molds," *Mechanical Engineering*. June 1945.

mold or pattern which, when complete, serves as the mold. Casting
is by centrifugal means, and metal temperatures up to 600 F can be
used. The flexibility of the mold permits intricate designs with
undercuts, but close dimensional accuracy cannot be maintained.
An alloy of 98% tin, 1% copper, and 1% antimony is frequently used
in this work.

Full-page newspaper type is cast in a mold (called a "mat") upon
which the type and illustration impressions have been made on
damp paper. The type metal is poured into the mold after the paper
is dry. End-grain wood may also be used as a mold material for
low-melting alloys where only a limited number of simple castings
are required.

Continuous Casting

Research and experimental work has proved that there are many
opportunities for saving in the continuous casting of metals. Briefly,
the process consists of continuously pouring molten metal into a
mold, which has the facilities for rapidly chilling the metal to the
point of solidification, and then withdrawing it from the mold. The
following processes are typical of those in use or in the process of
development.

Reciprocating mold process.[9] In the process shown in Figure 19, a reciprocating water-cooled copper mold is used, the down
stroke being synchronized with the discharge rate of the slab. Molten metal is poured into the holding furnace shown and is discharged
to the mold through a 1/2-inch tube at the rate of 20,000 pounds per
hour. The molten metal is distributed across the mold from a
submerged, horizontal crosspiece, the level of the metal being held
constant at all times. The pouring rate of the molten metal is
controlled by a needle valve through the top of the holding furnace.
As the metal becomes chilled in the lower part of the mold, it is
discharged at a constant rate and enters the withdrawing rolls. These
are synchronized with the downward movement of the mold and are
mounted just above a circular saw which cuts the slab to required
lengths. Brass slabs produced by this process are further processed,
by cold rolling, into sheets and strips.

Asarco process.[10] The Asarco process, shown in Figure 20,
differs from other continuous processes in that the forming die or
mold is integral with the furnace and there is no problem of con-

[9] Process used by the Scovill Manufacturing Company and a development of the
Junghans-Rossi process.

[10] This process in its present stage is the product of the work of a number of
collaborators. It has been developed by the American Smelting and Refining Company.

trolling the flow of metal. The metal is fed by gravity into the mold
from the furnace as it is continuously solidified and withdrawn by the

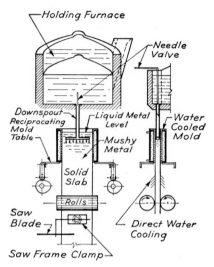

Fig. 19. Reciprocating mold process of continuous slab casting. (Courtesy Scovill
Manufacturing Company.)

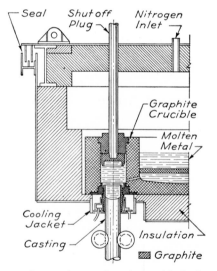

Fig. 20. Asarco process for continuous cast shapes (J. S. Smart, Jr., and A. A.
Smith, Jr., "Asarco Continuous Cast Shapes," *Iron Age*, September 22, 1949). (Courtesy American Smelting & Refining Company.)

rolls below. An important feature of this process is the water-cooled
graphite-forming die, which is self-lubricating, has excellent resist

ance to thermal shock, and is not attacked by copper-base alloys. The upper end, being in the molten metal, acts as a riser and compensates for any shrinkage which might take place during solidification, while simultaneously acting as an effective path for the dissipation of evolved gases. These dies are easily machined to shape, and products may be produced ranging from $\frac{7}{16}$ to $5\frac{1}{8}$ inches in diameter. Multiple production from a single die permits casting the small section rods.

In starting the process, a rod of the same shape as that to be cast is placed between the drawing rolls and inserted into the die. This rod is tipped with a short length of the alloy to be cast. As the molten metal enters the die, it melts the end surface of the rod, forming a perfect joint. The casting cycle is then started by the drawing rolls, and the molten metal is continuously solidified as it is chilled and withdrawn from the die. When the casting leaves the furnace, it ultimately reaches the sawing floor where it is cut to desired length while still in motion. A tilting receiver takes the work and drops it to a horizontal position, and from there it goes to inspecting and straightening operations.

The process has proved successful for phosphorized copper and many of the standard bronzes. The alloy compositions may be produced with satisfactory commercial finish as rounds, tubes, squares, or special shapes. Physical properties are superior to permanent-mold and sand castings.

Williams continuous-casting process.[11] Developed for continuous casting of carbon and alloy steels, this process utilizes thin-walled brass molds having cross-sectional areas up to 45 square inches. These molds are preferably oval in cross section. A small stream of metal is poured into the mold from an electric holding furnace at a rate controlled by the metal level in the mold. The mold must of necessity be constructed of a material having a high heat conductivity and one that is not easily wetted by the liquid metal. Rapid mold cooling is essential for the success of this process, and results in improved mold life, less segregation, smaller grain structure, and a better surface. Actually the metal next to the mold wall solidifies only a few inches below the top surface and shrinks slightly from the mold sides. As the cast section leaves the cooled mold, it passes through a section that controls the rate of cooling and then to the drawing and straightening rolls. Below this point it is cut to length by an oxyacetylene torch and finally lowered to a horizontal position.

[11] Original patents on this process by E. R. Williams. Process now being developed jointly by Republic Steel Corporation and Babcock & Wilcox Tube Company.

Steel blooms and billets, produced by this process, have good crystalline structure, little segregation, uniform section, and a size close to that required for many rolling mills.

Alcoa direct-chill process.[12]   This process consists of pouring molten aluminum from a holding furnace through a refractory trough into shallow, stationary molds, the bottoms of which rest on a hydraulic elevator.   When the metal at the bottom of the mold

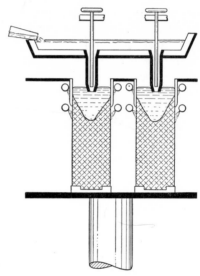

Fig. 21. Casting aluminum ingots by the direct-chill process. (Courtesy Aluminum Corporation of America.)

becomes chilled, the elevator drops at a rate of 2 to 5 inches per minute. As the ingots descend, they are sprayed with water to complete their solidification. This process is shown diagrammatically in Figure 21 although, in actual practice, three ingots are usually cast instead of two as shown. The shallow molds used are made in sizes of 12 by 36 and 12 by 48 inches and are rectangular in shape, although other sizes and circular shapes can be cast if desired. The length of the ingots is regulated to give a convenient size for rolling and is usually 136 inches. This process leaves a rough surface on the ingots which must be removed by milling before they can be further processed in the rolling mill. Most of the aluminum used in the United States is cast by this process.

[12] Based on patent of W. T. Ennor, November 3, 1942. Process developed and used by Aluminum Company of America.

Direct casting of sheet (Hazelett process).[13] Much work has been done in the attempt to cast various metals into sheet form between water-cooled rolls, as is done in the manufacture of glass by the continuous method. So far this process has not proved commercially successful, owing to the fact that the metal solidifies faster at the edges of the strip than at the center and, consequently, builds up a greater thickness at the edges than is desired. This forces the cooling rolls apart and changes the sheet thickness. Also, in casting solid-solution alloys, the process is affected by segregation problems, resulting ultimately in wide variations of metal analysis. Some progress has been made in the elimination of these difficulties by increasing rolling speeds and reducing the contact area that the metal has with the rolls.

REVIEW QUESTIONS

1. Describe the process of permanent-mold casting.
2. For what type of work is slush casting used?
3. Define die casting.
4. What are the advantages of the die-casting process over sand casting?
5. Distinguish between hot- and cold-chamber methods of die casting.
6. What is the difference between a multiple-cavity die and a combination die?
7. What are the limitations of the hot-chamber method of die casting?
8. What metals are usually die-cast by the cold-chamber process?
9. List the principal metals or alloys used in die casting.
10. What group of alloys are most widely used in die casting?
11. Describe how mercury patterns are used in making castings.
12. What are the advantages and limitations of the shell molding process?
13. State the differences between true centrifugal casting, semicentrifugal casting, and centrifuging.
14. How is cast-iron pipe made? Illustrate by sketch.
15. What is the average rotational speed for centrifugal casting, and on what does the speed depend?
16. State the advantages of centrifugal casting over other methods.
17. Describe the "lost-wax" casting process.
18. What alloys may be cast in plaster molds?
19. Compare the reciprocating-mold and draw-casting processes of continuous casting.
20. Why are ferrous metals difficult to cast continuously?
21. How are molds made by the CO_2 process?
22. What process should be used to make the following: small zinc castings, statuettes, aluminum pistons, aluminum ingots, and small brass gears?

[13] C. W. Hazelett, *Mechanical Engineering*, Vol. 61, 1939, p. 923.

REFERENCES

Anderson, E. A., and G. L. Werky, *Zamak Alloys for Zinc Alloy Die Casting*, New Jersey Zinc Company, 1944.

Bolz, R. W., (*a*) "Plaster-Mold Casting," *Machine Design*, December 1949. (*b*) "Die-Casting," *Machine Design*, November 1949.

Cady, E. L., *Precision Investment Castings*, Reinhold Publishing Company, 1948.

Casting Alcoa Alloys, Aluminum Company of America, 1954.

Charnock, G. F., and F. W. Partington, *Mechanical Technology*, Constable and Company, London, 1934.

Chase, Herbert, (*a*) *Die Casting*, John Wiley and Sons, 1934. (*b*) "Which Form of Non-Ferrous Casting," *Metals & Alloys*, September 1944.

Harvill, H. L., *High Pressure Die Casting*, H. L. Harvill Manufacturing Company, 1945.

Heine, R. W., and P. C. Rosenthal, *Principles of Metal Casting*, McGraw-Hill Book Company, 1955.

Lippert, T. W., "Continuous Casting of Semi-finished Steel," *Iron Age*, August 19, 1948.

Metals Handbook, The American Society for Metals, 1948.

Moxley, S. D., "Centrifugal Casting of Steel," *Mechanical Engineering*, 1944.

Sager, Alfred, "Permanent Mold Castings," *Metals & Alloys*, April 1945.

Smart, J. S., Jr., and A. A. Smith, Jr., "Continuous Casting—The Asarco Process," *Iron Age*, August 26, 1948, and September 22, 1949.

Smart, J. S., Jr., "Continuous Casting," *Metal Progress*, October 1955.

Wilkins, W. G., "Plaster-Mold Castings," *Machine Design*, June 1949.

CHAPTER 6

HEAT TREATMENT

OF STEEL

Heat treatment is the operation of heating and cooling a metal in its solid state to change its physical properties. According to the procedure used, steel can be made hard to resist cutting action and abrasion, or it can be softened to permit further machining. With the proper heat treatment, internal stresses may be removed; grain size, reduced; toughness, increased; or a hard surface, produced on a ductile interior. The analysis of the steel must be known since small percentages of certain elements, notably carbon, greatly change the physical properties.

Alloy steels owe their properties to the presence of one or more elements other than carbon, namely nickel, chromium, manganese, molybdenum, tungsten, silicon, vanadium, copper, and cobalt. Because of their improved physical properties, they are used commercially in many ways not possible with carbon steels.

The following discussion applies principally to the heat treatment of ordinary commercial steels, known as carbon steels. With this process, the rate of cooling is the controlling factor; rapid cooling from above the critical range results in hard structure, whereas very slow cooling produces the opposite effect.

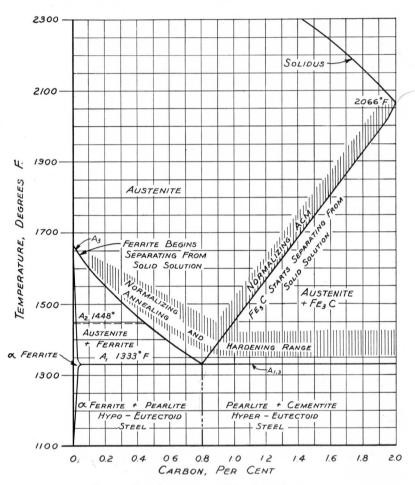

Fig. I. Partial iron–iron-carbide phase diagram.

Iron–Iron-Carbide Diagram

Under conditions of equilibrium, the knowledge of steel and its structure is best summarized in the iron–iron-carbide diagram shown in Figure 1. If a piece of 0.20% carbon steel is slowly and uniformly heated and its temperature recorded at definite intervals of time, a curve (as shown in Figure 2) may be obtained. Such a curve is called an inverse-rate curve, the abscissa being the heating rate or the time required to heat or cool the steel 10 degrees. The curve is a vertical line except at those points where the heating or cooling rates show marked change. It is evident that at three temperatures there is a definite change in the heating rate. In a similar fashion these same three points again show upon cooling, but occur at slightly lower temperatures. Where structural changes occur these points are known as *critical points* and are designated by the symbols Ac_1, Ac_2, and Ac_3. The letter c is the initial letter of the French word *chauffage*, meaning "to heat." The points on the cooling

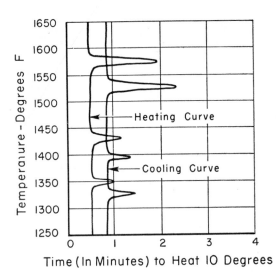

Fig. 2.   Inverse-rate curve for SAE 1020 steel.

curve are designated by Ar_1, Ar_2, and Ar_3, the r being taken from the word *refroidissement*, meaning "to cool."

Certain changes which take place at these critical points are called *allotropic changes*. Although the chemical content of the steel remains the same, its property is changed. Principal among these are changes in electrical resistance, atomic structure, and loss of magnetism. By definition, an allotropic change is a reversible change in the atomic structure of the metal with a corresponding change in the properties of the steel. These critical points should be known, as most heat-treating processes require heating the steel to a temperature above this range. Steel cannot be hardened unless it is heated to a temperature above the lower critical range and in certain instances above the upper critical.

If a series of time-temperature heating curves are made for steels of different carbon contents and the corresponding critical points plotted on a temperature-percent-carbon curve, a diagram similar to Figure 1 would be obtained. This diagram, which applies only under slow cooling conditions, is known as a partial iron–iron-carbide diagram. By referring to this diagram one may readily observe the proper quenching temperatures for any carbon steel.

Consider again the piece of 0.20% carbon steel which has been heated to a temperature around 1600 F. Above the Ar_3 point this

steel is a solid solution of carbon in gamma iron and is called *austenite*. The iron atoms lie in a face-centered cubic structure and are nonmagnetic. Upon cooling this steel, the iron atoms start to form a body-centered cubic lattice below the Ar_3 point. This new structure that is being formed is called *ferrite* or alpha iron and is a solid solution of carbon in alpha iron. The solubility of carbon in alpha iron is very

Fig. 3. Structure of SAE 1095 steel, furnace-cooled from 1550 F. Etched in 5% picral. Showing lamellae of cementite and ferrite in pearlite. Magnification × 1200.

much less than in gamma iron. At the Ar_2 point the steel becomes magnetic, and, as the steel is cooled to the Ar_1 line, additional ferrite is formed. At the Ar_1 line the austenite that remains is transformed to a new structure called *pearlite*. This constituent is lamellar in appearance under high magnification, the lamellae being alternately ferrite and iron carbide. Called pearlite because of its "mother-of-pearl" appearance, it is shown under high magnification in Figure 3.

As the carbon content of the steel increases above 0.20%, the temperature at which the ferrite is first rejected from the austenite drops until, at about 0.80% carbon, no free ferrite is rejected from the austenite. This steel is called *eutectoid* steel and is 100% pearlite in structure composition. The eutectoid point in any metal is the lowest temperature at which changes occur in a solid solution. If the carbon content of the steel is greater than the eutectoid, a new line is observed in the iron–iron-carbide diagram labeled *Acm*. The line denotes the temperature at which iron carbide is first rejected from the austenite instead of ferrite. The iron Carbide (Fe_3C) is known as *cementite* and is extremely hard and brittle. Steels con-

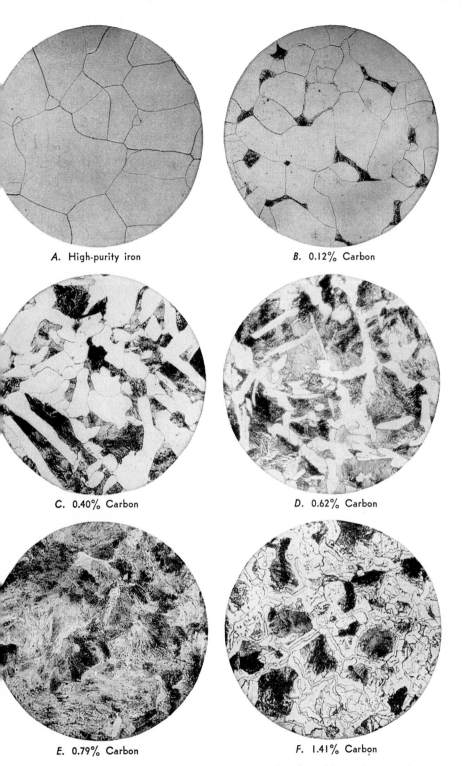

A. High-purity iron B. 0.12% Carbon

C. 0.40% Carbon D. 0.62% Carbon

E. 0.79% Carbon F. 1.41% Carbon

Fig. 4. Photomicrographs of iron-carbon alloys showing the effect of increasing amounts of carbon on the structure of the metal. (Courtesy Bureau of Standards.)

taining less carbon than the eutectoid are known as *hypoeutectoid* steels, and those with more carbon content are called *hypereutectoid* steels.

These steels, in structure, are shown in a series of photomicrographs in Figure 4. The first figure shows pure iron or ferrite. As the carbon content increases up to 0.79% carbon, the dark areas of the pearlite form and increase in quantity, while the white background area of ferrite decreases and the sample is nearly all pearlite. In the sample containing 1.41% carbon, the pearlitic area is smaller and the white background area is now cementite and ferrite. The maximum amount of cementite at 1.41% carbon would be about 11%. All these iron-carbon alloys have been cooled slowly to produce the constituents just described.

Grain Size

All steel is crystalline in structure, and the size of these crystals or grains has an important effect on the quality of the steel. Molten steel, upon cooling, starts solidifying at many small centers or nuclei, the atoms in each group tending to be positioned in a similar fashion. The irregular grain boundaries, seen under the microscope after polishing and etching, are the outlines of each group of atomic cells that have the same general orientation. The size of these grains depends on a number of factors, the principal one being the furnace treatment it has received.

It has long been known that coarse-grained steels are less tough and have a greater tendency for distortion than those having a fine grain; however, they have better machinability and greater depth-hardening power. The fine-grained steels, in addition to being tougher, are more ductile and have less tendency to distort or crack during heat treament. Control of grain size is possible through regulation of composition in the initial manufacturing procedure, but after the steel is made, the control is through proper heat treatment. Aluminum, when used as a deoxidizer, is the most important controlling factor during the manufacturing period since it raises the temperature at which rapid grain growth occurs.

When a piece of low-carbon steel is heated, there is no change in the grain size up to the Ac_1 point. As the temperature increases through the critical range, the ferrite and pearlite are gradually transformed to austenite, and, at the upper critical point, Ac_3, the average grain size is a minimum. Further heating of the steel causes an increase in the size of the austenitic grains, which in turn governs the final size of the grains when cooled. Quenching from the Ac_3 point would result in a fine-grained structure, whereas slow cooling or quenching from a higher temperature would yield a coarser structure. The final grain size depends entirely on the prior austenitic grain size in the steel at the time of quenching.

Not all steels start growing large crystals immediately upon being heated above the upper critical range; some steels can be heated to a higher temperature with little change in their structure. A temperature known as a *coarsening temperature* is eventually reached, and grain-size increase becomes rapid. This is characteristic of medium-carbon steels, many alloy steels, and steels that have been deoxidized with aluminum. The coarsening temperature is not a fixed temperature and may be changed by prior hot or cold working and heat treatment.[1] Hot work on steel is started at temperatures well above the critical range, with the steel in a plastic state, and has the effect of refining the grain structure and eliminating any coarsening effect due to the high temperature. Hot forging or rolling should not continue below the critical temperature.

The principal method of determining grain size is by microscopic examination, although it may be roughly estimated by examination of a fracture. For microscopic determination it is necessary for the grain boundaries to be clearly outlined by some constituent. Low-carbon steels have ferrite precipitated from the austenite upon slow cooling, and the outlines of these grains can be clearly brought out by polishing and etching. Since a very slow cooling rate may produce too much primary ferrite to permit evaluation of prior austenitic grain size, a cooling rate must be employed such that the proeutectoid constituent is restricted to merely outlining the pearlitic regions. Likewise, for medium-carbon steels the former austenitic grain size would be represented roughly by the pearlitic area plus one-half the surrounding ferrite. Hypereutectoid steels will have the grain boundaries outlined by the cementite that is precipitated.

An example of a large-grained steel is shown in the photomicrograph in Figure 5. This specimen has been heated to an excessively high temperature, resulting in large grain growth and some crystalline separation. Steel that has been "burnt" shows this separation owing to oxidation at the grain boundaries, and this cannot be remedied by heat treatment. The steel can be rendered fit for commercial use only by remelting.

[1] M. A. Grossman, "Grain Size in Metals with Special Reference to Grain Growth in Austenite," *Transactions ASM*, Vol. 22, no. 10, 1934.

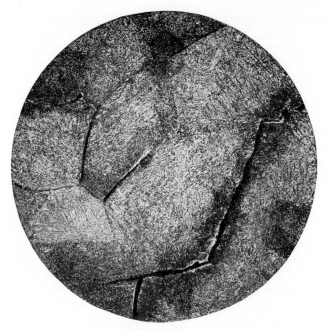

Fig. 5. Crystalline separation and excessive grain size. Magnification ×300.

Hardening

Hardening is the process of heating a piece of steel to a temperature within or above its critical range and then cooling it rapidly. If the carbon content of the steel is known, the proper temperature to which the steel should be heated may be obtained by reference to Figure 1, the iron-carbon diagram. However, if the composition of the steel is unknown, a little preliminary experimentation may be necessary to determine the range. A good procedure to follow is to heat and quench a number of small specimens of the steel at various temperatures and observe the results, either by hardness testing or by microscopic examination. When the correct temperature is obtained, there will be a marked change in hardness and other properties.

In any heat-treating operation the rate of heating is important. Heat flows from the exterior to the interior of steel at a definite maximum rate. If the steel is heated too fast, the outside becomes hotter than the interior, and uniform structure cannot be obtained. If a piece is irregular in shape, a slow rate is all the more essential to eliminate warping and cracking. The heavier the section, the longer must be the heating time to achieve uniform results. Even after the correct temperature has been reached, the piece should be held at that temperature for a sufficient period of time to permit its thickest section to attain a uniform temperature.

The hardness obtained from a given treatment depends on the quenching rate, the carbon content, and the work size. In alloy steels the kind and amount of alloying element influences only the hardenability of the steel and does not affect the hardness except in unhardened or partially hardened steels.

A very rapid quench is necessary to harden low- and medium plain-carbon steels. For these steels, quenching in a water bath is a method of rapid cooling which is common practice. For high-carbon and alloy steel, oil is generally used as the quenching medium, because its action is not so severe as that of water. Various commercial oils, such as mineral oil, have different cooling speeds and, consequently, impart different hardnesses to steel on quenching. For extreme cooling, brine or water spray is most effective. Certain alloys can be hardened by air cooling, but for ordinary steels, such a cooling rate is too slow to give an appreciable hardening effect. Large parts are usually quenched in an oil bath, which has the advantage of cooling the part down to ordinary temperatures rapidly and yet is not too severe. The temperature of the quenching medium must be kept uniform to achieve uniform results. Any quenching bath used in production work should be provided with means for cooling.

Steel with low carbon content will not respond appreciably to hardening treatments. The predominating constituent of such steel is ferrite, which is soft and not changed by the treatment. As the carbon content in steel increases up to around 0.60%, the possible hardness obtainable also increases. Above this point the hardness can be increased only slightly, because steels above the eutectoid point are made up entirely of pearlite and cementite in the annealed state. Pearlite responds best to heat-treating operations; any steel composed mostly of pearlite can be transformed into a hard steel.

As the size of parts to be hardened increases, the surface hardness decreases somewhat, even though all other conditions have remained the same. There is a limit to the rate of heat flow through steel. No matter how cool the quenching medium may be, if the heat inside a large piece cannot escape faster than a certain critical rate, there is a definite limit to the inside hardness. However, brine or water quenching is capable of rapidly bringing the surface of the quenched part to its own temperature and maintaining it at, or close to, this temperature. Under these circumstances there would always be some finite depth of surface hardening regardless of size. This is not true in oil quenching, when the surface temperature may be high during the critical stages of quenching.

Hardenability is that property of a steel which determines the depth and distribution of hardness obtained by the quenching treatment. Alloys increase the hardenability of steel and make it possible to harden small pieces uniformly from the outside to the inside. Because of this characteristic it is possible to harden alloy steels at

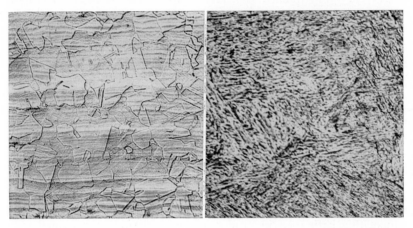

Fig. 6. Structure of 18–8 stainless steel, water-quenched to show austenite. Lines caused by hot rolling. Magnification ×125.

Fig. 7. Structure of SAE 1095 steel water-quenched. Etched with Villella's reagent to show martensite. Magnification ×562.

a slower cooling rate than plain carbon steels. Therefore, alloy steels may be effectively hardened by quenching in oil instead of water.

Constituents of hardened steel. It has been previously stated that austenite is a solid solution of carbon in gamma iron. All carbon steels are composed entirely of this constituent above the upper critical point. The appearance of austenite under the microscope is shown in Figure 6 at a magnification of 100. Extreme quenching of a steel from a high temperature will preserve some of the austenite at ordinary temperatures. This constituent is about one half as hard as martensite and is nonmagnetic.

If a hypoeutectoid steel is cooled down slowly, the austenite is transformed into ferrite and pearlite. Steel having these constituents is soft and ductile. Faster cooling will result in a different constituent, and the steel will be harder and less ductile. A rapid cooling, such as a water quench, will result in a martensitic structure, which is the hardest structure that can be obtained. Cementite, although somewhat harder, is not present in its free state except in hypereutectoid steels and then only in such small quantities that its influence on the hardness of the steel can be ignored.

The essential ingredient of any hardened steel is *martensite*. A. Martens, a German scientist, first recognized this constituent about 1878. Martensite is obtained by rapid quenching of carbon steels and is the transitional substance formed by the rapid decomposition of austenite. It is a supersaturated solution of carbon in alpha iron. Under the microscope it appears as a needlelike constituent, as may be seen in Figure 7. The hardness of martensite depends on the amount of carbon present and varies from Rockwell C45 to C67. It cannot be machined, is quite brittle, and is strongly magnetic.

If steel is quenched at slightly less than the critical rate, a dark constituent with somewhat rounded outlines will be obtained. The name of this constituent is *fine pearlite*. Under the microscope, at usual magnifications, it appears as a dark unresolved mass, but at very high magnification a fine lamellar structure can be seen. Fine pearlite is less hard than martensite, having a Rockwell C hardness varying from 34 to 45, but is quite tough and capable of resisting considerable impact. As the quenching rate is still further reduced, the pearlite becomes coarser and is definitely laminated under high magnification at slow rates of cooling.

Maximum hardness of steel. The maximum hardness obtainable in a given piece of steel depends on the carbon content. Although various alloys such as chromium and vanadium increase the rate and depth-hardening ability of alloy steels, their maximum hardness will not exceed that of a carbon steel having the same carbon content. This fact is illustrated in the curve shown in Figure 8, where Rockwell C hardness is plotted against percentage of carbon. This curve shows the maximum hardness that is possible for a given carbon percentage. To obtain maximum hardness, the carbon must be completely in solution in the austenite when quenched. The *critical quenching rate,* which is the slowest rate of cooling that will result in 100% martensite, should be used. Finally austenite must not be retained in any appreciable percentages, as it is considerably softer than martensite.

The curve in Figure 8 is made up of test points from both alloy and carbon steels, and it may be seen that there is little variation in the results. However, the same quenching rate cannot be used for both alloy and carbon steels of the same carbon content. The maximum hardness obtained in any steel represents the hardness of

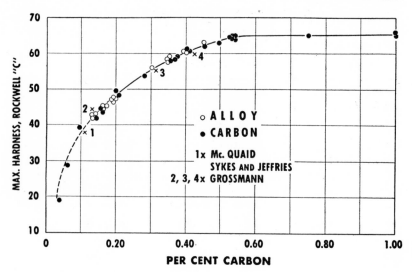

Fig. 8. Maximum hardness versus carbon content. From "Quantitative Hardening," by J. L. Burns, T. L. Moore, R. S. Archer, *Transactions ASM*, Vol. XXVI. 1938. (Courtesy American Society for Metals.)

martensite and is approximately 66 to 67 Rockwell. Carbon equal to, or in excess of, 0.60% is necessary to achieve this level.

Annealing

The primary purpose of *annealing* is to soften hard steel so that it may be machined or cold-worked. This is usually accomplished by heating the steel to slightly above the critical temperature, holding it there until the temperature of the piece is uniform throughout, and then cooling at a slow rate. This process is known as *full annealing* because it wipes out all trace of previous structure and refines the crystalline structure in addition to softening the metal. Annealing also relieves internal stresses previously set up in the metal and removes gases trapped in the metal during the initial casting.

When hardened steel is reheated to above the critical range, the constituents are changed back into austenite, and slow cooling then provides ample time for complete transformation of the austenite into the softer constituents. For the hypoeutectoid steels these constituents are pearlite and ferrite. It may be noted, by referring to the equilibrium diagram, that the annealing temperature for hypereutectoid steels is lower, being slightly above the A_1 line. There is no reason to heat above the Acm line, as it is at this point that the precipitation of the hard constituent cementite is started. All martensite is changed into pearlite by heating above the lower critical range and slowly cooling. Any free cementite in the steel is unaffected by the treatment.

The temperature to which a given steel should be heated in annealing depends on its composition, and for carbon steels it can be obtained readily from the partial iron–iron-carbide equilibrium diagram shown in Figure 1. The heating rate should be consistent with the size and uniformity of sections so that the entire part is brought up to temperature as uniformly as possible.

When the annealing temperature has been reached, the steel should be held there until conditions are uniform throughout. This usually takes about 45 minutes for each inch of thickness of the largest section. For maximum softness and ductility, the cooling rate should be very slow, such as allowing the parts to cool down with the furnace. The higher the carbon content, the slower must be this rate.

Process annealing, practiced in the sheet and wire industry between cold-working operations, consists of heating the steel to a temperature a little below the critical range and then cooling it slowly. This process is more rapid than the spheroidizing process and results in the usual pearlitic structure. It is similar to the tempering process but will not give so much softness and ductility as a full anneal. Also, at the lower heating temperature there is less tendency for the steel to scale or decarburize.

Normalizing

The process of normalizing consists of heating the steel about 50 to 100 F above the upper critical range and cooling, in still air, to room temperature. This process is principally used with low- and medium-carbon as well as alloy steels to make the grain structure more uniform, to relieve internal stresses, or to achieve desired results in physical properties. Most commercial steels are normalized after being rolled or cast.

Spheroidizing

Spheroidizing is the process of producing a structure in which the cementite is in a spheroidal distribution as shown in Figure 9. If a steel is heated slowly to a temperature just below the critical range and held there for a prolonged period of time, this structure will be obtained. It may also be accomplished by alternately heating and cooling between temperatures that are just above and below the Ac_1 range. The globular structure obtained gives improved machinability to the steel. This treatment is particularly useful for hypereutectoid steels that must be machined.

Tempering

Steel that has been hardened by rapid quenching is brittle and not suitable for most uses. By *tempering* or "drawing," the hardness and brittleness may be reduced to the desired point for service conditions. As these properties are reduced, there is also a decrease in tensile strength and an increase in the ductility and toughness of the steel. The operation consists of the reheating of hardened steel to some temperature below the critical range, followed by any rate of cooling. Although this process softens steel, it differs considerably from annealing in that the process lends itself to close control of the physical properties and in most cases does not soften the steel to the extent that annealing would.

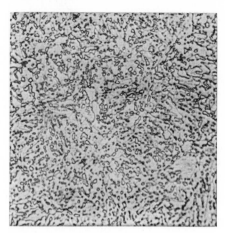

Fig. 9. SAE 1095 steel quenched from 1550 F and tempered at 1250 F for 8 hours. Structure is spheroidized cementite in a ferritic matrix. Magnification × 900.

Tempering is possible because of the instability of the martensite, the principal constituent of hardened steel. At about 400 F this constituent will start to break down to the softer constituents. Low draws from 300 to 400 F do not cause much decrease in hardness and are used principally to relieve internal strains. As the tempering temperatures are increased, the breakdown of the martensite takes place at a faster rate, and at about 600 F the change to a structure called tempered martensite is very rapid. The tempering operation may be described as one of precipitation and agglomeration, or coalescence of cementite. A substantial precipitation of cementite begins at 600 F, which produces a decrease in hardness. Increasing the temperature causes coalescence of the carbides, with continued decrease in hardness. Alloying elements have a profound influence on tempering, the general effect being to retard the softening rate so that alloy steels will require a higher tempering temperature to produce a given hardness.

In the process of tempering some consideration should be given to time as well as to temperature. Although most of the softening action occurs in the first few minutes after the temperature is reached, there is some additional reduction in hardness if the temperature is maintained for a prolonged time. Usual practice is to heat the steel to the desired temperature and hold it there only long enough to have it uniformly heated.

Interrupted Quenches

The conventional method of hardening and tempering steel just described is illustrated by the time-temperature curve shown in Figure 10. In another process, known as *martempering,* the steel is quenched from the austenite region to a temperature just above that where martensite starts to form. The steel is held at this temperature long enough to enable the surface and the center of the piece being

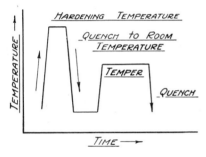
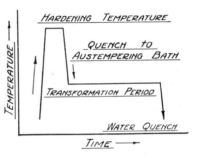

Fig. 10. Customary quench and temper process.

Fig. 11. Austempering process.

treated to come to the same temperature. When this occurs, the piece is usually cooled in air to room temperature, thus forming martensite. The temperature at which the steel is held varies with the carbon and alloy content, although for steels containing around 0.40% carbon the temperature is 400 F. The main purpose of martempering is to minimize distortion, cracking, and internal stresses that result from normal quenching in oil or water.

The process of *austempering* is depicted in Figure 11. Steel is heated to a temperature above the critical range until it is all converted to austenite. It is then quenched into a molten salt or metal bath held at some predetermined temperature ranging from 350 to 800 F and held there for a definite period of time until the transformation is complete. The structure obtained is called *bainite.* Under the microscope this structure is similar in appearance to martensite, etching somewhat darker. Although the steel is of the same hardness, it is tougher and more ductile than quenched and tempered steel.

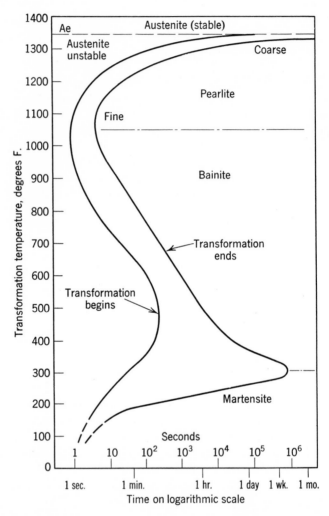

Fig. 12. The process of austenite transformation at constant temperatures. (Courtesy Carnegie-Illinois Steel Corporation.)

The foundation for the austempering process is based upon investigation of austenitic transformation at constant temperatures. It is represented diagrammatically by the S curve in Figure 12. This figure is drawn for steel of eutectoid composition, but is similar to curves of other carbon and alloy steels. Because of the long intervals required for some transformations, the temperatures are plotted against time on a logarithmic scale. The distance between the two curves indicates the time required for complete transformation from austenite to the final constituent. This constituent will depend upon the rate of quench and the temperature at which it is held. Above the upper hump in the curves it will be pearlite; from 350 to 800 F, bainite; and below the lower hump, martensite. These constituents vary in structure within each range, and the change is gradual from one to the other. Because of the curves extending far to the left at the upper hump, steel must be rapidly quenched to the desired transformation temperature to clear the curve and eliminate the formation of some pearlite. Most alloying elements in steel have the effect of shifting the curves to the right, thus allowing more time to harden the steel fully without hitting the upper bend of the curve. This increase in hardenability of the steel permits the hardening of thicker sections than would otherwise be possible. Complete austempering is limited to steels of a size that can be quenched at a rate that will not cut through this portion of the curve. However, large sections will be benefited by having a hard tough surface of bainite with fine pearlite at the interior. This process is widely used for treating such articles as small tools, springs, lock washers, firearm parts, link chains, shovels, and miscellaneous machinery parts.

Surface Hardening

Carburizing. The oldest known method of producing a hard surface on steel is case hardening or *carburizing*. This process, in brief, is merely heating iron or steel to a red heat, in contact with some carbonaceous material. Iron, at temperatures close to and above its critical temperature, has an affinity for carbon. The carbon enters the metal to form a solid solution with iron and converts the outer surface into a high-carbon steel.

The steel used for this process is usually a low-carbon steel of about 0.15% carbon, which does not respond appreciably to heat treatment. In the course of the process, the outer layer is converted into a high-carbon steel with a content ranging from 0.9% to 1.2% carbon. If it receives proper heat treatment, it will have an extremely hard surface on the outside and a soft ductile center.

This process is merely one of changing the carbon content of the surface steel, which makes it possible to obtain different physical properties in a given piece of steel. A steel with varying carbon content and, consequently, different critical temperatures requires a special heat treatment. Since there is some grain growth in the steel during the prolonged carburizing treatment, the work should be heated to the critical temperature of the core and then cooled, thus refining the core structure. The steel should then be reheated to a point above the transformation range of the case (Ac) and quenched to produce a hard, fine structure. The lower, heat-treating temperature of the case results from the fact that hypereutectoid steels are normally austenized for hardening just above the lower critical. A third tempering treatment may be used to reduce strains.

Nitriding. Nitriding is somewhat similar to ordinary case hardening, but it uses a different material and treatment to create the hard-surface constituents. In this process the metal is heated to a temperature of around 950 F and held there for a period of time, in contact with ammonia gas. Nitrogen from the gas is introduced into the steel, forming very hard nitrides, which are finely dispersed through the surface metal.

It has been found that nitrogen has greater hardening ability with certain elements than with others; hence, special nitriding alloy steels have been developed. Aluminum, in percentages of 1 to 1½, has proved to be especially suitable in steel, since it combines with the gas to form a very stable and hard constituent. The temperature of heating ranges from 850 to 1200 F, although 960 to 975 F is the temperature range generally used.

The nitriding process develops extreme hardness in the surface of steel. This hardness ranges from 900 to 1100 Brinell, which is considerably higher than that obtained by ordinary case hardening. Nitriding steels, by virtue of their alloying content, are stronger than ordinary steels and respond readily to heat treatment. It is recommended that these steels be machined and heat-treated before nitriding, because there is no scale or further work necessary after this process. Fortunately, the structure and properties are not affected appreciably by the nitriding treatment, and, since no quenching is necessary, there is little tendency to warp, develop cracks, or change condition in any way. The surface effectively resists corrosive action of water, salt-water spray, alkalies, crude oil, and natural gas.

Nitriding is used on many automotive, airplane, and diesel-engine wearing parts, as well as on numerous miscellaneous parts, such as pump shafts, gages, drawing dies, gears, clutches, and mandrels. Its use is limited by the expense necessary for the treatment and the comparatively thin case obtained (0.001 to 0.005 inch).

Cyaniding. Cyaniding is a process which combines the absorption of carbon and nitrogen to obtain surface hardness in low-carbon steels that do not respond to ordinary heat treatment. The part to be case-hardened is immersed in a bath of fused, sodium cyanide salts at a temperature of approximately 1600 F, the time of soaking depending on the depth of case. The part is then quenched in water or oil to obtain a hard surface. Case depths of 0.005 to 0.020 inch may be readily obtained by this process. Disadvantages are the toxicity of the salts used and the size limitation of the parts that can be treated.

Induction Hardening

In recent years the use of induced electric current has had widespread acceptance by industry. Principal applications for this method of heating include melting of metals, hardening and other heat-treatment operations, preheating metals for hot work, and heating for sintering, brazing, and similar operations. High-frequency alternating current obtained from motor generator sets, mercury-arc converters, spark-gap oscillators, or vacuum-tube oscillators are used for this type of heating. Although there are different power and frequency limitations for each type of equipment, most do not exceed frequencies of 500,000 cycles.

Induction heating has proved satisfactory for many surface hardening operations as required on crankshafts and similar wearing surfaces. It differs from ordinary case-hardening practice in that the analysis of the surface steel is not changed, the hardening being accomplished by an extremely rapid heating and quenching of the wearing surface which has no effect on the interior core. The hardness obtained in induction hardening is the same as that obtained in conventional treatment and depends on carbon content.

An inductor block, acting as a primary coil of a transformer, is placed around, but not touching, the journal to be hardened. A high-frequency current is passed through this block, inducing a current in the surface of the bearing. The heating effect is due to induced eddy currents and hysteresis losses in the surface material. As the steel is heated to the upper critical range, the heating effect of these losses is gradually decreased, thereby eliminating any possibility of overheating the steel. The inductor block surrounding the heated surface has water connections and numerous small holes on its inside surface; and, as soon as the steel has been brought up to the proper temperature, it is automatically spray-quenched under pressure.

An important feature of this method of hardening is its rapidity of action, since it requires only a few seconds to heat steel to a depth of ⅛ inch. The actual time will depend primarily upon the frequency used, power input, and depth of hardening required. Although the equipment cost is high, it is offset by the advantages of the process, which include fast operation, freedom from scaling, clean

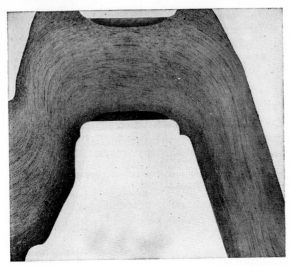

Fig. 13.   Section of an induction-hardened crankpin bearing.   (Courtesy The Ohio Crankshaft Company.)

operation, little tendency for distortion, no manual handling of hot parts, and low treating cost. Medium-carbon steel has proved satisfactory for parts, and the nature of the process has practically eliminated the necessity for using costly alloy steels. Figure 13 illustrates the local heating obtained in a hardened crankpin bearing which has been induction-hardened.

Flame hardening

Flame hardening, like the induction-hardening process, is based on rapid heating and quenching of the wearing surface. The heating is accomplished by means of an oxyacetylene flame, which is applied for a sufficient length of time to heat the surface above the critical temperature of the steel. Integral with the flame head are water connections which cool the surface by spraying as soon as the desired temperature is reached. By proper control, the interior surface is not affected by the treatment, the depth of the case being a function of the heating time and flame temperature. Figure 14 shows an etched cross section of a gear tooth and the hardened areas.

Several methods are employed in this process. In the stationary method of spot hardening, both torch and work are stationary, and the effect is local. In progressive harden-ing, the flame and work move with respect to one another as, for example, in rail hardening. As the flame progresses, the work is immediately quenched behind the flame. Spinning or rapidly rotating cir-cular work may be used, employing one or more flames. As soon as the work is brought up to the proper temperature, it is quenched while rotating. This method is usually applied to fairly small work when the heating time is short. Spinning may also be used in connection with a progressive movement of the torch along the side of the work.

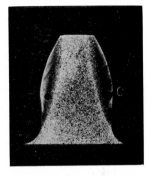

Fig. 14. Section through a gear tooth showing structure obtained by flame hardening. (Courtesy The Linde Air Products Company.)

With this process, hard surfaces having a ductile backing may be obtained, large pieces may be treated without heating the entire part, the case depth is easily controlled, the surface is free of scale, and the equip-ment is portable.

REVIEW QUESTIONS

1. What are the principal microconstituents found in all annealed steels?
2. Describe what takes place when an allotropic change occurs in steel.
3. What changes take place in steel at the critical points?
4. Describe the process known as hardening.
5. What is martensite? How does it appear under the microscope?
6. What determines the maximum hardness that can be obtained in a piece of steel?
7. What is meant by each of the following terms: eutectoid, pearlite, cementite, austenite, and alpha ferrite?
8. What microconstituents will be found in annealed 0.50% carbon steel? 1.2% carbon steel?
9. What is the purpose of annealing, and how is it done?
10. Distinguish between normalizing and spheroidizing.
11. How is martempering done, and why is it used?
12. What is the difference between austempering and ordinary tempering?
13. Describe the process of carburizing.
14. For what type of work is cyanizing used?

15. What is nitriding, and what advantages does the process have over carburizing?

16. How is induction hardening accomplished?

17. Describe the methods used in flame hardening.

18. How does a variation in grain size affect the properties of steel?

REFERENCES

Bullens, D. K., *Steel and Its Heat Treatment,* 5th edition, Vols. I and II, John Wiley and Sons, 1948.

Camp, J. M., and C. B. Francis, *The Making, Shaping, and Treating of Steel,* 5th edition, Carnegie-Illinois Steel Corporation, 1940.

Clark, D. S., and W. R. Varney, *Physical Metallurgy,* D. Van Nostrand Company, 1952.

Coonan, F. L., *Principles of Physical Metallurgy,* Harper and Brothers, 1943.

Davenport, E. S., and E. C. Bain, *Transformation of Austenite at Constant Subcritical Temperatures,* AIME Technical Publication 348, 1930.

Doan, G. E., *The Principles of Physical Metallurgy,* 3d edition, McGraw-Hill Book Company, 1953.

Dowdell, R. L., H. S. Jerabek, A. C. Forsyth, and C. H. Green, *General Metallography,* John Wiley and Sons, 1943.

Heyer, R. H., *Engineering Physical Metallurgy,* D. Van Nostrand Company, 1939.

Hultgren, R., *Fundamentals of Physical Metallurgy,* Prentice-Hall, 1952.

Keller, J. F., *Lectures on Steel and Its Treatment,* 2d edition, American Society for Steel Treating, 1930.

Keyser, C. A., *Basic Engineering Metallurgy,* Prentice-Hall, 1953.

Metals Handbook, American Society for Metals, 1948.

Newton, J., *An Introduction to Metallurgy,* 2d edition, John Wiley and Sons, 1947.

Rosenholtz, J. L., and J. F. Oesterle, *The Elements of Ferrous Metallurgy,* 2d edition, John Wiley and Sons, 1938.

Sachs, G., and K. R. Van Horn, *Practical Metallurgy,* American Society for Metals, 1940.

Sisco, F. T., *Modern Metallurgy for Engineers,* Pitman Publishing Company, 1948.

Smith, M. C., *Principles of Physical Metallurgy,* Harper and Brothers, 1956.

Stoughton, B., and A. Butts, *Engineering Metallurgy,* 3d edition, McGraw-Hill Book Company, 1938.

Teichert, E. J., *Ferrous Metallurgy,* 3 Vols., McGraw-Hill Book Company, 1944.

Williams, R. S., and V. Homerberg, *The Principles of Metallography,* 4th edition, McGraw-Hill Book Company, 1939.

Woldman, N. E., *Materials Engineering of Metal Products,* Reinhold Publishing Corporation, 1949.

CHAPTER 7

POWDER
METALLURGY

Powder metallurgy is the art of producing commercial products from metallic powders by pressure. Heat, which may or may not be used in the process, must be kept at a temperature below the melting point of the powder. The application of heat during the process, or subsequently, is known as *sintering* and results in bonding the fine particles together, thus improving the strength and other properties of the finished product. Products made by powder metallurgy are frequently alloyed or contain nonmetallic constituents to improve the bonding qualities of the particles or to improve certain properties or characteristics of the final product. Cobalt, or some other metal, is necessary in the bonding of tungsten carbide particles, whereas graphite is added with bearing-metal powders to improve the lubricating qualities of the finished bearing.

Metal in powder form is higher in cost than in solid form, and the process which must produce in large quantities economically requires expensive dies and machines. This higher cost is often justified by the unusual properties obtained. Some products cannot be made by any other process; others made by this process compete favorably with their counterparts made by other methods, because the close tolerances maintained in this process eliminate the necessity of any further processing.

Important Characteristics of Metal Powders

Since the particle size, shape, and size distribution of metal powders have definite effects on the characteristics and physical properties of the compacted product, powders are produced according to specifications, such as structure of shape, fineness, particle-size distribution, flowability, chemical properties, compressibility, apparent specific gravity, and sintering properties.

The *shape* of a powder particle, depending largely on how it was produced, may be spherical, ragged, dendritic, flat or angular. *Fineness* may be determined by passing the powder through a standard sieve or by microscopic measurement. Standard sieves ranging from 100 to 325 mesh are used for checking sizes and also for determining particle-size distribution within that range. *Particle-size distribution* has considerable influence in determining the flowability and apparent density, as well as the final porosity, of the product. Once it is established for a product, it cannot be varied appreciably without affecting the size of the compact. *Flowability* is that characteristic of a powder which permits it to flow readily and conform to the mold cavity. It can be described as the rate of flow through a definite orifice. *Chemical* properties have to do with the purity of the powder, amount of oxides permitted, and the percentage of other elements allowed. Clean surfaces on particles are essential for attaining desired mechanical properties. *Compressibility* of powders, which varies considerably, is influenced by the particle-size distribution and shape. Dependent on this characteristic is the green strength of the powders which must be sufficient to hold the pressed forms together in the manufacturing operations. Compressibility is the ratio of the volume of initial powder to the volume of the compressed piece. The *apparent density* or specific gravity of a powder may be expressed in grams per cubic centimeter. As the apparent density decreases, it is necessary to use more powder to produce a part. It should therefore be kept constant so that the same amount of powder can be fed into the die each time. *Sintering* ability should be good and should not require too narrow a temperature range. Procedures for testing most of the foregoing characteristics may be found in ASTM and Metal Powder Association Standards.

Methods of Producing Powders

Although all metals can be produced in the powder form, only a few find wide application in the manufacture of pressed-metal parts. Some lack the desired characteristics or properties described above which are necessary for economical production. The two principal kinds in use are the iron- and copper-base powders. Both lend themselves well to this process and are produced in a wide variety of alloys. Whereas bronze is used in porous bearings, brass and iron are more often used in small machine parts. Other powders of steel, nickel, silver, tungsten, and aluminum alloys have a limited but important application in the field of powder metallurgy.

All metal powders, because of their individual physical and chemical characteristics, cannot be manufactured in the same way. The procedures vary widely, as do the sizes and structures of the particles obtained from the various processes. *Machining* results in coarse particles and is used principally for producing magnesium powders. *Milling* processes, utilizing various types of crushers, rotary mills, and stamping mills, break down the metals by crushing and impact. Brittle materials may be reduced to irregular shapes of almost any fineness by this method. The process is also used in pigment manufacture for ductile materials, where flake particles are obtained, an oil being used in the process to keep them from sticking together. *Shotting* is the operation of pouring molten metal through a sieve or orifice and cooling by dropping into water. Spherical or pear-shaped particles are obtained by this process. Most metals can be shotted, but the size of the particles is too large in many instances. *Atomization,* or the operation of metal spraying, is an excellent means of producing powders from many of the low-temperature metals such as lead, aluminum, zinc, and tin. The particles are irregular in shape and are produced in many sizes. A few metals can be converted into small particles by rapidly stirring the metal while it is cooling. This process, known as *granulation,* depends on the formation of oxides on the individual particles during the stirring operation. *Electrolytic deposition* is a common means for processing copper, iron, tantalum, silver, and several other metals. The characteristic structure obtained by this method is dendritic, and the apparent density is low. The *reduction method,* economical for some metals, reduces metal oxides in powder form by contact with a gas at temperatures below the melting point. Tungsten, iron, molybdenum, nickel, and cobalt are produced commercially by this process.

Various other methods involving precipitation, condensation, and other chemical processes have been developed for producing powdered metals. These methods, as well as some of those previously mentioned, are not widely used but prove satisfactory for some metals.

Pressing to Shape

Powder for a given product must be carefully selected to insure economical production and to obtain the desired properties in the final compact. If only one powder is to be used and the particle size distribution is right, no additional processing or blending will be necessary before pressing. In some cases various sizes of powder particles are mixed together to change such characteristics as flowability or density, but most powder is produced with sufficient particle-size variation. Mixing or blending becomes necessary in production when the powders are alloyed or when nonmetallic particles are added. Any mixing or processing of the powder must be done under favorable conditions to prevent oxidation or defects.

Practically all powders have lubricants added in the blending operation to reduce die wall friction and to aid in the ejection. Although these lubricants add to the porosity, they permit a greatly increased production rate and are necessary in presses using automatic powder feed. Lubricants may include stearic acid, lithium stearate, and powdered graphite. If hand feeds are used, the lubricant can be omitted in the powder and the die cavity coated manually.

Powders are pressed to shape in steel dies under pressures ranging from a few thousand to 200,000 psi. Because the soft particles can be pressed or keyed together quite readily, powders that are plastic do not require so high a pressure as the harder powders to obtain adequate density. Quite obviously, the density and hardness increase with the pressure, but in every case there is an optimum pressure above which little advantage in improved properties can be obtained. Owing to the necessity for strong dies and large capacity presses, production costs increase with high pressures.

Many of the commercial presses developed for other materials are adaptable for use in powder metallurgy. Though mechanically operated presses are generally used because of their high rate of production, hydraulic presses may be employed if the part is large and high pressures are required. The single-punch press and the high-speed rotary multiple-punch press are designed so that their operation, from the filling of the cavity with powder to the ejection of the finished compact, can be either a continuous or a single cycle. Rotary table presses have a high rate of production, since they are equipped with a series of die cavities, each provided with top and bottom punches. In the course of production the table indexes around, and the operations of filling, pressing, and ejecting the product, are accomplished at the various stations. The presses are designed with 6 to 35 stations, and production rates up to 1000 compacts per minute can be obtained. A simple punch and die arrangement for compacting metal

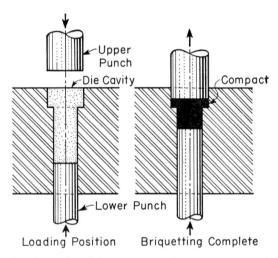

Fig. I. Simple punch and die arrangement for compacting metal powder.

powder is shown in Figure 1. Two punches are involved, an upper punch which conforms to the top shape of the part, and a lower punch which conforms to the lower end of the die cavity. The lower punch also acts as an ejector to remove the briquetted part from the die. The die cavity must be very smooth to reduce friction and must also be provided with a slight draft to facilitate removal of the part. Wall friction prevents much of the pressure from being transmitted to the powder, and, if pressure is exerted only from one side, there will be considerable variation in density from top to bottom. This accounts for the use of both top and bottom punches in most dies. The travel of the punches depends upon the compression ratio of the powder, which, for iron and copper, is roughly 3 to 1. The die cavity is filled level to a depth three times the height of the finished compact. The ejected part, known as a *green compact,* resembles the finished part, but has only the little structural strength derived from the interlocking of the power particles obtained by compression. Final strength is obtained by sintering.

A recent development in powder metallurgy is the *centrifugal com-*

pacting of heavy metal powders to obtain uniform density. Molds are filled with the powder and then centrifuged to provide pressures around 400 psi. Uniform density is obtained since the centrifugal force acts independently on each particle of powder. Upon removal from the molds the compacts are processed the same as pressed compacts. The use of this technique is limited to parts made of heavy powders such as tungsten carbide. Parts made in this way should be of nearly uniform section, since small irregular thicknesses are not successfully compacted. Otherwise the process yields products low in cost, uniform in density, and having a strength comparable to other methods of manufacture.

Green compacts for tungsten and molybdenum powders have also been made by preparing them as a slurry and pouring them into a plaster-of-Paris mold. Upon drying, they are processed in the usual manner. Such procedure is simple and permits considerable varia tion as to size or shape.

A press setup for compacting small pinions from metal powders is shown in Figure 2. Many products similar to this are entirely completed by the pressing operation and require no further processing other than sintering. The sintering operation increases the strength and improves the crystalline structure.

Sintering

The operation of heating a "green compact" to an elevated temperature is known as *sintering*. As previously stated, it is the process by which solid bodies are bonded by atomic forces. Baeza[1] states that by the application of heat the particles are pressed into more intimate contact, and the effectiveness of surface-tension reactions is increased. Plasticity is increased, and there is a possibility that better mechanical interlocking is produced by building a fluid network. Also, any interfering gas phase present is removed by the heat. The temperatures used in sintering are usually well below the melting point of the principal powder constituent but may vary over a wide range up to a temperature just below the melting point. Tests have proved that there is usually an optimum sintering temperature for a given set of conditions, with nothing to be gained by going above this temperature. Aside from the temperature, other factors in sintering are time and atmosphere. The time element varies with different metals, but in most cases the effect of the heating is complete in a very short time, and there is no economy in prolonging the operation. Atmosphere is nearly always important, as the product, being made up of small

[1] W. J. Baeza, *A Course in Powder Metallurgy*, Reinhold Publishing Company, 1943.

particles, has a large surface area exposed. The problem is to provide a suitable atmosphere of some reducing gas or nitrogen to prevent the formation of undesirable oxide films during the process.

Fig. 2. Pressing small pinions from powdered metal. (Courtesy Moraine Products Division of General Motors Corporation.)

Furnaces for sintering may be either the batch or continuous type. The continuous type, which has a wire mesh belt to carry the compacts through the furnace, is shown in Figure 3. Pusher and roller hearth furnaces are also used and are similar in appearance. There is always some dimensional change in the operation of sintering; it may be either a growth or a shrinkage.[2] What happens depends on the shape and particle-size variation of the powder, the powder composition, sintering procedure, and briquetting pressure. Accurate

[2] R. P. Koehring, "Sintering Atmospheres for Production Purposes," *Powder Metallurgy*, American Society for Metals, 1942.

size is maintained by compensating for the change in making the green compact and then maintaining uniform conditions.

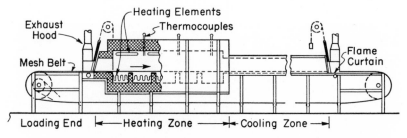

Fig. 3.   Continuous-type furnace for sintering powder metal compacts.

Hot Pressing

Many attempts have been made to combine the pressing and sintering operations.   Experiments have demonstrated that this method can produce compacted products with improved strength and hardness, greater accuracy, and higher densities than the products obtained by the usual methods.   Factors which limit its greater use include high cost of dies, difficulties in heating and atmospheric control, and the length of time required for the cycle.   Hot pressing is used to some extent in the manufacture of cemented carbides, but in most cases attempts to combine sintering with pressing have not met with success.

Sizing and Finishing Operations

Products requiring close tolerance or sizing may necessitate a final operation such as coining, hot pressing, or swaging.   All these operations increase the density by closing the pores and give added strength to the part.   It is also possible to close the voids by *infiltration,* the introduction of molten metal into the sintered compact by capillary attraction.   This procedure results in improved physical properties by eliminating the voids which act as internal notches.   For successful results the infiltrate should have a much lower melting point than the compact and the operation should be done as quickly as possible.   The infiltration of copper into iron is a good example of this procedure.

All pressed-metal parts may be heat-treated although the results do not conform in all cases to those obtained in solid metals.   Best results are obtained with dense structures.   Porosity influences the rate of heat flow through the part and permits internal contamination if certain salts are used in the process.

Porous Metal Sheet

Porous metal sheets having controlled porosity are now being made by two processes. One process, known as gravity sintering, has been developed for stainless steel powder. A uniform layer of powder is placed upon ceramic trays and sintered up to 48 hours in dissociated ammonia at high temperature. The sheets are then rolled to obtain thickness uniformity and a better surface finish. They may then be fabricated into suitable shapes in the same manner as working sheet metal. Porous sheets of stainless steel are corrosion resistant and are used for gasoline, oil, and chemical filters.

In a somewhat similar process powders are fed from a hopper between two rolls, which compress and interlock them into a sheet of sufficient strength to be conveyed through a sintering furnace. The sheet can then be passed through another set of rolls and heat-treated if necessary. By blending the powders before they enter the rolls, alloy sheets can be made. Metal powders that can be rolled into sheets include copper, brass, bronze, Monel, and stainless steel. Both uniform mechanical properties and controlled porosity can be obtained by this process.

Advantages and Limitations

The use of powder metallurgy is rapidly increasing, and many products are being made better and more cheaply than by other manufacturing methods. Some of the advantages obtained by this process are as follows: [3,4]

1. Many products such as sintered carbides and porous bearings cannot be produced by any other method or process. This applies also to a number of products from alloys containing both metallic and nonmetallic powders. It is also possible to mold layers of different metal powders to form bimetallic products.

2. It is possible to produce parts with controlled porosity, such as those found in self-lubricating bearings made from nonferrous powders and graphite.

3. Large-scale production of many small parts can compete favorably with machined parts because of the close tolerances and surface finish that are obtained. On parts up to 2 inches in diameter, tolerances of ± 0.001 inch or less can be maintained.

[3] E. Schumacher and A. G. Souden, "Powder Metallurgy," *Metals & Alloys*, November 1944.

[4] P. Schwarzkopf and C. G. Goetzel, "Processing Trends in Powder Metallurgy," *Iron Age*, September 19, 1940.

4. Products of extreme purity can be made, since it is possible to obtain powders in a very pure state. In the operation of pressing there is little chance for impurities to enter.

5. The process is economical in material, since there are no losses of material in the fabrication, and in most cases the dimensional accuracy is so close that no material allowance is needed for machinery.

6. Labor cost is low; skilled mechanics are not required to operate presses or other necessary equipment.

7. A wide range of physical properties is possible with any given material. These can be controlled by varying the die pressure, particle size, or sintering temperature, or by introducing alloying elements.

Powder metallurgy has certain limitations which will restrict its use, particularly with those products that can be made economically by other manufacturing processes. In addition there are certain other limitations as to the mechanical equipment, the thermal characteristics of the powder, safety, and design. Some of these limitations are:

1. Metal powders are expensive and in some cases difficult to store without some deterioration.

2. Equipment costs are high. Presses with capacities up to 100 tons per square inch are required for some products. Dies operating in these presses must be accurately machined and capable of withstanding high pressures and temperatures. Sintering furnaces present problems of temperature and atmospheric control. These facts preclude the use of this process for short-run jobs.

3. The size of powder-fabricated parts is controlled by the capacity of the presses available and also by the compression ratio of the various powders. Compression ratios of different powders vary considerably. Since pressure is not distributed uniformly in a powder as it is in a liquid, a large product is not likely to have uniform density.

4. Intricate designs in products are difficult to attain, since there is no flow of the metal particles during compacting. Abrupt changes in thickness must be avoided; and it is not possible to mold undercuts, internal threads, and grooves. Uniform density is difficult to attain in long pieces.

5. Some thermal difficulties appear in sintering operations, particularly with the low-melting powders such as tin, lead, zinc, and cadmium. Most oxides of these metals cannot be reduced at temperatures below the melting point of the metal; hence, if such oxides

exist, they will have detrimental effects on the sintering process and result in an inferior product.

6. Some powders, in a finely divided state, present explosion and fire hazards, and precaution must be taken to keep dust out of the air. Such metal powders include aluminum, magnesium, zirconium, and titanium.

7. A completely dense product is not possible by this process. However, porosity can be reduced materially if the heating accompanies the pressing operation, or by infiltration.

Metal-Powder Products[5]

Many metals are now available for use in powder-metal parts, and the number of products made by this process is steadily increasing. A representative selection of machine parts made from a wide variety of metal powders is shown in Figure 4. It is interesting to note the intricate shape and design of the parts, most of which are made complete without the necessity of machining. Some of the prominent powder-metal products are as follows:

Cemented carbides. Tungsten-carbide particles are mixed with a cobalt binder, pressed to shape, and then sintered at a temperature above the melting point of the matrix metal. The metal cobalt binds the carbide particles together and gives strength and toughness to the final product. Cemented carbides are used for cutting tools, dies, and various wear-resistant products.

Motor brushes. Brushes for motors are made by mixing copper with graphite in sufficient quantities to give the compact adequate mechanical strength. Tin or lead may also be added in small quantities to improve wear resistance.

Porous bearings. Most bearings are made from copper, tin, and graphite powders, although other metal combinations are used. After sintering, the bearings are sized and then impregnated with oil by a vacuum treatment. Porosity in the bearings can be controlled readily and may run as high as 40% of the volume.

Metallic filters. Porous metal filters, having greater strength and shock resistance than ceramic filters, are made with porosities up to 80%. Bronze and nickel are common metals used for this purpose.

Gears and pump rotors. Gears and pump rotors are made from powdered iron, mixed with sufficient graphite to give the product the desired carbon content. Parts are produced with close dimensional accuracy, requiring a minimum of machining. A porosity of around

[5] H. E. Hall, "Development in Metal Powders and Products," *Powder Metallurgy,* American Society for Metals, 1942.

Fig. 4. Machine parts made from a wide variety of metal powders. (Courtesy Chrysler Corporation—Amplex Divisions.)

20% is obtained in the process, and after the sintering operation the pores are impregnated with oil to promote quiet operation. The physical properties of iron-powder parts are close to those of ordinary gray cast iron.

Magnets. Excellent small magnets can be produced from iron, aluminum, nickel, and cobalt when combined in powder form. Alnico magnets, made principally from iron and aluminum powders, are superior to those cast. A finer grain structure is obtained, there are no internal defects, and the magnets are produced with close dimensional tolerances.

Contact parts. Electric-contact parts lend themselves well to powder-metallurgy fabrication, since it is possible to combine several metal powders and still maintain some of the principal characteristics of each. Contact parts must be wear-resistant and somewhat refractory and at the same time must have good electrical conductivity.

Many combinations such as tungsten-copper, tungsten-cobalt, tungsten-silver, silver-molybdenum, and copper-nickel-tungsten have been developed for electrical applications. Numerous other parts, including clutch faces, tungsten filaments, diamond cutting wheels, brake bands, laminated metals, and welding rods are produced by powder metallurgy. There are many other uses for powdered metals which are not pressed to shape, such as paint pigments and other protective coatings. Aluminum powder is used in Thermit welding; and, in the field of pyrotechnics and explosives, powdered aluminum and magnesium are both prominent. The addition of powdered metals to plastics increases their strength and contributes other metallic properties.

REVIEW QUESTIONS

1. What is powder metallurgy?
2. What is meant by sintering, and how is it accomplished?
3. What characteristics should be included in specifying a metal powder?
4. Why is particle-size distribution important in a given product?
5. What determines the compressibility of a powder, and how is it expressed?
6. What two powders have greatest use in compressed-powder products?,
7. Name and describe five methods of producing powders.
8. What is the purpose of adding certain lubricants to the powder before processing?
9. Describe the usual steps in producing a metal-powder part.
10. What types of presses are generally used in this work?
11. What are the various factors that must be considered in the operation of sintering?
12. Why not hot-press all products and eliminate the sintering operation?
13. How are porous metal sheets manufactured?
14. What are the advantages claimed for powder-metal parts?
15. List the limitations of this manufacturing process.
16. Name three products made by powder metallurgy that cannot be made by other processes.
17. What advantages do bearings made by this process have over cast bearings?
18. What uses are found for metal powders that are not compressed to a solid form?

REFERENCES

Adler, Arthur, "Stainless Steel Powder Parts," *Materials & Methods*, March 1955, p. 119.
Baeza, W. J., *A Course in Powder Metallurgy*, Reinhold Publishing Company, 1943.
Balke, C. C., "Powder Metallurgy—Some Theoretical Aspects," *Iron Age*, April 17, 1941.

Campbell, John B., Porous Metal Sheet, *Materials & Methods,* April 1955, p. 98.

Clauser, H. R., "Structural Parts from Metal Powders," *Materials & Methods,* September 1949.

Goetzel, C. G., "Sintered, Forged, and Rolled Iron Powders," *Iron Age,* October 1, 1942.

Lenel, F. V., "Powder Metallurgy," *Mechanical Engineering,* July 1943.

Powder Metallurgy Today, F. S. Stokes Company, 1949.

Schumacher, E. E., and A. G. Souden, "Some Aspects of Powder Metallurgy," *Bell System Technical Journal,* Vol. XXIII, October 1944.

Schwarzkopf, P., "Infiltration of Powder Metal Compacts with Liquid Metal," *Metal Progress,* January 1950, p. 64.

Schwarzkopf, P., and C. G. Goetzel, "Processing Trends in Powder Metallurgy," *Iron Age,* September 19, 1940.

Skaupy, F., *Principles of Powder Metallurgy,* Philosophical Library, 1944.

Victor, M. T., and C. A. Sorg, "Design of Powder Metallurgy Parts," *Metals & Alloys,* March 1944.

Wulff, J., *Powder Metallurgy,* American Society for Metals, 1942.

Wulff, J., H. F. Taylor, and A. J. Shaler, *Metallurgy for Engineers,* John Wiley and Sons, 1952.

CHAPTER 8

PLASTICS

The manufacture of plastic products on a large scale is of comparatively recent date. The discovery of ebonite or hard rubber by Charles Goodyear in 1839 and the development of Celluloid by Hyatt about 1869 marked the beginning of this industry. It was not until 1909, however, that one of the most important materials, phenol formaldehyde resin, was developed by Dr. L. H. Baekeland and his associates. Since then, research has added numerous other synthetic materials which vary widely in physical properties.

In general, the term "plastic" is applied to all materials capable of being molded or modeled. Modern usage of this word has changed its meaning to include a large group of synthetic organic materials that become plastic by the application of heat and are capable of being formed to shape under pressure. They replace materials like glass, wood, and metals in construction and make many useful articles, including coatings and filaments for weaving. Products made from plastic materials can be produced rapidly with close-dimensional tolerance and excellent surface finish. Often they have replaced metals where lightness in weight, corrosion resistance, and

dielectric strength are to be considered. Another important characteristic of these products is that they may be made either transparent
or in colors. There are over fifty different kinds of plastics in commercial production today, offering a wide variety of physical
properties.

Fig. I. A group of parts molded from thermosetting resins. A majority of these parts
were compression-molded. (Courtesy The Hydraulic Press Manufacturing Company.)

Plastic Materials

Plastic materials may be broadly classified as *thermosetting* and
thermoplastic. Thermosetting compounds are formed to shape under
heat and pressure, resulting in a product that is permanently hard.
The heat first softens the material; but, as additional heat and pressure are applied, the plastic is hardened by a chemical change known
as *polymerization*.[1] A group of parts molded from thermosetting
resins is shown in Figure 1. Thermoplastic materials undergo no

[1] Polymerization is a chemical process resulting in the formation of a new compound
whose molecular weight is a multiple of that of the original substance.

chemical change in molding and do not become hard with the application of pressure and heat. They remain soft at elevated temperatures until they are hardened by cooling, and they may be remelted repeatedly by successive applications of heat, as in the melting of paraffin.

The raw materials for plastics are various agricultural products and numerous other minerals and organic materials, including coal, gas, petroleum, limestone, silica, and sulfur. In the process of manu-facture still other ingredients are added such as color powders, solvents, lubricants, plasticizers, and filler material. Wood powder, flour, cotton, rag fibers, asbestos, powdered metals, graphite, and other constituents are employed as fillers. Their use reduces manu-facturing costs, minimizes shrinkage, improves heat resistance, pro-vides impact strength, or imparts other desired properties to the product. Plasticizers or solvents are used with some compounds to soften them or to improve their flowability in the mold. Lubricants also improve the molding characteristics of the compound. All these materials are mixed with the granulated resins before mold-ing.

Some of the common thermosetting compounds are as follows:

Phenol formaldehyde. This compound, originally developed by Dr. Baekeland, is one of the principal thermosetting plastics used in industry today. The synthetic resin, made by the reaction of phenol with formaldehyde, forms a hard, high-strength, durable material which is capable of being molded under a wide variety of conditions. This material has high heat and water resistance, and may be pro-duced in a wide range of colors. It is used in the manufacture of coating materials, laminated products, grinding wheels, and metal and glass bonding agents, and may be cast into many useful items. Products made from this material include molded cases, appliance plugs, bottle caps, knobs, dials, knife handles, radio cabinets, and numerous electrical parts.

Urea formaldehyde. This plastic component, also thermosetting, may be obtained in the form of molding power or in solution for laminating and similar treatments. It also has wide use as an ad-hesive since it possesses good bonding qualities and strength as well as resistance to water. The chemical combination of urea with formaldehyde forms a colorless resin especially adapted to light-colored articles which resist ultraviolet light and remain colorless for a long period of time. These products, which have a hard surface and high dielectric strength, are light in weight, and may be produced in all colors. They include tableware, light fixtures, buttons, instrument dials, veneer bonds, and clock cases. As a binder for sand cores urea resins are used in the casting of light metals.

Phenol furfural. Furfural is obtained by processing waste farm products like corncobs and hulls from rice and cottonseeds with certain acids. The thermosetting resin obtained flows readily at low molding temperatures and cures rapidly when the proper temperature is reached. Products of furfural are dark in color and water resistant, have excellent electrical qualities, and can be fabricated by most processes. Commercial products of this material are used for instrument housings, brake linings, electrical parts, binder for abrasive wheels, and varnish for impregnating laminates.

Melamine. Melamine resins, principally melamine formaldehyde, are comparatively recent additions to the plastic family. The compound melamine, made from carbon, nitrogen, and hydrogen, produces an excellent shock- and heat-resisting product. It is a thermosetting plastic and is adapted to processing by either compression or transfer molding. Being arc-resistant and having high dielectric strength, it is highly useful for electrical parts such as telephone sets, circuit breakers, and terminal blocks. Other uses include laminated products, tableware, and enamel.

Epoxides. Epoxy resins, first manufactured in the United States in 1947, are used for casting, laminating, molding, potting (the encasing of electrical parts), as paint ingredients, and as adhesives. Cured resins are low in shrinkage, have good chemical resistance, excellent electrical characteristics, strong physical properties, and adhere well to both glass and metal. As adhesives they are employed in aircraft structures to replace other forms of fastening. Likewise in the manufacture of laminates they are used with glass fibers to make panels for printed circuits, tanks, jigs, and dies. Because of their resistance to wear and impact, epoxy resins have recently been used extensively in the manufacture of press dies for metal forming operations.

Silicones. Silicon-base polymers differ materially from most other plastics which are based on the carbon atom. They possess a desirable combination of properties for a large group of industrial products such as oils, greases, resins, adhesives, and rubber compounds. Their outstanding properties include stability, resistance to high temperatures over long periods of time, good low temperature and high electric characteristics, and water repellence. Some oils and greases operate well over a temperature range of −40 to 500 F. The silicone resins may be molded, used in laminates or as coatings, or they may be processed into foam sheets or blocks. Silicone rubbers are used in moldings, extrusions, gaskets, in insulation, or as a shock-absorption material. Because of their high cost the use of silicone products is often limited where their unusual properties would be most useful.

Thermoplastic compounds available in quantity include the following: THERMOPLASTICS

Cellulose derivatives. Cellulose derivatives are widely used in the United States because of the availability of cellulose material in cotton and wood.

Cellulose nitrate, the first to be used, is highly inflammable, but has the advantage of being extremely tough, water resistant, and clear in color. It is used in fountain pens, ping-pong balls, jewelry, handles for toothbrushes, and fish lures.

Cellulose acetate is a more stable compound, having considerable mechanical strength and ability to be fabricated into sheets or molded by injection, compression, and extrusion. Display packaging, toys, knobs, flashlight cases, bristle coating for paint brushes, radio panels, and extruded strips are successfully made of this compound.

Cellulose acetate–butyrate molding compound is similar to cellulose acetate, and both are produced in all colors and by the same processes. In general, cellulose acetate–butyrate is recognized for its low moisture absorption, toughness, dimensional stability under various atmospheric conditions, and ability to be continuously extruded. Typical butyrate products include steering wheels, football helmets, goggle frames, trays, belts, furniture trim, insulation foil, and extruded tubing for gas and water.

Ethylcellulose, one of the newer cellulose plastics, is the lightest of the cellulose derivatives. In addition to its use as a base for coating materials, it is employed extensively in the various molding processes because of its stability and resistance to alkalies. Other outstanding properties are surface hardness, good electrical properties, and mechanical strength. Typical applications include containers, drill jigs and forming dies, trim moldings, heads for golf clubs, and flexible coatings. It may also be produced in thin sheets or extruded shapes.

Cellophane (regenerated cellulose) is produced in thin sheets by an extruding process and is useful for packaging materials since it provides a protective coating against moisture and other contaminating influences. Because of its durability, pleasing appearance, and fire resistance, this material is also being used for curtains and draperies.

Polystyrene. Polystyrene is a thermoplastic material especially adapted for injection molding and extrusion, although some other methods of processing can be used. Some of its outstanding characteristics are low specific gravity (1.07), availability in colors from clear to opaque, resistance to water and most chemicals, dimensional stability, and insulating ability. Electrical insulation has been one of its major applications to date because it is an excellent rubber substitute. In addition, styrene resins are molded into such products as battery boxes, dishes, radio parts, lenses, and wall tile.

Polyethylene. Polyethylene products are flexible at both room and low temperatures, waterproof, unaffected by most chemicals, capable of being heat-sealed, and can be produced in a variety of colors. Polyethylene is one of the lighter plastics and in solid form can float on water. Although one of the newer plastics, it has many applications, including such products as ice-cube trays, developing trays, fabrics, film for packaging, collapsible nursing bottles, coaxial cable, and insulating parts for high-frequency fields. Polyethylene products may be made by molding, blow molding, or may be extruded into sheets and monofilaments.

Vinyl resins. A number of vinyl resins commercially available include copolymers of vinyl chloride and vinyl acetate, polyvinyl butyrals, polyvinyl chloride, polyvinyl alcohol, and polyvinyl acetate. All are thermoplastic materials capable of being processed by compression, injection, or extrusion into a wide variety of products. The *copolymers* of *vinyl chloride* and *vinyl acetate* are obtained with a wide range of properties by varying the ratio of the two resins. They are especially suitable for surface coatings and for both flexible and rigid sheeting. In addition, they are extruded and molded into many products, a special grade being used in the manufacture of fibers that have chemical resistance and considerable strength. *Polyvinyl butyral,* used for interlayers in safety glass, raincoats, sealing fuel tanks, and flexible molded products, is a clear tough resin. It has resistance to moisture, great adhesiveness, and stability toward light and heat. *Polyvinyl chloride* resin has a high degree of resistance to many solvents and will not support combustion. It has found wide industrial use in resilient rubberlike products. *Polyvinyl alcohol* products which are durable and have excellent resistance to oils and chemicals include extruded tubing, molded trim, seals, gaskets, binders, and abrasive-resistant linings. *Polyvinyl acetate* is used as an adhesive for bonding many materials and as a base for various coatings, lacquers, ink, and plastic wood.

Acrylic resins. This resin is of special value because of its excellent light-transmitting power, ease of fabrication, and resistance to moisture. The acrylic resin most commonly used is *methyl methacry-*

late, but it is better known by the commercial names Lucite (du Pont) and Plexiglas (Rohm & Haas). It is a thermoplastic material which can be fabricated by casting, extruding, molding, and stretch forming into such products as airplane windows, shower doors, gage covers, toilet articles, transparent models, and covers where visibility of operation is desirable.

Many other synthetic and natural resins, protein substances, and other materials are used in the manufacture of plastics. *Nylon* monofilaments are used for hosiery, parachute shroud line, glider tow ropes, and brush bristles. Examples of molded and extruded products of nylon are bearings, tumblers, kitchen accessories, luggage, tubes, and furniture trim. The *shellac* resins are used as coating material, binder for abrasive wheels, phonograph records, and insulators. A variety of cold-molding compounds consisting of materials such as asbestos fibers with bituminous, cement, or shellac binders are made into such products as knobs, handles, connector plugs, and arc shields. Nonflammable casein and protein plastics of all colors are made into buttons, novelties, sheets, and tubing.

Synthetic rubber. Attempts to synthesize natural rubber have been made for many years. The fact that many highly industrialized nations had no source of raw rubber under their control was a contributing factor in developing research along this channel which has produced many synthetics. Among these synthetics Thiokol, Neoprene, GR-S, Buna N, butyl, and silicone rubbers[2] have had commercial acceptance. GR-S is produced in largest quantity, being particularly adapted for tire use. Similar to natural rubber, it can be substituted in most instances. It is a copolymer of butadiene and styrene and can be cured to any degree of hardness desired. The strength of GR-S is improved by adding carbon black, and for tire use is frequently compounded with natural rubber. The butadiene-acrylonitrile copolymers (known as Buna N or nitrile rubbers), employed principally because of their resistance to oils, find use in such products as oil hose, gaskets, and diaphragms. They also serve to some extent as a blending material with phenolics and vinyl plastics. The organic polysulfides, known as Thiokols, are very resistant to gasoline, oils, and paints, as well as to sunlight, and are used in the manufacture of hose, shoe heels and soles, coated fabrics, and insulation coatings. Resilient solid objects can be molded in conventional machines used for other plastics.

The chloroprene polymer, known as Neoprene, is produced from

[2] A. Black, "Recent Developments in Engineering Materials," *Mechanical Engineering,* April 1945.

coal, limestone, water, and salt. Calcium carbide, a product of coal and limestone, when added to water, forms acetylene gas (C_2H_2). This gas, in combination with hydrogen chloride, forms chloroprene, which is changed to Neoprene by polymerization. Neoprene has good resistance to oils, heat, and sunlight, and is used for such articles as conveyor belts, shoe soles, protective clothing, insulation, hose, printing rolls, tires and tubes, and as a bonding material for abrasive wheels. It has a wider application than other synthetic rubbers and can replace natural rubber in any of its present uses. Butyl, an isobutylene copolymer, has many of the properties and characteristics of natural rubber. Because of its strength, resistance to abrasion, and low permeability to gases, it is used most in the manufacture of inner tubes. Other uses include steam hose, conveyor belting for heated materials, and tank linings.

Methods of Processing

Plastic materials differ greatly from each other and lend themselves to such processing methods as compression molding, transfer molding, injection molding, jet molding, casting, extrusion, blowing, and laminating. Each material is best adapted to some one of the methods, although many can be fabricated by several. In most processes the molding material is in powder or granular form, although for some there is a preliminary operation of *preforming* the material before use.

Preforming. This operation consists of compressing a powder into small pellets of a size and shape that conform to a known mold cavity. All preforms are of the same density and weight, and the operation avoids waste of material in loading molds and, in general, speeds up production by rapid-mold loadings, with no possibility of overloading the molds. In the preforming operation the thermosetting powder is cold-molded, and no curing takes place. Preforms are used only in compression- and transfer-molding processes.

A rotary preforming press used in making disk pellets of various molding compounds is shown in Figure 2. The powder is fed by gravity from the hopper into the mold cells, and any excess powder is scraped off. The amount of material fed into each cell is controlled by regulating the lower punch. As the table revolves, pressure is applied uniformly on both sides, compressing the powder charge, and at the end of the cycle the tablet is ejected. In some cases tablets of more than one size are made at the same time, the only objection to this procedure being that there is some difficulty encountered in sorting the tablets.

Reciprocating machines, having only a single set of dies, are also used for a wide variety of preforming operations. The dies can be changed quickly, but the output is much lower than that of the

Fig. 2. Close-up view of rotary preforming press used in making disk pellets of various molding compounds. (Courtesy General Electric Company.)

rotary machines. When preforms are used in multiple-cavity molds, they are first transferred to a loading tray. The tray locates them accurately with reference to the mold cavities in the machine, and all preforms are molded simultaneously.

Compression molding. Compression molding is illustrated in Figure 3. A given amount of material is placed into a heated, metallic mold; and, as the mold closes, pressure is applied, causing the softened material to flow and conform to the shape of the mold. The material can be used either in a granulated state or preformed into a tablet. Pressures used in compression molding vary from 100 to 8000 psi, depending on the material used and the size of the product. The temperature range is from 250 to 400 F. Heat is very important for thermosetting resins, since it is used first to plasticize and then to polymerize or make them hard. Uniform heating of the powder is desirable, but not always easy to attain, because of the poor heat conductivity of the material.

Some thermoplastic materials are processed by compression, but the cycle of rapid heating and cooling of the mold adds to the difficulty in using such material. Unless the mold is sufficiently cooled before ejection, distortion of the piece is likely to result.

A large variety of hydraulic presses, ranging from hand-operated to completely automatic, are available for compression molding. The function of the press is to apply the necessary pressure and at the

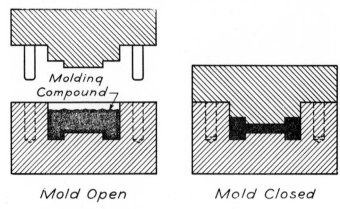

Mold Open   **Mold Closed**

Fig. 3.   Diagrammatic view of compression-molding process.

same time sufficient heat to plasticize properly and cure the plastic materials. Heat may be transferred from heated platens or applied directly to the metal mold. It is supplied by steam, heated liquids, electrical resistance, or ultrahigh-frequency electric currents.

The simplest type of press is the hand-operated one. Separate molds, which are loaded and unloaded outside the press, are used, and the only function of the press is to supply the necessary pressure for the operation. Other presses, also manually controlled, have the molds permanently mounted and consequently can use much larger molds. Semiautomatic presses are those that operate automatically for one cycle only. This type eliminates variations due to the personal element, as the operator need only load and unload the machine. A self-contained, semiautomatic press used for both compression and transfer molding is shown in Figure 4. The mold is closed and clamped by the upward-acting press platen. Molding that requires the addition of a high-frequency unit for plasticizing the molding material can also be done on this press.

Completely automatic presses are those that operate continuously for a long period of time. All operations, such as measuring and feeding the raw material, are automatically controlled and accurately timed so as to maintain uniform molding conditions. Automatic presses are rapid in operation and require a minimum of attention.

Transfer molding. In the process of transfer molding, the thermosetting powder or preforms are placed into the pressure chamber above the mold cavities, as illustrated in Figure 5. They are then plasticized by heat and pressure and injected into the mold cavities as a hot liquid, where the material is cured and becomes hard. This

Fig. 4. Semi-automatic toggle compression-molding press, capacity 50 tons. (Courtesy F. J. Stokes Machine Company.)

process is especially desirable for producing parts requiring small metal inserts, since the hot plastic material enters the mold gradually and without great pressure. Intricate parts and those having large variation in section thickness can also be produced to advantage by this method. The process differs from the injection molding of thermoplastic materials in that the mold is kept heated at all times and parts are ejected without cooling. In some equipment provision is made to use high-frequency electric current as a means of heating the preformed tablets.

Injection molding. The injection molding machine of 8-ounce capacity, shown in Figure 6, can be controlled automatically at a rate of around 300 shots per hour and, in operation, is quite similar to that of some die-casting machines. A schematic sketch showing the operation of injection molding machines is shown in Figure 7. Molding material is fed by gravity from a hopper and a metering

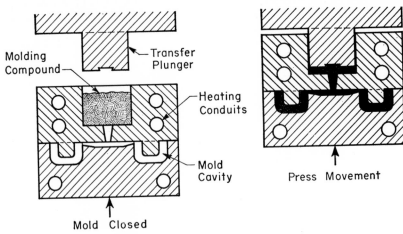

Fig. 5. Diagrammatic sketch of transfer-molding process.

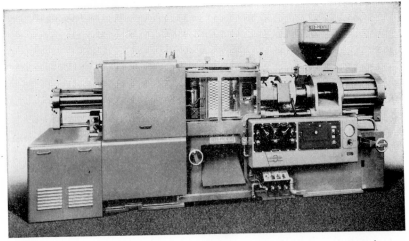

Fig. 6. Plastic injection-molding machine. (Courtesy Reed Prentice Corp.)

device to a cylindrical heating chamber, where it is plasticized and injected into the closed mold under considerable pressure. The finished product is hardened in the mold by the cooling effect of water circulated through conduits in the mold. After the injection plunger retracts, the mold is opened and the product ejected.

The heating-chamber construction of all injection machines is about the same. It is cylindrical in shape with a torpedolike spreader in the center so that the incoming material is kept in a layer thin enough to be heated both uniformly and rapidly. The heating chamber temperature ranges from 250 to 500 F, depending on the kind of material being charged and the size of the mold. Heat is

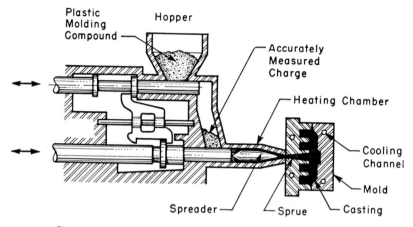

Fig. 7. Sketch showing operation of injection-molding machine.

furnished by a series of electrical-resistance coils. These chambers must be of substantial construction, as injection pressures may reach as high as 30,000 psi.

Injection machines are built in three general styles: of horizontal construction, as shown in Figure 7; with the heating and injection unit in a vertical position, as illustrated in Figure 8; and a completely vertical unit such as a compression-type machine, with the molds held in a horizontal position. The machine shown in Figure 8, with the injection unit in a vertical position, has certain desirable construction features which facilitate the feeding of the material into and through the heating chamber. The entire heating-chamber unit can be swung away from the mold for purposes of cleaning, repairing, and changing of molds. The insert of the figure shows in detail the method of heating the plastic material as it is fed to the heating cylinder from the overhead hopper.

Thermoplastic materials are generally used in injection molding, because they are especially suited for rapid production. Compared to compression molding, this process is much faster, since the mold does not have to be alternately heated and cooled. The mold is

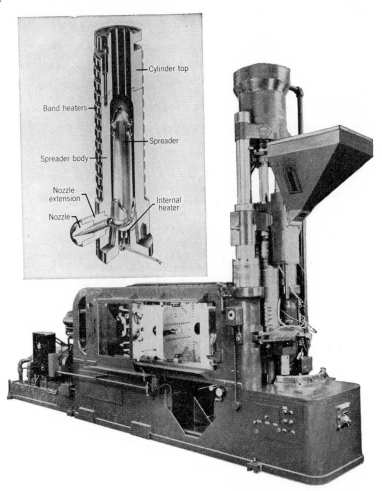

Fig. 8. An automatic injection-molding machine, 48-ounce capacity, having the heating cylinder assembly in a vertical position. Insert shows heating cylinder assembly. (Courtesy Lester-Phoenix, Inc.)

maintained at a constant temperature, usually 165 to 200 F, by circulating water, and a production cycle of two to six shots per minute is possible. Mold costs are lower, since fewer cavities are necessary to maintain equivalent production by injection molding. Articles of difficult shapes and of thin walls are successfully produced, as illustrated in Figure 9. Metal inserts, such as bearings, contacts, or screws, can be applied in the mold and cast integrally with the product. Material loss in the process is low, as sprues and gates can be re-used. Although the capacities of injection machines vary from 2 ounces to 8 pounds, small-parts machines of 8- to 16-ounce capacity are most popular.

Thermosetting materials can be injection-molded by a process known as *jet molding*. With a few minor changes, nearly any standard thermoplastic injection-molding machine can be converted

Fig. 9. Mold for making berry baskets in an injection-molding machine. (Courtesy Nalle Plastics.)

to a jet-molding machine. The torpedo spreader in the heater is removed, and the main heating of the resin materials is concentrated at the nozzle passage to the sprue. As soon as the mold is filled, the nozzle area is cooled by circulating water, and the pressure in the chamber is released. No further chemical changes of the material take place until the cycle is repeated.

Extruding. Thermoplastic materials, such as the cellulose derivatives, vinyl resins, polystyrene, polyethylene, and nylon, may be extruded through dies into simple shapes of any desired length. Thermosetting compounds are not well adapted to this process because of the rapidity with which they harden but are used to a limited extent in the production of thick-walled tubes. A schematic diagram of an extruding press is shown in Figure 10. Granulated or powdered material is fed into the hopper and then forced through a heated chamber by a spiral screw. In the chamber the material becomes a thick viscous mass, in which form it is forced through the die. As it leaves the die, it is cooled by air or water and gradually hardens as it rests on the conveyor. Long tubes, rods, molding sections, and many special sections are readily produced in this manner. Because they can be bent or curved to various shapes after extrusion by immersion in hot water, such products as conduits for electric conductors and for handling chemicals are made by this process. Much insulation, now extruded directly on wire, is economical to produce and has excellent physical properties. Filaments for plastic fabrics and sheeting for curtains and packaging purposes are both important products of this process.

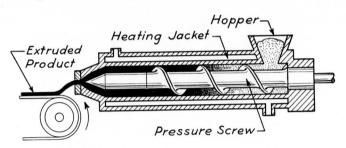

Fig. 10.   Schematic diagram of typical plastic extrusion press.

Casting. Thermosetting materials used for casting include the phenolics, the polyesters, and the allyl resins, the last being especially useful for optical lenses and other applications requiring excellent clarity. These resins have a wider use in casting than the thermoplastics, as they have greater fluidity in pouring. Ethycellulose and cellulose acetate butyrate, both thermoplastics, are used where impact strength and rigidity are needed for drop-hammer and stretch dies. Acrylics are used in the casting of transparent articles and flat sheets.

Plastics are cast when the number of parts desired is not sufficient to justify the making of expensive dies. Frequently, open molds of lead are formed by dipping a steel mandrel of desired shape into molten lead and stripping the shell from the sides of the mandrel after it solidifies. Cores of lead, plaster, or rubber may be introduced if desired. Hollow castings are also produced by the slush-casting method. Solid objects may be made from molds of plaster, glass, wood, or metal. When parts have numerous undercuts, the molds are made of synthetic rubber.

Casting is recommended for preparing short rods, tubes, and various shapes that are to be used in subsequent machining operations or carving. Machined surfaces have a dull white appearance which may be removed by tumbling with wood blocks and abrasive particles or by buffing. Costume jewelry and novelties are cast because of the pleasing color combination that can be obtained and the fact that frequent style changes do not justify the preparation of expensive die equipment. Other examples of cast products are knobs, clock and instrument cases, handles, drilling jigs, and punches and dies for sheet-metal fabrication in the airplane industry.

Laminated plastics. Laminated plastics consist of sheets of paper, fabric, asbestos, wood, or similar materials which are first impregnated or coated with resin and then combined under heat and pressure to form commercial materials. These materials are hard, strong, impact-resisting, and unaffected by heat or water, and have desirable properties for numerous electrical applications. The final product may consist of either a few sheets or over a hundred, depending on the thickness and properties desired. Although most laminated stock is made in sheet form, rods and tubes as well as special shapes are avail-

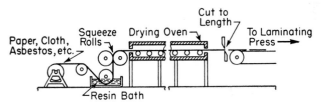

Fig. II. Diagrammatic sketch of process for preparing sheet material for lamination.

able. The material has good machining characteristics which permit its fabrication into gears, handles, bushings, furniture, and many other articles.

In the manufacture of laminated products, the resinoid material is dissolved by a solvent to convert it into a liquid varnish. Rolls of paper of fabric are then passed through a bath for impregnation, as shown in Figure 11. This is a continuous operation; and, as the sheet leaves the resinoid bath, it goes through a drier, which evaporates the solvent, leaving a fairly stiff sheet impregnated with the plastic material. To facilitate lamination, the sheets are then cut into convenient sizes and stacked together in numbers sufficient to make up the desired thickness of the final sheet. Each group is assembled between polished metal plates at top and bottom and is then stacked in a hydraulic press. Under the action of heat and pressure, a hard rigid plate having desirable properties for many industrial applications is obtained. Tubes, made by machine-winding strips of the prepared stock around a steel mandrel, are cured by being placed in a circulating-hot-air oven or are subjected to both heat and pressure in a tube mold. Properties of laminates depend largely on the sheet material or filler used. Paper-base materials are used often in electrical products because of their excellent characteristics and their ability to be held to close tolerances.[3] Fabric-base materials are stronger and tougher and, hence, better for stressed parts. Gears made of a canvas base are quiet in operation and have proved very satisfactory. Asbestos and fiber-glass cloth are recommended for heat-resisting and low water-absorption uses. Thin sheets of wood are now being laminated to produce a light material equal in strength to some metals and resistant to moisture. These sheets, produced with a smooth surface, can be formed into panels without expensive machining operations. Safety glass is, in effect, a laminated-plastic product, since thermoplastic layers are used between the glass sheets to make it nonshattering. In addition, many other materials, including rubber, metal, rayon, and spun glass, are used in the manufacture of laminated products.

Blowing or vacuum forming. Many plastic materials can be formed into thin hollow shapes by air-pressure differentials when the sheet material is heated and is in a soft, pliable condition. To accomplish this, the sheet is clamped to the top surface of a vacuum or pressure container and is drawn or blown into a form approximating a section of a sphere. No dies are required, and upon cooling it retains its formed shape.

A somewhat similar process, known as vacuum snapback forming, is illustrated in Figure 12. After the heated sheet is clamped, a vacuum is created in the chamber, which causes the sheet to be drawn down as shown by the dotted lines. The male mold is then introduced into the formed sheet, and the vacuum is gradually reduced, causing the sheet to snap back against the mold form. Movement of the sheet after contact with the form should be kept at a minimum to avoid surface markings. By having ample draft on the mold form the part is easily removed. In Figure 13 is shown a setup where sheets are formed to shape by air pressure and are actually blown into the mold. This process is used where more complicated shapes are desired and possible surface defects are not objectionable. By using special, synthetic greases on the mold, the tendency for marks to show on the formed part is materially decreased. Similar results may be obtained by vacuum drawing, but there are likely to be surface defects from air bubbles in the grease.

[3] According to NEMA (National Electrical Manufacturers Association) there are twelve grades of laminates which are standard for most applications. Six grades have paper base, four have fillers of cotton fabric, one has an asbestos paper filler, and one uses asbestos fibers.

Certain plastics can be formed into bottles and containers in a fashion similar to the methods used in blowing glass bottles. In this

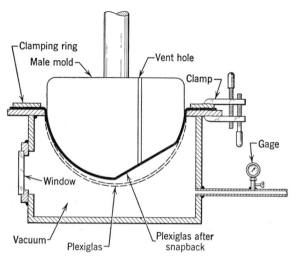

Fig. 12. Vacuum snapback forming of heated thermoplastic sheets. (Courtesy Rohm & Haas Company.)

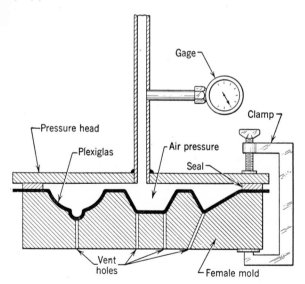

Fig. 13. Forming heated thermoplastic sheets by blowing into a mold. (Courtesy Rohm & Haas Company.)

operation a tube or parison of thermoplastic material is either injected or extruded into an open mold, as shown in Figure 14. With

the tube still in contact with the extruding nozzle, the mold closes
and air pressure from an outlet within the nozzle expands the plastic
against the walls of the mold. The extrusion is then cut from the
nozzle, and the mold indexes to the next position. Here a blow
head descends on the mold and holds the blown container under

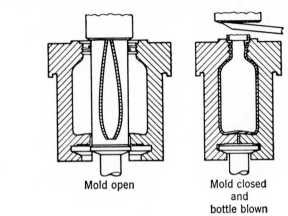

Mold open   Mold closed
and
bottle blown

Fig. 14. Blow-molding a thermoplastic bottle using an extruded parison. (Courtesy
Plax Corporation and Modern Plastics Encyclopedia.)

pressure until it is removed. It is ejected from the mold by an air
jet and cooled to room temperature by a water spray. Articles made
by blowing include Christmas tree ornaments, atomizer bulbs, cos-
metic containers, bottles, floats, and certain synthetic-rubber articles
like hot-water bottles. Polyethylene, cellulose nitrate, and the acrylics
are among those plastics that can be formed by blowing techniques.

Molds for Plastics

Molds for both the compression and injection processes are made of
steel and are heat-treated. The production of these molds demands
the same type of machine work and the usual precision required for
dies used in pressure casting. There are, however, some differences
in construction because of varying characteristics in the materials
being processed. Ample draft and fillets should be provided to facilitate removing the article from the mold. Ejector pins are usually
provided for this purpose and should be located at points where the
pin marks are not noticeable. Like metals, plastic materials shrink
on cooling, and some allowance must be provided. Shrinkage varies
according to the type of material and method of processing but is
usually 0.003 to 0.009 inch per inch.

Compression molds are made in *hand* and *semiautomatic* types.

Each type might be further subdivided into *positive, semipositive,* and *flash* designs. The hand molds are charged and unloaded on a bench. Heating and cooling are accomplished by plates on the presses which are provided with the necessary circulating facilities. The semiautomatic molds are fastened rigidly to the presses and are heated or cooled by adjacent plates. As they open, work is ejected automatically from the molds which are single or multiple cavity.

Further classification of hand and positive molds may refer to the method of confining the plastic material in the mold. A positive mold is one that entirely confines the material in the mold. An example of this is a cylinder with a close-fitting plate at the bottom and a plunger which enters the cylinder to compress the powder. The thickness of the part being molded is controlled by the amount of powder charged. Such molds are commonly used in mounting metallurgical specimens. Semipositive molds are designed so that there is some provision for overflow. A landed mold of this type, shown in Figure 15, permits the escape of some material, but, owing to the telescoping feature, has some of the characteristics of a positive mold. This mold is very successful and is used more than either the positive or the flash types. Ejector pins are brought into play as the mold opens, to force the parts from the mold. The flash-type mold has no telescoping action whatsoever, and the material is not confined until the end of the stroke. As a result there is a slight fin, a few thousandths of an inch thick, around the lands of the mold where the closing is made.

Since most compression molding is done with thermosetting materials, alternate heating and cooling of the mold are not required. The molding temperature for these plastics is obtained from gas, steam, electricity, or heated liquids. Heat not only softens the plastic material so that it can be shaped to the mold, but also causes the chemical change which hardens it.

Injection molds are made in two pieces, one half being fastened to the fixed platen and the other half to the movable platen. Contact between the halves is made on accurately ground surfaces or lands, surrounding the mold cavities. Neither half telescopes with the other, which is the case with many of the compression molds. The cavities should be centrally located with reference to the sprue hole in the fixed half so as to obtain an even distribution of material and pressure in the mold. For locating purposes, guide pins, which are similar to those employed on metal-press dies, are fastened in the fixed half of the mold and enter hardened bushings in the movable part of the mold.

Mold cavities can extend into both halves of the mold. It is best, however, to have the outside of the molded part in the fixed half, provided that the shape is suitable for this arrangement. In the cooling process the plastic material tends to shrink away from the cavity walls and is withdrawn from this half as the mold opens. It is retained on the cores of the movable half until the ejector mechanism operates.

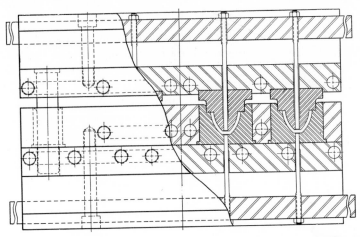

Fig. 15. Multicavity compression mold. (Courtesy Detroit Mold Engineering Company.)

Injection molds have cooling channels in both halves to permit the maintenance of a uniform temperature for chilling the molded part, since most materials fabricated by this process are thermoplastic. The material is forced into the mold from the heated cylinder under pressures ranging from 2 to 20 tons psi and is ejected from the mold at a temperature of approximately 125 F. Ejection of the parts occurs as the mold opens and is accomplished by either ejector pins or stripper plates.

Any cores required in injection molding are placed on the movable half of the mold. The normal shrinkage of the molded part tends to cling to the cores, causing it to withdraw freely from the stationary half as the mold opens. Vents, to permit the escape of entrapped air, are extremely small and are located in such a way as to permit all air to escape quickly.

REVIEW QUESTIONS

1. List the principal materials used in the manufacture of plastic articles.
2. Distinguish between thermosetting and thermoplastic materials.
3. Name the various methods used in forming plastic materials.
4. Describe the process of injection molding.
5. What is meant by polymerization?
6. Which resin is widely used in the manufacture of flexible products?
7. What resin is used for making transparent products?
8. How does synthetic rubber differ from natural rubber?
9. What are the basic raw materials used in making Neoprene?
10. What is the purpose of preforming molding powder?
11. Describe the process of compression molding.
12. What advantages does transfer molding have over compression molding?
13. What type of plastic material is generally used in injection molding? Why?
14. What plastic products are formed by the extruding process?
15. What kind of molds are used in plastic casting?
16. List the various materials that are laminated with plastics.
17. Describe the vacuum snapback method of forming.
18. How are plastic bottles made?
19. What is the difference between positive and flash-type molds?
20. How are molds for plastics vented?

REFERENCES

ASTM Standards on Plastics, American Society for Testing Materials, 1943.
Bakelite Molding Plastics, Bakelite Corporation, 1940.
Bell, L. M. T., *The Making and Moulding of Plastics,* Chemical Publishing Company.
Dearle, D. A., *Plastic Molding,* Chemical Publishing Company, 1941.
Delmonte, J., *Plastics in Engineering,* Penton Publishing Company, 1940.
DuBois, J. H., *Plastics,* American Technical Society, 1945.
Flynn, H. L., "How to Work With Plastics," *American Machinist,* April 11, 1946.
Huscher, J. L., "Fabrication and Use of Rigid Polyvinal Chloride Plastics," *Materials & Methods,* June 1954, pp. 119–134.
Lehmann, George P., "Proper Molds for Plastics," *American Machinist,* June 25, 1941.
Lougee, E. F., *Plastics from Farm and Forest,* Plastic Institute, Chicago, 1943.
Plastics Encyclopedia, Plastics Catalog Corporation, 1954.
Plastics Engineering Handbook, The Society of the Plastics Industry, Reinhold Publishing Corporation, 1954.
Sasso, J., *Plastics for Industrial Use,* McGraw-Hill Book Company, 1942.
Simonds, H. R., and C. Ellis, *Handbook of Plastics,* D. Van Nostrand Company, 1943.
Simonds, H. T., *Industrial Plastics,* 3d edition, Pitman Publishing Company, 1945.
Tenite Injection Molding, 3d edition, Tennessee Eastman Company, 1949.
Tenite Extrusion, Tennessee Eastman Company, 1950.
Thayer, G. B., *Plastic Mold Designing,* American Industrial Publisher, 1941.
Young, J. R., *Materials & Processes,* 2nd edition, John Wiley and Sons, 1954.

CHAPTER 9

WELDING

Welding is the fusion or uniting of two pieces of metal by means of heat. Many welding processes have been developed which differ widely in the manner in which the heat is applied and in the type of equipment used. Some processes require hammering, rolling, or pressing to effect the weld; others bring the metal to a fluid state and require no pressure. The processes that use pressure require bringing the surfaces of the metal to a temperature sufficient for cohesion to take place. This is nearly always a subfusion temperature. However, if the fusion temperature is reached, the molten metal must be confined by surrounding solid metal. No additional weld metal is required in welds of this type. Most welds are made at fusion temperature and require the addition of weld metal in some form. In the welding of dissimilar metals, it is often possible to make a satisfactory bond by bringing only one of the metals to a fusion temperature. Welds are also made by casting, in which case the metal is heated to a high temperature and poured into the cavity between the two pieces to be joined. In this method the heat in the weld metal must be sufficient to cause it to fuse properly with the parent metal.

Soldering is the uniting of two pieces of metal with a different metal, which is applied between the two in a molten state and at a temperature not exceeding 800 F. In this process some alloying with the base metal takes place, and additional strength is obtained by mechanical bonding. The usual metals for soldering are low-melting alloys of lead and tin. Brazing is a similar process in which the metal parts are joined by nonferrous metals, such as copper-zinc and silver alloys, having melting points below that of the parent metal but above 800 F. The filler metal is distributed between the joint surfaces by capillary attraction. Soldering is not considered a welding process, but brazing now is.[1] Temperatures in this process range from 1100 to 1983 F, which makes it possible to choose from a wide selection of possible filler metals.

Most of the developments of modern welding have taken place since the first World War as a result of the demands of industry for more rapid means of fabrication and assembly of metal parts. Welding processes are employed extensively in the manufacture of automobile bodies, aircraft, high-speed railroad cars, machine frames, structural work, tanks, and general machine-repair work. In the oil industry welding is extensively used at refineries and in pipe-line fabrication. During war the largest single use for welding has been in shipbuilding; in peacetime it is the fabrication of metal structures. The competition of welding has also been felt in the casting industry, since many machine parts that were formerly cast are now made up of steel members welded together. Such construction has the advantage of being lighter and stronger than cast iron. Gas cutting has likewise had its influence on forged products. Many parts are now accurately cut from thick steel plates, thus saving the cost of expensive dies. There is hardly an industry today that is not affected in some way by welding and cutting processes.

The first welding processes were all limited to low-carbon steel and wrought iron, which are easily welded and have a wide welding range. As the carbon content increases or as alloying elements are added, the welding range decreases, and good welds become increasingly difficult. However, the development of new electrodes and new welding techniques has greatly altered our concept of what is weldable material. Practically all alloy steels can now be welded if proper equipment and materials are used. Cast iron at first presented serious difficulties, because of its low ductility, poor fusion, and tendency to crack on cooling. Most of these difficulties are now overcome by proper methods and the selection of suitable welding materials. Such non-

[1] *Welding Handbook*, American Welding Society.

ferrous metals as brass, bronze, Monel metal, aluminum, copper, and nickel can be successfully welded, although special precaution must usually be taken to prevent oxidation.

General Conditions for Welding

Welding is facilitated if surfaces are cleaned and freed from foreign matter by wire brushing, machining, or sand blasting. Impurities tend to weaken a weld, causing the metal to be either brittle or filled with gas and slag inclusions. They also cause poor cohesion of the metals.

Tendencies toward oxidation increase with temperature. At the high temperatures used in many welding processes, the oxidation of the weld metal is likely to have serious weakening effects in the weld. In some processes this influence is counteracted by the use of a flux which removes the oxides and permits perfect cohesion of the metals. In the electric-arc process the flux is coated on the electrodes and, when melted, forms a protective coating of slag over the weld metal, as well as a nonoxidizing atmosphere. In gas welding and forge welding it is usually added in powder form. Other processes eliminate any oxidation tendencies by creating a nonoxidizing atmosphere at the point where the welding is done.

Inasmuch as oxidation takes place rapidly at high temperature, speed in welding is important. Some processes are naturally quicker than others, but the work should be done as rapidly as possible.

Principal Welding Processes

The principal welding processes, listed in Table 11, are discussed briefly in the text matter that follows.

Welded Joints

The six principal types of joints used in most welding processes (see Figure 1) are butt, lap, edge, corner, plug, and tee. Some of these types, such as butt welds, may be further subdivided, as they vary in form according to the thickness of the material. Joints for forge welding differ in their manner of preparation and do not resemble those shown in the figure. Lap and butt joints are the principal types used in resistance welding. In general, resistance-welded joints must be prepared more accurately and must be considerably cleaner than those used in other processes. Both gas and arc welding use the same types of joints.

Forge welding. Forge welding was the first form of welding used and for many centuries the only one in general use. Briefly, the

TABLE II.   Welding Processes*

I. Forge welding
   A. Manual
   B. Machine
     1. Rolling
     2. Hammer
     3. Die

II. Resistance welding
   A. Spot
   B. Seam
   C. Projection
   D. Flash
   E. Butt
   F. Percussion

III. Gas welding
   A. Air-acetylene
   B. Oxyacetylene
   C. Oxyhydrogen
   D. Pressure

IV. Braze welding
   A. Torch
   B. Twin-carbon arc
   C. Furnace
   D. Induction
   E. Resistance
   F. Dip
   G. Block
   H. Flow

V. Arc welding
   A. Carbon electrode
     1. Shielded
     2. Unshielded
   B. Metal electrodes
     1. Shielded
       (*a*) Shielded metal arc
       (*b*) Impregnated tape
       (*c*) Atomic hydrogen
       (*d*) Inert gas
       (*e*) Submerged arc
       (*f*) Shielded stud
     2. Unshielded
       (*a*) Bare metal
       (*b*) Stud

VI. Thermit welding
   A. Pressure
   B. Nonpressure

VII. Flow welding

VIII. Induction welding

IX. Cold welding

* This table follows closely the chart prepared by The American Welding Society.

process consists of heating the metal in a forge to a plastic condition and then uniting it by pressure. The heating is usually done in a coal- or coke-fired forge, although modern installations frequently employ oil or gas furnaces. The manual process is naturally limited to light work because all forming and welding are accomplished with a hand sledge. Before the weld is made, the pieces are formed to correct shape, so that, when they are welded, they will unite at the center first. As they are hammered together from the center to the outside edges, any oxide or foreign particles will be forced out. The process of preparing the metal is known as *scarfing*.

Forge welding is naturally rather slow, and there is considerable danger of an oxide scale forming on the surface. The tendency to oxidize can be counteracted somewhat by using a thick fuel bed and by covering the surfaces with a fluxing material which dissolves the

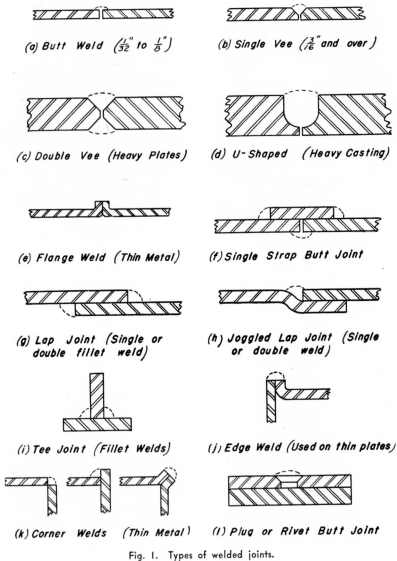

(a) Butt Weld $\left(\frac{1}{32}"\ to\ \frac{1}{8}"\right)$ (b) Single Vee $\left(\frac{3}{16}"\ and\ over\right)$

(c) Double Vee (Heavy Plates)   (d) U-Shaped (Heavy Casting)

(e) Flange Weld (Thin Metal)   (f) Single Strap Butt Joint

(g) Lap Joint (Single or double fillet weld)   (h) Joggled Lap Joint (Single or double weld)

(i) Tee Joint (Fillet Welds)   (j) Edge Weld (Used on thin plates)

(k) Corner Welds (Thin Metal)   (l) Plug or Rivet Butt Joint

Fig. I. Types of welded joints.

oxides. Many special fluxes have been prepared; however, borax in combination with sal ammoniac is commonly used. Heating must be slow because of unequal section thickness. As soon as the desired uniform temperature is reached, the pieces are removed to the anvil and hammered together.

For this type of welding, low-carbon steel and wrought iron are recommended, since they have a large welding-temperature range. This range decreases rapidly as the carbon content increases. High-carbon steels and alloy steels require considerably more care in controlling temperature and producing the welds.

Large work may be welded in hammer forges driven by air or steam. Such equipment is especially valuable for forming and shaping work in the plastic state and has the additional advantage of refining the grain size when worked above the critical temperature of the metal. Welded steel pipe is made mechanically by running the preheated steel strips through rolls which form the pipe to size and apply the necessary pressure for the weld.

Electrical-Resistance Welding. In this process a heavy electric current is passed through the metals to be joined, causing a local heating, and the weld is completed by the application of pressure. This process dates back to the latter part of the nineteenth century and was first used by Elihu Thompson. When the current passes through the metal, the greatest resistance is at the point of contact; hence, the greatest heating effect is at the point where the weld is to be made. Alternating current is generally used, coming to the machine with the usual commercial voltages. A transformer in the machine reduces the voltage 4 to 12 volts and raises the amperage sufficiently to produce a good heating current. The amount of current necessary is 30 to 40 kva per square inch of area to be united, based on a time of about 10 seconds. For other time intervals the power varies inversely with the time. The necessary pressure to effect the weld will vary from 4000 to 8000 psi.

Resistance welding is essentially a production process adapted to the joining of light-gage metals which can be lapped. Usually the equipment is suitable for only one type of job, and the work must be moved to the machine. The process is especially adapted to quantity production and includes a large amount of the welding done at the present time. It is the only process that permits a pressure action at the weld, while allowing an accurately regulated heat application. Also, the operation is extremely rapid.

The weldability of a given metal depends to some extent on its melting point. Practically all metals can be welded by resistance welding, although some few, such as tin, zinc, and lead, can be welded only with great difficulty.

In all resistance welding the three factors that must be given consideration are expressed in the formula: Heat $= I^2RT$, where I is the welding current in amperes, R the resistance of the metal being welded, and T the time. The amperage of the secondary or welding current is determined by the transformer. To provide possible variation of the secondary current, the transformer is equipped with a regulator on the primary side to vary the number of turns on the primary coil. This may be seen in Figure 2. For good welds these three variables, current, resistance, and time, must be carefully considered and determined by such factors as material thickness, kind of material, type and size of electrode.

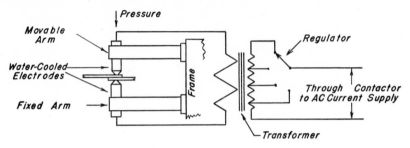

Fig. 2. Diagram of spot welder.

The timing of the welding current is very important. There should be an adjustable delay after the pressure has been applied until the weld is started. The current is then turned on by the timer and held a sufficient time for the weld. It is then stopped, but the pressure remains until the weld cools, thus eliminating any tendency for the electrodes to arc and also protecting the weld from discoloration. The pressure on the weld may be obtained manually, by mechanical means, by air pressure, by springs, or by hydraulic means. Its application must be controlled and co-ordinated with the application of the welding current.

Resistance welding may be subdivided as (1) spot welding, (2) projection welding, (3) seam welding, (4) butt welding, (5) flash welding, and (6) percussion welding.

Spot welding. In this form of resistance welding, two or more sheets of metal are held between metal electrodes as shown in Figure 2. The welding cycle is started with the electrodes contacting the metal under pressure before the current is applied, and for a period known as the *squeeze time*. A low-voltage current of sufficient amperage is then passed between the electrodes, causing the metal in contact to be rapidly raised to a welding temperature. As soon as the temperature is reached, the pressure between the electrodes squeezes the metal together and completes the weld.   This period, usually 3 to 30 cycles, is known as the *weld time*.   Next, while the pressure is still on, the current is shut off for a period called the *hold time*, during which the metal regains some strength by cooling.   The pressure is then released, and the work is either removed from the machine or moved so that another portion can be welded.   This is the *off time*.   All times are measured in terms of current cycles and usually range from 3 to 60 (1 cycle = $\frac{1}{60}$ sec).

Spot welding is probably the simplest form of resistance welding and for ordinary sheet steel does not present much of a problem. Good welds require sheet steel which is free from scale or foreign substances.   Such films cause variations in surface resistance and tend to increase the heating effect of metal in contact with the electrodes.

Surface imperfections, variations in weld strength, and electrode pickup are defects to be encountered if sheet surfaces are not properly prepared.   It may be noted that in spot welding there are five zones of heat generation: one at the interface between the two sheets, two at the contact surfaces of the sheets with the electrodes, and the other two in the metal of the sheets.   The contact resistance at the interface of the two sheets is the point of highest resistance where the weld formation starts.   The heat is not readily conducted from this point by the two electrodes on either side.   Contact resistance at this point, as well as between the electrodes and the outsides of the sheets, depends upon surface conditions, magnitude of electrode force, and the size of the electrodes.   If the sheets are the same in both thickness and analysis, the heat balance will be such that the weld nugget will be at the center.   With uneven sheet thicknesses or welding sheets of different thermal conductivities it may be necessary to use electrodes of different size or conductivity to obtain a proper heat balance.

Machines for spot welding are made in three general types: *stationary single-spot, portable single-spot,* and *multiple-spot* machines. Stationary machines may be further classified as *rocker-arm* and *direct-pressure* types.   The rocker-arm type, shown in Figure 3, is the simplest and cheapest but generally limited to machines of small capacity.   This machine is so designated because the motion for applying pressure and raising the upper electrode is made by rocking the upper arm.   The larger machines usually employ direct straight-line motion of the upper electrode.   This arrangement permits them to be used also for projection welding.

As assemblies to be welded increase in size, it is not always possible to bring them to a machine.   Portable spot welders, connected to the transformer by long cables, and capable of being moved to any position, are then used. Where all welds cannot be made by a single machine setup, welding jig assemblies are served best by portable welders. A wide variety of portable welding guns is made, as indicated in Figure 4, the principal differences among them being the manner of applying the pressure and the shape of the tips. Pressure is applied manually, pneumatically, or hydraulically, depending on the size and the type of gun.

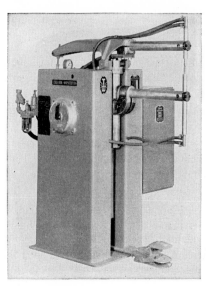

For production work, multiple-spot-welding machines have been developed which are capable of producing two or more spots simultaneously. In machines of this type several direct welds can be made from either one or more transformers. In some cases a system known as *indirect welding* is used, where two electrodes are in series, and the current passes through a heavy plate underneath the sheets and between the electrodes.

Fig. 3. Air-operated rocker-arm spot welder, 15-kva capacity. (Courtesy The Taylor Winfield Corporation.)

Spot welding lends itself readily to production work because of its simplicity and the rapidity with which welds can be made. Most ferrous and nonferrous alloys

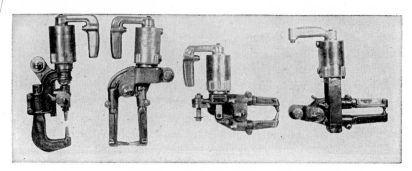

Fig. 4. Different types of welding guns. All may be operated by either air or hydraulic means. (Courtesy Progressive Welder Company.)

may be spot-welded, but each metal requires special manipulation and current regulation. Spot welding has a wide application, from thin foils in which low currents are used to heavy plates requiring high current and long time. Theoretically, any material of reasonable thickness can be spot-welded; however, as the thickness increases, the tremendous force necessary becomes a limiting factor. One-half inch is the usual upper limit. Spot welding is widely used in the manufacture of automobiles, refrigerators, and metal toys, and in numerous other metal-stamping assemblies.

Projection welding. Projection welding, a process similar to spot welding, is illustrated in the line diagram shown in Figure 5. Projection welds are produced at localized points in workpieces held under pressure between suitable electrodes. Sheet metal to be welded in this manner is first put through a punch press, which makes small projections or buttons in the metal. These projections are made with a diameter on the face equal to the thickness of the stock and project above the stock about 60% of its thickness.

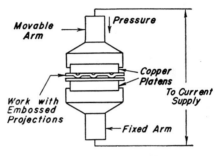

Fig. 5. Projection welding.

Such projection spots or ridges are made at all points where a weld is desired. This process is also used for cross-wire welding and for parts where the ridges are produced by machining. One advantage of this form of welding is that a number of welds can be made simultaneously, the only limit to the number being the ability of the press to furnish and distribute equally to the work the correct current and pressure. Results are generally uniform, and weld appearance is often better than in spot welding. Electrode life is long, since only flat surfaces are used and little maintenance is required.

In actual welding the sequence of operation is identical with that of spot welding. The current per weld is slightly less than for spot welds, but, because multiple welds are made, greater current and pressure capacity must be available. Only press-type machines are recommended for this process. It is possible to weld all metals by this method as readily as by other resistance-welding processes.

Seam welding. Seam welding consists in making a continuous weld on two overlapping pieces of sheet metal. Coalescence is produced by heat, obtained from the resistance of current. The current passes through the overlapping sheets which are held together under pressure between two circular electrodes. This method is, in effect, a continuous spot-welding process, since the current is not usually on continuously but is regulated by the timer on the machine. In high-speed seam welding using continuous current, the frequency of the current acts as an interrupter.

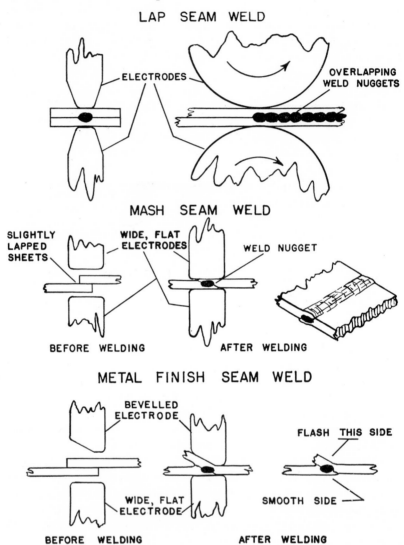

Fig. 6. Types of seam welds.

The three types of seam welds commonly used in industry are illustrated in Figure 6. The most common type is the simple lap seam weld shown in the upper part of the figure. This weld consists of a series of overlapping spot welds with sufficient overlap of the weld nuggets to provide a pressure-tight joint. If the pressure-tight quality of the lap seam weld is not required, the individual nuggets may be spaced so as to give a stitch effect. This process is known as *roll-spot* welding. In the center of the figure, a *mash seam* weld is shown which is produced by reducing the amount of sheet lapping to a small value. Broad-faced, flat electrodes are used, which forge the sheets together while welding. This forging action by the electrodes is

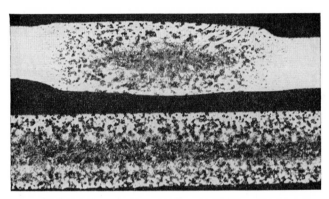

Fig. 7. Longitudinal and cross section of mash seam welds made with 0.050-inch steel at 80 ipm. Current 19,000 amps, electrode force 1500 lb, and initial overlap 150%. Magnification × 12.5.

known as "mash-down" and occurs simultaneously with the fusing on the sheets. Since the joint is covered above and below by the electrodes and on either side by the sheets, any extrusion or spitting from the weld is prevented. Micrographs showing longitudinal and transverse sections of two pieces of 0.050-inch steel are shown in Figure 7. Alterations can be made in electrode face contour and the amount of lap increased so that the mash-down takes place on only one side, which can be finished later, leaving no trace of the joint. This type of mash seam welding, shown in the lower part of the figure, is often referred to as *finish seam* welding and finds application where the product is normally viewed from one side only.

All the heat generated in a seam-welding circuit is a result of current passing through the resistance of the welding circuit. The current magnitude obviously becomes one of the most significant factors in controlling the amount of heat generated in the weld. A second variable is the resistance of the welding circuit, which has several sources of resistance. The heat at the electrode contact surfaces is kept at a minimum by the use of copper-alloy electrodes and is dissipated by flooding the electrodes and weld area with water. Heat, generated at the interface by contact resistance, may be increased by decreasing the electrode force. The third variable which influences the magnitude of the heat is the weld time, which, in seam welding, is controlled by the speed of rotation of the electrodes. The amount of heat generated is decreased, with an increase in welding speed.

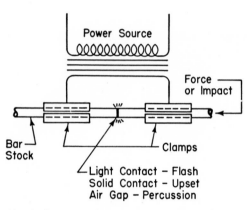

Fig. 8.   Sketch illustrating different forms of butt-welding bar stock.

Seam welding is used in the manufacture of metal containers, automobile mufflers and fenders, stove pipes, refrigerator cabinets, and gasoline tanks. Advantages of this type of fabrication include neater design, saving of material, tight joints, and low-cost construction.

Butt welding. This form of welding, illustrated in Figure 8, is the gripping together of two pieces of metal that have the same cross section and pressing them together while heat is being generated in the contact surface by electrical resistance. Although pressure is maintained while the heating takes place, at no time is the temperature sufficient actually to melt the metal. The joint is upset somewhat by the process, but this defect can be eliminated by subsequent rolling or grinding. Both parts to be welded should be of the same resistance in order to have uniform heating at the joint. If two dissimilar metals are to be welded, the metal projecting from the die holders must be in proportion to the specific resistance of the materials to be welded. The same treatment must be used where materials of different cross section are butt-welded.

In actual operation, the work is first clamped in the machine and a pressure is applied on the joints. The welding current is then started, and heating takes place, the rate depending on the pressure, the material, and the condition of surfaces. Since the contact resistance varies inversely with the pressure, the pressure is less at the start and is then increased to whatever is necessary to effect the weld (2500 to 8000 psi) when the welding temperature is reached. As soon as the weld is completed, the current is cut off and the work unclamped from the machine. This process differs from flash-butt welding in that there is no flashing or arcing at the joint during the operation.

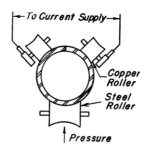

Fig. 9. Continuous butt welding of pipe.

Practically all metals that can be spot- or projection-welded can also be butt-welded, with the strength of the weld being about equal to the strength of the metal being welded. This type of welding is especially adapted to rods, pipes, small structural shapes, and many other parts of uniform section. Areas up to 70 square inches have been successfully welded, but generally the process is limited to small areas because of current limitations. Figure 9 illustrates a special type of butt-seam welding used in pipe manufacture.

Flash welding. Butt and flash-butt welding, though similar in application, differ somewhat in the manner of heating the metal. Again, in Figure 8, it is noted that for flash welding the parts must be brought together in a very light contact. A high voltage starts a flashing action between the two surfaces and continues as the parts advance slowly and the forging temperature is reached. The weld is completed by the application of sufficient forging pressure to effect a weld. A small fin or projection left around the joint can be easily removed. The entire operation is quite rapid, and it is important to have proper timing and current for the size section involved. Insufficient heat traps oxides, making it impossible to obtain a good weld. Overheating may result in molten metal being blown from the weld, causing a cavity. High forces ranging from 5000 to 25,000 psi are used in forging the joint together.

Welding of small areas is usually done by the butt-welding method, large areas are done by the flash-butt method; however, there is no clear demarcation between the two. The shape of the piece and the nature of the alloy are frequently the determining factors. Areas ranging from 0.002 to 50 square inches have been successfully welded by flash welding. In this process, less current is required than in ordinary butt welding; there is less metal to remove around the joints; the metal that forms the weld is protected from atmospheric contamination; the operation consumes little time; and end-to-end welding of sheets is possible. Because of these advantages, flash welding is more widely used than the ordinary butt or upset process. Many nonferrous metals can be flash-welded satisfactorily; however, alloys containing high percentages of lead, zinc, tin, and copper are not recommended for this process. Flash welding is widely used for tubular furniture, rear-axle housings, steel rims, sheets in body manufacture, steel forgings, and rolled sections.

Percussion welding. This is a recent development in welding, and, like the flash-weld process, relies on arc effect for heating rather than on the resistance in the metal. Pieces to be welded are held apart, one in a stationary holder and the other in a clamp mounted in a slide and backed up against heavy spring pressure (see Figure 8). When the movable clamp is released, it moves rapidly, carrying with it the piece to be welded. When the pieces are about $\frac{1}{16}$ inch apart, there is a sudden discharge of electric energy, causing intense arcing over the surfaces and bringing them to a high temperature. The arc is extinguished by the percussion blow of the two parts coming together with sufficient force to effect the weld.

The electric energy for the discharge is built up in one of two ways. In the electrostatic method, energy is stored in a capacitor, and the parts to be welded are heated by the sudden discharge of a heavy current from the capacitor. The electromagnetic welder uses the energy discharge caused by the collapsing of the magnetic field linking the primary and secondary windings of a transformer or other inductive device. In either case intense arcing is created, which is followed by a quick blow to make the weld.

The action of this process is so rapid (about 0.1 second) that there is little heating effect in the material adjacent to the weld. Heat-treated parts may be welded without being annealed. Parts differing in thermal conductivity and mass can be successfully joined, since the heat is concentrated only at the two surfaces. Some applications are welding Stellite tips to tools, copper to aluminum or stainless steel, silver contact tips to copper, cast iron to steel, lead-in wires on electric lamps, and zinc to steel. Butt welds are made without any upset or flash at the joint. The principal limitation of the process is that only small areas (up to $\frac{1}{2}$ square inch) of nearly regular sections can be welded. Thin sheets of equivalent area cannot be joined by this process. The equipment is expensive, since it must be extremely rugged and must be provided with accurate holding fixtures and with elaborate electric timing devices and large transformer capacity.

Gas welding. Gas welding includes all the processes in which gases are used in combination to obtain a hot flame. Those commonly used are acetylene, natural gas, and hydrogen in combination with oxygen. Oxyhydrogen welding was the first gas process to be commercially developed. The maximum temperature developed by this process is 3600 F. *Hydrogen* is produced either by the electrolysis of water or by passing steam over coke. The most-used com-

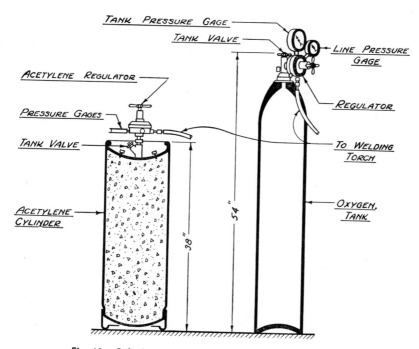

Fig. 10. Cylinders and regulators for oxyacetylene welding.

bination is the oxyacetylene process which has a flame temperature of 6300 F.

Oxyacetylene welding. An oxyacetylene weld is produced by heating with a flame obtained from the combustion of oxygen and acetylene and with or without the use of a filler metal. In most cases the joint is heated to a state of fusion, and, as a rule, no pressure is used.

Oxygen is produced by electrolysis and liquefying air. Electrolysis separates water into hydrogen and oxygen by passing an electric current through it. Most of the commercial oxygen is made by liquefy-

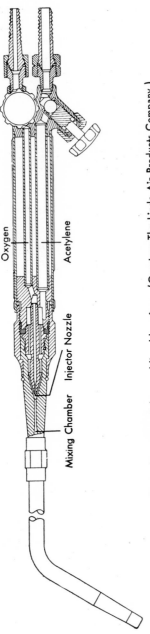

A. Cross section of an oxyacetylene welding blowpipe. (Courtesy The Linde Air Products Company.)

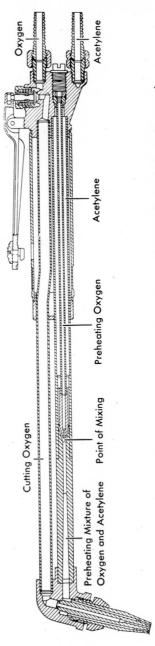

B. Cross section of an oxyacetylene cutting blowpipe. (Courtesy The Linde Air Products Company.)

Fig. 11.

ing air and separating the oxygen from the nitrogen. It is stored in steel cylinders, as shown in Figure 10, at a pressure of 2000 psi.

Acetylene gas (C_2H_2) is obtained by dropping lumps of calcium carbide in water. The gas bubbles up through the water, and the remainder of the calcium carbide is converted into slaked lime. The reaction that takes place in an acetylene generator is

$$CaC_2 + 2H_2O = Ca(OH)_2 + C_2H_2$$

Calcium   Water   Slaked   Acetylene
carbide   lime   gas

The calcium carbide used for making this gas is a hard, gray, stonelike material formed by smelting calcium with coal in an electric furnace. This material is crushed, sized, and stored in air-tight steel drums before its use. Acetylene gas can be obtained either from acetylene generators, which generate the gas by mixing the carbide

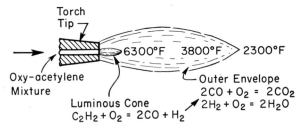

Fig. 12. Sketch of neutral flame showing temperatures attained.

with the water, or purchased in cylinders ready for use. Because this gas may not be safely stored at pressure much over 15 psi, it is stored in combination with acetone. Acetylene cylinders are filled with a porous filler, saturated with acetone, in which the acetylene gas can be compressed. These cylinders hold 300 cubic feet of gas at pressures up to 250 psi.

A cross section of a welding torch is shown in Figure 11. It consists of a series of brass tubes through which and into which the gases are conducted and finally mixed, valves for controlling the volumes of acetylene and oxygen, and a copper tip from which the gas mixture is burned. Regulation of the proportion of the two gases is of extreme importance, because the characteristics of the flame may be varied.

Three types of flames that can be obtained are *reducing, neutral, and oxidizing*. Of the three the neutral flame shown in Figure 12 has the widest application in welding and cutting operations. The inner, luminous cone at the tip of the torch requires approximately a one-to-one mixture of oxygen and acetylene and is the result of the reaction indicated on the figure. This cone is surrounded by an outer-envelope flame which is only faintly luminous and slightly bluish in color. The oxygen required for this flame comes from the atmosphere. The maximum temperature of 6000 to 6300 F is obtained at the tip of the luminous cone.

When there is an excess of acetylene used, there is a decided change in the appearance of the flame. In this flame there will be found three zones instead of the two just described. Between the luminous cone and the outer envelope there is an intermediate cone of whitish color, the length of which is determined by the amount of the excess acetylene. This flame, known as a reducing or carbonizing flame, is used in the welding of Monel metal, nickel, certain alloy steels, and many of the nonferrous, hard-surfacing materials, such as Stellite and Colmonoy.

If the torch is adjusted to give excess oxygen, a flame similar in appearance to the neutral flame is obtained, except that the inner luminous cone is much shorter, and the outer envelope appears to have more color. This oxidizing flame may be used in fusion welding of brass and bronze, but it is undesirable in other applications.

The advantages and uses of oxyacetylene welding are numerous. The equipment is comparatively inexpensive and requires little maintenance. It is portable and can be used with equal facility out in the field and in the factory. With proper technique, practically all metals may be welded, and the equipment can be used for cutting as well as welding. The process is especially adapted to the welding of sheet metal, to flame hardening, and to the application of many hard-facing materials.

Oxyhydrogen welding. Since oxyhydrogen burns at a much lower temperature (3600 F) than oxygen and acetylene, it is used primarily for welding thin sheets and low-melting alloys and in some brazing work. While the same equipment can be used for both processes, flame adjustments are more difficult in hydrogen welding because there is no distinguishing color to judge the gas proportions. A reducing atmosphere is recommended, and the process is characterized by the absence of oxides formed on the surface of the weld. The quality of these welds is equal to that obtained by other processes.

Air-acetylene welding. The torch used in this process is similar in construction to a *Bunsen burner*—air is drawn into the torch as required for proper combustion. Since the temperature is lower than those attained by other gas processes, this type of welding has limited use. Principal applications of the process include lead welding and low-temperature brazing or soldering operations.

Pressure gas welding. In pressure gas welding, the abutting areas of parts to be joined are heated with oxyacetylene flames to a welding temperature (around 2200 F), and pressure applied. It is a butt-welding process and similar to the resistance method except that heat is applied by a gas flame instead of by electrical resistance. Two methods are in common use. In the first, known as the closed-joint method, the surfaces to be joined are held together under pressure during the heating period. Multiflame water-cooled torches, de-

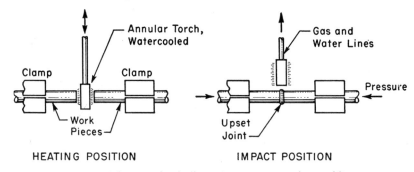

HEATING POSITION   IMPACT POSITION

Fig. 13. Schematic sketch illustrating pressure gas butt welding.

signed to go completely around the joint, are used in this operation. During the heating operation the torches are oscillated slightly back and forth to eliminate excessive local heating. As the heating progresses, the ends, which are prepared with a slight bevel, close up. When the correct temperature is reached, an additional upsetting pressure is applied. For low-carbon steel the initial pressure is below 1500 psi and the upsetting pressure around 4000 psi. Pressures vary with the material, and for high-carbon steel and many alloys, a constant pressure is applied throughout the entire welding cycle.

The second or open-joint method (shown in Figure 13) employs a flat multiflame torch which is placed between the two surfaces to be joined. This torch uniformly heats these surfaces until there is a film of molten metal over each of them. The torch is then quickly withdrawn, and the two surfaces are forced together and held under pressure (around 4000 psi) until solidification takes place. The appearance of this joint is similar to that obtained by flash welding, whereas the closed-joint method produces a joint with a bulging appearance.

This process is successfully used in the welding of rods, tubes, railroad rails, and pipe lines. Dissimilar metals can be joined, for example, high-speed steel can be joined to carbon shanks in the manufacture of certain tools. No filler metal is used, and the quality of the weld is determined by the properties of the metal being joined.

Oxyacetylene torch cutting. The cutting of steel with a flame-cutting torch has developed into a very important production process. A simple hand torch for flame cutting is shown in Figure 11. It

Fig. 14. Cutting a square billet with a portable bar-cutting machine. (Courtesy The Linde Air Products Company.)

differs from the welding torch in that it has several small holes for preheating flames, surrounding a central hole through which pure oxygen passes. The preheating flames are exactly like the welding flames and are intended only to preheat the steel before the cutting operation. The principle on which flame cutting operates is that oxygen has an affinity for iron and steel. At ordinary temperatures this action is slow, but eventually an oxide in the form of rust materializes. As the temperature of the steel is increased, this action becomes much more rapid. If the steel is heated to a red color and a jet of pure oxygen is blown on the surface, the action is almost instantaneous, and the steel is actually burned into an iron oxide slag-like appearance. About 1.3 cubic feet of oxygen is required to burn up 1 cubic inch of iron. This action is illustrated in Figure 14, where a square steel billet is being cut with a portable machine. In the operation shown, the blowpipe starts and finishes at an angle, while a constant clearance is maintained at all times between the cutting nozzle and the billet. Metal up to 30 inches in thickness can be cut by this process.

Many cutting machines have been developed that automatically control the movement of the torch to cut any desired shape. Such a

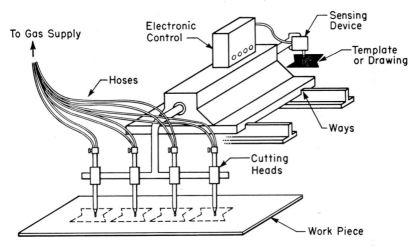

Fig. 15. Schematic sketch of oxyacetylene torch-cutting machine.

machine cutting several parts simultaneously is shown diagrammatically in Figure 15. In all such machines there is provided some sort of control or sensing device to guide the torches along a predetermined path. This control, in its simplest form, may be a hand-guided pointer, following a drawing or held against a template. Usually these machines are electrically driven and are provided with a knurled, magnetized drive spindle which follows a steel template and controls the movement of the machine at the proper cutting speed. There is also an electronically controlled sensing device which is provided with an electric eye capable of following a line drawing, thus eliminating the need for template construction.

Most cutting torches use acetylene in combination with oxygen to provide the necessary flame for preheating. This is not essential, however, as hydrogen, natural gas, or propane can be used. Hydro-

gen gas is recommended for underwater cutting, while the others
are often used because of lower cost.

Many parts that previously required shaping by forging or casting
are now cut to shape by this process. Flame-cutting machines, which
replace many machining operations where accuracy is not paramount,
are widely used in the shipbuilding industry, structural fabrication,
maintenance work, and the production of numerous items made from
steel sheets and plates. Cast iron, nonferrous alloys, and high-man-
ganese alloys are not readily cut by this process.

Flame machining.[2]   Flame machining is the term used to describe
the operation of removing metal with a cutting blowpipe. It differs
from ordinary flame cutting in that it does not sever the main body
of metal but merely removes metal as is done in machining operations.
The torch is held at a small angle to the work surface and, as it progresses, cuts out a groove instead of penetrating. The process is rapid,
requiring no power, and the work setup need not be rigid. On the
other hand, the surface finish is not good and close dimensional
accuracy cannot be attained. However, for many rough machining
operations involving the removal of a large amount of metal, this
method of cutting should be considered.

Arc welding.   Arc welding is a process in which coalescence is
obtained by heat, produced from an electric arc, between the work
and an electrode. The electrode or filler metal is heated to a liquid
state and deposited into the joint to make the weld. Contact is first
made between the electrode and the work to create an electric circuit, and then, by separating the conductors, an arc is formed. The
electric energy is converted into intense heat in the arc, which attains
a temperature around 10,000 F.

Either direct or alternating current can be used for arc welding,
direct current being preferred for most purposes. A d-c welder (see
Figure 16) is simply a motor-generator set of constant-energy type
(constant potential may also be used), having the necessary characteristics to produce a stable arc. There should not be too great a
current surge when the short circuit is made, and the machine should
compensate to some extent for varying lengths of the arc. D-c
machines are built in capacities up to 600 amperes, having an open-
circuit voltage of 40 to 95 volts. A 200-ampere machine has a rated
current range of 40 to 250 amperes, according to the standard of
the National Electrical Manufacturers Association. While welding is
going on, the closed-circuit voltage is 18 to 25 volts. In *straight*

[2] E. L. Cady, "Flame Cutting and Machining Methods," *Metals & Alloys*, May 1945.

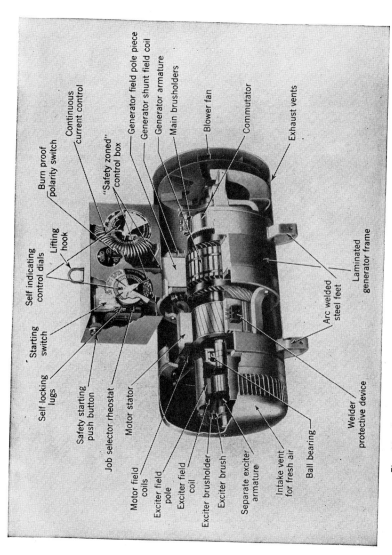

Fig. 16. D-c arc-welding machine. (Courtesy The Lincoln Electric Company.)

polarity the electrode is the negative terminal, whereas in *reverse polarity* the electrode is the positive terminal.

Carbon-electrode welding. The first methods of arc welding, which employed only carbon electrodes, are still in use to some extent for both manual and machine operation. The carbon arc is used only as a source of heat, and the torch is handled in a fashion similar to that used in gas welding. Filler rods supply weld metal if additional metal is necessary. The twin-carbon-arc method was one of the first used, the arc being between the two electrodes and not with the work. In operation the arc is held ¼ to ⅜ inch above the work, and best results are obtained with the work in a flat position. The use of this method is limited to brazing and soldering.

A second process, utilizing a single, carbon electrode of negative polarity, is considerably simpler. The arc is created between the carbon electrode and the work, and any weld metal needed is supplied by a separate rod. Such an arc is easy to start, as there is no tendency for the electrode to stick to the metal. Straight polarity must always be used, as a carbon arc is unstable when held on the positive terminal.

Most carbon-arc welding of this type is done with the use of automatic welding equipment where the arc voltage and current, rate of travel, and rate of feeding the filler rod are all properly controlled. Since a carbon arc is easily affected by magnetic fields, a separate magnetic field is built into the electrode holder to stabilize the arc and control its direction. Protection of the metal can be obtained by introducing either inert gases or slag-forming fluxes into the arc. Carbon-arc welding is used for welding cast iron, steel, copper, bronze, galvanized iron, and aluminum, as well as for rough cutting of metals.

Metal-electrode welding. Shortly after the development of carbon-electrode welding, it was discovered that, by the use of a metal electrode with the proper current characteristics, the electrode itself could be melted down to supply the necessary weld metal. A basic patent for this process which is in general use today was issued to Charles Coffin in 1889. In actual operation, an arc is started by striking the work with an electrode and quickly withdrawing it a short distance. As the electrode end is melted by the intense heat, most of it is transferred across the arc in the form of small globules to a molten pool. A small amount is lost by being vaporized, and some globules are deposited alongside the weld as spatter. The arc is maintained by uniformly moving the electrode toward the work at a rate that compensates for that portion of it which has been melted and transferred to the weld. At the same time the electrode is gradually moved along the joint being welded.

For ordinary welding there is little difference in the quality of the welds made by a-c and d-c equipment. The a-c machines consist principally of static transformers which are simple pieces of equipment having no moving parts. Their efficiency is high, their loss at no load is negligible, and their maintenance and initial costs are low. Welders of this type are built in six sizes specified by NEMA, and are rated at 150, 200, 300, 500, 750, and 1000 amperes. For welding requiring 750 amperes or higher, a-c equipment is preferred. The fact that there is less magnetic flare of the arc or "arc blow" with a-c than with the d-c equipment is important in the welding of heavy plates or fillet welding. For jobs requiring medium- or small-amperage current loads the a-c equipment is limited by the type of electrodes required. Most of the nonferrous metals and many of the alloys cannot be welded with a-c equipment, because electrodes have not been developed for this purpose.

The welding speed, the quality of welds, and the ease of welding of a-c and d-c welders are comparatively the same. D-c machines may be used with all types of carbon and metal electrodes since the polarity can be changed to suit the electrode. With the a-c welder the alternating current is constantly reversing with every cycle, and electrodes have to be selected that will operate on both polarities. A-c welders operate at slightly higher voltages, and hence the danger of shock to the operator is increased. In spite of these limitations. there is a growing demand for the a-c type of welder in fabrication and maintenance shops, sheet-metal work, and jobbing machine shops.

Electrodes. The three types of metal electrodes (or "rods") are *bare, fluxed,* and *heavy coated.* Bare electrodes have a limited use for the welding of wrought iron and mild steel. Straight polarity is generally recommended. Improved welds may be made by applying a light coating of flux on the rods with a dusting or washing process. The flux assists both in eliminating undesirable oxides and in preventing their formation. However, the heavily coated arc electrodes are by far the most important ones used in all types of commercial welding. Over 95% of the total manual welding that is being done today is with coated electrodes.

Figure 17 is a diagrammatic sketch showing the action of an arc using a heavy-coated electrode. In the ordinary arc with bare wire the deposited metal is affected to some extent by the oxygen and nitrogen in the air. This causes undesirable oxides and nitrides to be formed in the weld metal. The effect of heavy coatings on electrodes is to provide a gas shield around the arc to eliminate such conditions and also to cover the weld metal with a protective slag coating which prevents oxidation of the surface metal during cooling. Welds made from rods of this type have superior physical characteristics. Manufacturers' recommendations should always be followed in the selection of an electrode for a given job.

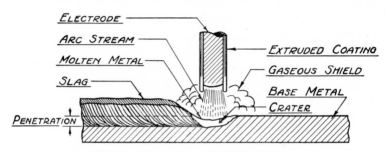

Fig. 17.   Diagrammatic sketch of arc flame.

Electrode coatings.   Electrodes coated with slagging or fluxing materials are particularly necessary in the welding of alloys and nonferrous metals.   Some of the elements in these alloys are not very stable and are lost if there is no protection against oxidation. Heavy coatings also permit the use of larger welding rods, higher current, and greater welding speeds.   In summary, the coatings perform the following functions:

1. Provide a protecting atmosphere.
2. Provide slag of suitable characteristics to protect the molten metal.
3. Facilitate overhead and position welding.
4. Stabilize the arc.
5. Add alloying elements to the weld metal.
6. Perform metallurgical refining operations.
7. Reduce spatter of weld metal.
8. Increase deposition efficiency.
9. Remove oxides and impurities.
10. Influence the depth of arc penetration.
11. Influence the shape of the bead.
12. Slow down the cooling rate of the weld.

These functions are not common to all coated electrodes, since the coating put on a given electrode is largely determined by the kind of welding it has to perform.   It is interesting to note that the coating composition is also a determining factor in electrode polarity. By varying the coating, rods may be used with either the positive or the negative terminal. Properly coated electrodes produce a weld metal having physical properties equal to the base metal.

Coating compositions which have been developed to accomplish these results may be classified as organic and inorganic coatings, although in some cases both types might be used. Inorganic coatings can be further subdivided into flux compounds and slag-forming compounds. These are some of the principal constituents used:

1. Slag-forming constituents: SiO_2, MnO_2, and FeO. Al_2O_3 is sometimes used, but it makes the arc less stable.
2. Constituents to improve arc characteristics: Na_2O, CaO, MgO, and TiO_2.
3. Deoxidizing constituents: graphite, aluminum, and wood flour.
4. Binding material: sodium silicate, potassium silicate, and asbestos.
5. Alloying constituents to improve strength of weld: V, Ce, Co, Mo, Al, Zr, Cr, Ni, Mn, W, and C_B.

Contact electrodes. The term *contact electrode* has been given to those electrodes which have a coating with a high metal powder content and are suitable for welding with a drag or contact technique. In most cases the electrode has an automatic striking or self-igniting characteristic due to the iron in the coating. By adding appreciable quantities of metal powder to the coating and increasing its thickness, the deposition rate is substantially increased. In some cases the coating may furnish as much weld metal as the core wire. Since the core melts at a slower rate than the wire, a deep cup is formed, providing excellent protection for the arc. This also prevents the wire from sticking to the work. Contact electrodes which have proved to be quite successful and economical, are still in a developmental stage; and their ultimate value and use still have to be determined.

Impregnated-tape metal-arc welding. This form of welding utilizes a tape impregnated with materials that have a shielding effect on the arc when they are consumed. The results are comparable with those obtained by using a heavy-coated electrode. This procedure is used only in automatic machine welding, in which case the tape is wrapped around the bare wire just ahead of the arc. Excellent welds are made in this fashion and are of a quality equal to those obtained when a heavy-coated rod is used.

Atomic-hydrogen arc welding.   In this process a single-phase a-c
arc is maintained between two tungsten electrodes, and hydrogen is
introduced into the arc as shown in Figure 18.   As the hydrogen
enters the arc, the molecules are broken up into atoms, which recom-
bine into molecules of hydrogen outside the arc.   This reaction is
accompanied by the liberation of an intense heat, attaining a tem-

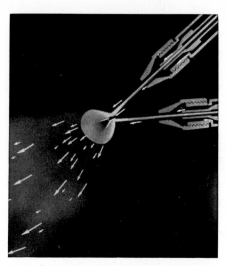

Fig. 18. Atomic-hydrogen welding arc drawn to show flow of gas and heat. Electrode holder shown in longitudinal section. (Courtesy General Electric Company.)

perature of about 11,000 F.   Weld metal may be added to the joint
in the form of welding rod, the operation being very similar to the
oxyacetylene process.   The atomic-hydrogen process differs from
other arc-welding processes in that the arc is formed between two
electrodes, as shown in Figure 19, rather than between one electrode and the work.   This makes the electrode holder a mobile tool,
since it can be moved from place to place without the arc being
extinguished.

The outstanding advantage of this process over others is its ability
to provide high heat concentrations.   In addition, the hydrogen also
acts as a shield and protects the electrodes and molten metal from
oxidation.   Metal of the same analysis as the metal being welded
can be used with both manual and automatic equipment, and many
alloys, difficult to weld by other processes, can be successfully treated.
The welds are clean, smooth, and free from scale, and they respond
to heat treatment in the same way as the parent metal when weld
metal of the same composition is used.   The process has wide use in

die repair; it successfully welds heat-resisting alloys; it has proved to be an excellent means of applying carbides and many other hard-surfacing alloys; and it is widely used in production work where special ferrous and nonferrous alloys are used.

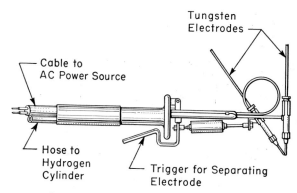

Fig. 19. Torch for atomic-hydrogen welding.

Inert-gas-shielded arc welding. In this process, coalescence is produced by heat from an arc between a metal electrode and the work which is shielded by an atmosphere of either *argon* or *helium*. Two methods of welding are employed: one using a tungsten electrode with filler metal added as in gas welding, and the other using consumable metal wire as the electrode. Both methods are adaptable to either manual or automatic machine welding, and no flux or wire coating is required for protection of the weld.

A hand torch using a tungsten electrode is shown in Figure 20. This torch is water-cooled and constructed with a gas nozzle surrounding the tungsten electrode so that the gas, as it leaves the nozzle, completely envelops the tip of the electrode and the work beneath it. Either alternating or direct current can be used, the selection being determined by the kind of metal to be welded. Direct current with straight polarity is required for welding copper alloys and stainless steel, whereas reverse polarity is used for magnesium. Alternating current is more versatile in its application and is used for steel, cast iron, and aluminum, as well as those metals mentioned above.

The manually controlled, consumable electrode is fairly new and differs considerably in operation from the afore-mentioned method. Figure 21 shows one of a number of manually operated guns available for this type of welding. As may be seen, the wire is pulled to the torch by knurled rollers and fed on through to the arc. The wire size ranges from 0.030 to 0.093 inch in diameter. This torch

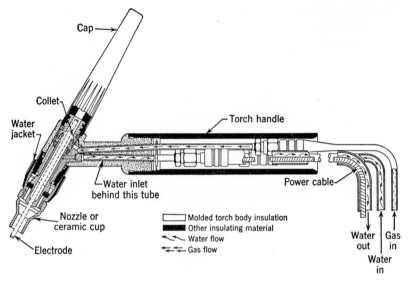

Fig. 20. Hand-welding torch for inert-gas-shielded arc welding. (Courtesy The Linde Air Products Company.)

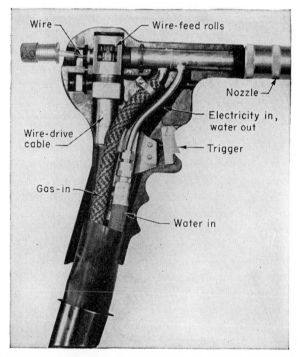

Fig. 21. Gun for consumable electrode gas-shielded welding torch with cover removed. (Courtesy General Electric Company.)

uses direct current with either helium or argon and is water-cooled. The entire equipment for the process, other than the gun, includes a wire reel and drive unit and a self-regulating welding generator. The generator has controls for setting arc length only and will automatically supply the proper current for any wire speed required. This process has the characteristics of an automatic process and can be used manually in all welding positions. It is adapted for welding aluminum, mild and stainless steel, aluminum bronze, nickel, and magnesium.

Inert-gas metal-arc cutting. A new process[3] for cutting non-ferrous metal has been developed which utilizes an inert-gas consumable-electrode gun similar to the one shown in Figure 21. An arc is established on the metal and the $\frac{3}{32}$-inch steel electrode is fed through at a speed such that the tip of the wire is at the bottom of the work piece. The cutting action, shielded with an inert gas, extends from the entire surface of the leading side of the wire rather than from the tip. For this reason it is very important that the wire feed and cutting speed be held constant. The inert gas best suited for cutting is argon. Direct current, ranging from 450 to 900 amperes, is recommended for most thicknesses. The process is particularly adapted to the cutting of aluminum, although plates of brass, nickel, and copper have also been cut.

Automatic arc-welding machines. Much metal electrode welding is now being done by machine or automatic units. Such welding is essentially the same as manual welding, except that machine units are supplied with controls that feed the wire as it is consumed and move either the welding head or work along at a proper welding rate. Some control systems vary the feed rate of the electrode as the voltage across the arc varies. If the voltage increases, indicating a longer arc than desired, the rate of feed increases. A lower voltage indicates a shorter arc and the feed is reduced, the goal being to hold a uniform arc length. Other systems feed the electrode at a constant rate of speed. This also gives a uniform arc length when used with a power source having constant voltage output. The electrode and molten base metal are protected from oxidation by shields of argon, helium, or carbon dioxide.

Prerequisites[4] for economic machine welding are a sufficient volume of production to justify expensive equipment and a uniform product. Assemblies must fit together readily, and each piece must be of the same size and similar in contour. Often jigs and handling

[3] R. S. Babcock, "Inert-Gas Metal-Arc Cutting," *The Welding Journal*, April 1955.
[4] R. F. Wyer, "Progress in Automatic Arc Welding," *Machinery*, November—December 1944.

devices are necessary to position the work. If these conditions are fulfilled, machine welding will be economical. The use of automatic-welding machines results in increased welding speed and uniform quality of the weld. In addition, the operator is relieved of tedious work, since he does not have to maintain the proper arc length and travel speed.

Fig. 22.   Filler-arc automatic-welding equipment.   (Courtesy General Electric Company.)

An 800-ampere d-c arc welding unit designed for the consumable electrode, gas-shielded welding process, is shown in Figure 22. The bare wire electrode is mechanically fed through the torch and provides the filler metal in the weld. The generator is self-regulating and supplies the right current to consume the amount of wire being fed. The operator sets the arc length on the generator and, even though the wire speed is changed while welding, the current will always be correct to burn off the wire uniformly. Satisfactory results depend on holding the arc length constant regardless of wire speed. Gas, such as argon and carbon dioxide, flows out of the torch around the arc and forms a protective shield. Wire sizes range from 0.020 to 0.125 inch with automatic units of this general type. Automatic welding machines find wide use in production welding of both straight and circumferential seams.

Carbon dioxide gas as a means of shielding the arc is being used extensively because of its low cost. Compared with argon and helium the cost ratio is around 9 : 1 and 7 : 1, respectively, in favor of carbon dioxide. However, welding in an atmosphere of carbon dioxide results in much spatter and loss of certain elements in the electrode unless close control of operating conditions is maintained. It is important that a very short and uniform arc be used. High current densities are required so the wire feed is high. Because of the close control required most carbon-dioxide-shielded arc welding is performed on automatic welding machines.

Arc spot welding. An interesting application of inert-gas arc welding is in the making of spot, plug, or tack welds by an argon shielded electric arc using consumable electrodes. To effect a weld, a small welding gun with pistol grip is held tightly against the work to be welded. As the trigger is released, the argon valve is opened, and the current is allowed to pass through the electrode for a preset interval (2 to 5 seconds), and then both are shut off. An advantage of this equipment is that spot welds can be made on thin sheets from one side of the work only. Being a low cost process, it is particularly useful in welding large or irregularly shaped assemblies that are difficult to spot-weld with resistance equipment.

Submerged-arc welding. This process is so named because the metal arc is shielded by a blanket of granular, fusible flux during the welding operation. Aside from this feature, its operation is quite similar to other automatic arc-welding methods. In operation, a bare electrode is fed through the welding head into the granular material, as shown in Figure 23. This material is laid down along the seam to be welded, and the entire welding action takes place beneath it. The arc is started either by striking beneath the flux on the work or initially by placing some conductive medium like steel wool beneath the electrode. The intense heat of the arc immediately produces a pool of molten metal in the joint and at the same time melts a portion of the granular flux. This material floats on top of the molten metal, forming a blanket which eliminates spatter losses and protects the welded joint from oxidation. Upon cooling, the fused slag solidifies and is easily removed; granular material not fused is recycled and used again.

This process is limited to flat welding although welds can be made on a slight slope or on circumferential joints. It is advisable to use a backing strip of steel, copper, or some refractory material on the joint to avoid losing some of the molten metal. The process uses high currents, 300 to 4000 amperes, which permits high rates of metal transfer and welding speeds. Deep penetration is obtained, and most commercial thicknesses of plate metal can be welded with

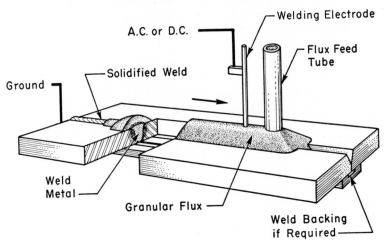

Fig. 23. Schematic sketch of submerged arc welding.

one pass. As a result, thin plates can be welded without any preparation, whereas only a small vee is required on most others. Most submerged-arc welding is done on low-carbon and alloy steels, but it may also be used on many of the nonferrous metals.

Stud arc welding. Stud welding is a d-c arc-welding process developed to end-weld metal studs to flat surfaces. It is accomplished with a pistol-shaped welding gun which holds the stud or fastener to be welded. When the trigger of the gun is pressed, the stud is lifted to create an arc and then forced against the molten pool by a backing spring. The entire operation is controlled by a timer, preset according to the size of the stud being welded. Shielding of the arc is usually accomplished by surrounding it with a ceramic ferrule which also confines the metal to the weld area and protects the operator from the arc. Stud welding has much use in ship construction as well as in many industrial applications involving the use of metal fasteners.

Thermit welding. Thermit welding is the only welding process employing an exothermal chemical reaction for the purpose of developing a high temperature and is based on the fact that aluminum has a great affinity for oxygen and can be used as a reducing agent for many oxides. The usual Thermit mixture or compound consists of finely divided aluminum and iron oxide, mixed at a ratio of about 1 to 3 by weight. The iron oxide is usually in the form of roll mill scale. This mixture is not explosive and can be ignited only at a temperature of about 2800 F. A special ignition powder is used to start the reaction. The chemical reaction requires only about 30 seconds and attains a temperature around 4500 F. The mixture reacts according to the chemical equation

$$8Al + 3Fe_3O_4 = 9Fe + 4Al_2O_3$$

The resultant products are a highly purified iron (actually steel) and an aluminum oxide slag, which floats on top and is not used. Other reactions also take place, as most Thermit metal is alloyed with manganese, nickel, or other elements.

Figure 24 illustrates the method of preparing the material for such a weld. Around the break where the weld is to be made, a wax pattern of the weld is built up. Refractory sand is packed around the joint, and necessary provision is made for riser and gates. A preheating flame is used to melt and burn out the wax, to dry the mold, and to bring the joints to a red heat. The reaction is then started in the crucible, and, when it is complete, the metal is tapped and allowed to flow into the mold. Since the weld-metal temperature is approximately twice the melting temperature of steel, it readily fuses in the joint. Such welds are sound, because the metal solidifies from the inside toward the outside, and all air is excluded from around the mold.

In Thermit pressure welds, the ends of joints to be welded are pressed tightly together, and a mold is built around a joint. After the reaction starts, the slag is poured in first to form a glasslike surface around the joint, and then the superheated metal is added. When the heat from the slag and metal bring the joint up to welding temperature, the weld is made by pressure, similar to the procedure followed in resistance butt welding.

There is no limit to the size of welds that can be made by Thermit welding. It is used primarily for the repairs of large parts which would be difficult or uneconomical to weld by other processes.

Cold-pressure welding. Cold-pressure welding is a method of joining nonferrous metals by applying pressure and causing the

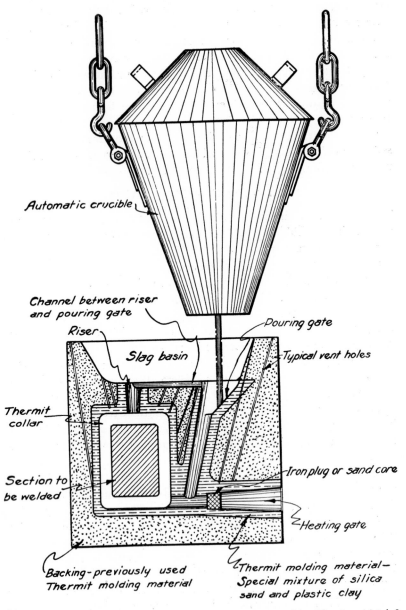

Automatic crucible

Channel between riser
and pouring gate

Riser

Slag basin

Pouring gate

Typical vent holes

Thermit
collar

Section to
be welded

Iron plug or sand core

Heating gate

Backing-previously used
Thermit molding material

Thermit molding material—
Special mixture of silica
sand and plastic clay

Fig. 24. Line drawing of mold and crucible for a Thermit weld. (Courtesy Metal &
Thermit Corporation.)

metals to flow in a manner necessary to produce a weld. The type of bond obtained is shown by the micrograph in Figure 25. Before a weld is made, the surfaces or parts to be joined must be wire-brushed thoroughly at a surface speed around 3000 fpm to remove oxide films on the surface. Other methods of cleaning seem to be unsatisfactory. In making a weld, the pressure is applied over a narrow strip so that the metal can flow away from the weld on both sides. It may be applied either by impact or with a slow squeezing

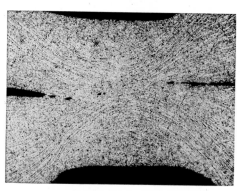

Fig. 25. A microsection of an aluminum cold weld, showing lines of flow. (Courtesy Koldweld Corporation.)

action, both methods being equally effective. Pressure required for aluminum ranges from 25,000 to 35,000 psi. Spot welds are rectangular in shape and in terms of gage thickness are approximately $t \times 5t$ in size. In addition, both ring welds and continuous seam welds can be made. The greatest success of this method of welding has been with aluminum and copper; however, lead, nickel, zinc, and Monel can also be joined by cold pressure.

TABLE 12. Brazing and Soldering

Dipping	Furnace	Gas torch	Electric	Soft soldering
1. Metal	1. Gas	1. Oxyacetylene	1. Resistance	1. Soldering iron
2. Chemical	2. Electric	2. Oxyhydrogen	2. Induction	2. Wiping
			3. Arc	

Brazing and Soldering

In the processes of brazing and soldering, which unite metals by means of a different metal, as shown in Table 12, joints are made without pressure, the joining metal merely being introduced into the

joint in a liquid state and allowed to solidify. Both processes have
wide commercial use in the uniting of small assemblies and electrical parts.

Brazing. In *brazing*, a nonferrous alloy is introduced in a liquid
state, between the pieces of metal to be joined, and allowed to
solidify. The filler metal has a melting temperature of over 800 F,
but lower than the melting temperature of the parent metal, and is
distributed between the surfaces by capillary attraction. *Braze welding* is similar to ordinary brazing except that the filler metal is not
distributed by capillary attraction. In both cases special fluxes are
required to remove surface oxide and to give to the filler metal the
fluidity necessary to wet the joint surfaces completely. The brazing
metals and alloys commonly used are as follows:

1. Copper: melting point 1982 F.
2. Copper alloys: brass and bronze alloys having melting points
   ranging from 1600 F to 2250 F.
3. Silver alloys: melting temperatures ranging from 1165 to 1550 F.[5]
4. Aluminum alloys: melting temperatures ranging from 1025 F to
   1785 F.[6]

In the brazing of two pieces of metal, the joint must first be
cleaned of all oil, dirt, or oxides, and the pieces properly fitted
together with appropriate clearance for the filler metal. Mechanical
or chemical cleaning may be necessary in the joint preparation in
addition to the flux used during the process. Borax, either alone or
in combination with other salts, is commonly used as a flux.

According to Table 12 the following four methods can be used in
heating the metal to complete a joint:

1. *Dipping* the assembled parts in a bath of filler metal or flux.
When dipped in a flux bath, which is held at a temperature sufficient
to melt the filler metal, the assembly must be held together securely
in a jig and the joint preloaded with the brazing alloy.

2. In *furnace brazing* the assemblies are held in position by jigs
and are introduced into a controlled-atmosphere furnace maintained
at the proper temperature to melt the brazing metal. These furnaces
can be either gas- or electric-heated, and of the batch or continuous
type.

3. *Torch brazing* is similar to oxyacetylene welding. Heat is
applied locally by an oxyacetylene or oxyhydrogen torch, and the
filler metal, in wire form, is melted into the joint. Flux is applied
by immersing the wire.

[5] *Metals Handbook*, American Society for Metals, 1948, p. 80.
[6] *Welding and Brazing of Alcoa Aluminum*, Aluminum Company of America, p. 99.

4. In *electric brazing* the heat may be applied by resistance, by induction, or by an arc. Of these methods, the first two are most often used because of their speed and accurate temperature control.

To facilitate speed in brazing, the filler metal is frequently prepared in the form of rings, washers, rods, or other special shapes, to fit the joint being brazed. This insures having the proper amount of filler metal available for the joint as well as having it placed in the correct position.

Joints in brazing may be of the lap, butt, sleeve, or scarf types, or of various shapes obtained by curling, upsetting, or seaming processes. The strength of the joint is determined principally by the strength of the brazing material used, although other influencing factors are strength of the parent metal, amount of clearance, cleanness of the joint, and method of heating and cooling.

One advantage of the brazing process is the effecting of joints in materials difficult to weld, in dissimilar metals, and in exceedingly thin sections of metal. In addition, the process is rapid and results in a neat-appearing joint requiring a minimum of finishing. Brazing is used for the fastening of pipes and fittings, tanks, carbide tips on tools, radiators, heat exchangers, electrical parts, and the repair of castings.

Soldering. Soldering differs from brazing in that lower-temperature filler metals (below 800 F) are used in the joint. Lead and tin alloys having a melting range of 300 to 700 F are used principally in soldering, and the strength of the joint is determined by the adhesive qualities and the strength of these alloys. Although any heating method used in brazing can be employed in this process, much soldering is done with the common soldering iron which is especially suitable for small parts and light-gage metal. Heat is supplied by the iron, and solder is fed to the joint in the form of wire. Cleaning of the joint surface is equally as important in soldering as in brazing, and a flux is necessary. Electric connections, wire terminals, and similar small parts are typical of the joints made by soft soldering. A form of soldering known as *wiping* is used in making connections of lead pipe.

REVIEW QUESTIONS

1. Distinguish between soldering, brazing, and braze welding.
2. What effect does carbon content in steel have on weldability?
3. What four stages are involved in the process of spot welding?
4. Give the various zones of heat generation in a resistance weld.

5. Describe indirect welding as applied to spot welding.
6. Distinguish between lap seam, mash seam, and finish seam welding.
7. What are the variables in seam welding that control the heat?
8. What advantages are claimed for projection welding?
9. How does ordinary butt welding differ from flash welding?
10. For what type of work is percussion welding used?
11. How is oxygen made and stored? Acetylene?
12. Give approximate temperatures obtained by oxyacetylene welding, oxyhydrogen welding, arc welding, Thermit welding, and atomic hydrogen welding.
13. List the advantages and limitations of oxyacetylene welding.
14. Describe two methods of pressure gas welding.
15. How does the oxyacetylene cutting torch operate?
16. What is meant by straight polarity?
17. Compare a-c and d-c arc welding machines, giving the advantages of each.
18. What are the methods used in controlling the arc length in automatic welding?
19. What is the purpose of a coating on an arc welding electrode?
20. What advantages are obtained by the use of contact electrodes?
21. Under what conditions would you recommend the use of the atomic-hydrogen process?
22. Describe the methods used for inert-gas shielded arc welding.
23. What is Thermit metal, and how is it used?
24. What metals respond to cold welding?

REFERENCES

Cady, E. L., "Flame Cutting and Machining Methods," *Metals & Alloys,* May 1945.
Design for Welding, James F. Lincoln Arc Welding Foundation, 1947.
Kerwin, H., *Arc and Acetylene Welding,* McGraw-Hill Book Company, 1944.
Mample, A. Z., "Soldering with Tin-Lead Alloys," *Metals & Alloys,* May 1945.
Mathias, D. L., "Recent Developments on Contact Electrodes," *The Welding Journal,* Vol. 34, No. 4, April, 1955.
Morris, J. L., *Welding Principles for Engineers,* Prentice-Hall, 1951.
Procedure Handbook of Arc Welding Design and Practice, 9th edition, Lincoln Electric Company, 1950.
Recommended Practices for Resistance Welding, American Welding Society, 1950.
Resistance Welding Manual, Resistance Welder's Manufacturing Association, 1948.
Resistance Welding—Theory and Use, American Welding Society, Reinhold Publishing Company, 1956.
Rossi, B. E., *Welding Engineering,* McGraw-Hill Book Company, 1954.
Rothschild, G. R., "Carbon-Dioxide-Shielded Consumable Electrode," *The Welding Journal,* Vol. 35, No. 1, January 1956.
Singleton, R. C., "Electric Arc Stud Welding," *Welding Journal,* December 1947.
The Oxwelder's Handbook, 15th edition, Linde Air Products Company, 1939.
The Welding Encyclopedia, 11th edition, Welding Engineer Publishing Company, 1943.

Udin, F., E. R. Funk, and J. Wulff, *Welding for Engineers,* John Wiley and Sons, 1954.

Welding Handbook, 3d edition, American Welding Society, 1950.

Wyer, R. F., "Some Developments in Gas-Shielded Arc Welding," paper presented at Philadelphia Chapter of American Welding Society, May 1944.

CHAPTER 10

ELECTROFORMING
AND
COATING PROCESSES

Electroforming

Electroforming is one of the primary processes of forming metals, in which parts are produced by electrolytic deposition of metal upon a conductive removable mold or matrix. The mold establishes the size and surface smoothness of the finished product. Metal is supplied to the conductive mold from an electrolytic solution in which a bar of pure metal acts as an anode for the plating current. The process differs from plating in that a solid shell is produced which is later separated from the form upon which it was deposited.

Electroforming is particularly valuable for fabricating thin-walled parts requiring a high order of accuracy, internal surface finish, and complicated internal forms which are difficult to core or machine. It may also be used to advantage in producing a small number of parts which would otherwise require expensive tooling.

Electroforming process. The first step in production is to fabricate a negative image of the part. This is known as a matrix, mold, or pattern which may be either permanent or expendable. Permanent molds can be used if there is sufficient draft to withdraw them without damage to the formed part, for example, in producing metal fountain pen caps, trumpet bells, and circular-to-rectangular transition-area wave guides. Such molds are generally machined from metal and are economical when many parts are to be made.

Where it is impossible to use permanent patterns, expendable ones, which are either chemically soluble or have a low melting temperature, can be used. Soluble metals have the advantage of good internal finish and close tolerance. Also, they may often be made cheaply by die casting or plastic molding. Principal materials include aluminum, zinc alloys, and plastics. Low-melting materials, like wax and lead-tin-bismuth alloys, can be molded at low cost but are easily scratched and sometimes difficult to remove. Both the fusible and the soluble molds have their principal use in complex internal forms that would be difficult or impossible to make by other processes.

Since some of the materials used for forms are nonconducting, they must first be coated with a metallic film. This can be done in a variety of ways, including brushing, spraying, and chemical reduction. Wax molds can be coated with graphite.—The conductivity of the film must not be too low, and good electrical contacts are important.

After the forms are prepared, they can be placed in the electrolytic solution and processed. When sufficient time has elapsed to build up the required thickness, the part is removed from the bath, rinsed, and stripped from the mold.

Materials used. All metals that can be used for plating can also be electroformed. Copper, nickel, iron, silver, zinc, lead, tin, cadmium, gold, aluminum, and a few others fall into this category. Copper, nickel, iron, and silver, used extensively in electroforming, contain properties such as good reproducibility, resistance to corrosion, electrical conductivity, good bearing surface, and adequate strength which are required in most products. A dendritic structure, aligned normally to the conductive form surface (as shown in Figure 1) is common to all electroformed metals. While the physical properties depend upon the characteristics of the metal used, they are also influenced by the rate of deposition, plating temperature, and other bath variables. Dense structures can be obtained, and for some metals the properties changed materially by heat treatment.

Advantages and limitations. Metallurgically, parts made by electroforming do not differ materially from parts made by other processes. The importance of electroforming as a process is its ability to produce complex parts requiring intricate detail, that are almost impossible to make by other processes.

Fig. I. Cross section of copper deposit from acid sulphate bath in a sharp right angle shows weak plane formed by juncture of columnar crystals growing from sides of the angle. Magnification ×50. (Courtesy National Bureau of Standards.)

Some advantages of electroforming are:

1. Extreme dimensional accuracy can be held on surfaces next to the conducting form. ⁀ Identical parts can be made with practically no dimensional variation.

2. Surface finishes of 8 rms or less can be maintained.

3. Parts of extreme thinness can be made.

4. Laminated metals can be produced.

5. Extreme metal purity can be obtained.

6. Intricate internal or external surfaces, difficult to form by other processes, can be produced.

7. Surfacing of parts to provide special physical or metallurgical properties is possible.

When compared with most normal processes, electroforming is not an economical method of fabrication, except for precision parts which are costly to produce by other processes. Limitations of electroforming are:

1. Rate of production is normally very slow.

2. Cost is high.

3. Accuracy of exterior surfaces cannot be controlled.

4. Process is confined to relatively thin products, seldom exceeding ⅜ inch.

5. Limited selection of materials.

6. Recesses are difficult to form. They should be shallow, and sharp internal angles must be avoided.

Parts presently being produced by this process include radar wave guides (see Figure 2), spiral pin cams, heat exchanger tubes, pen caps, metal bellows, metal screens, clad metals, bearing liners, venturi nozzles, instrument bells, and parts made of laminated metals.

Fig. 2. Electroformed wave guides.

Metallic Coatings

With few exceptions, any marketable product of metal must be surface-finished. While the primary purpose of a coating or finish may often be to improve the appearance and sales value of the item, coatings must be used on most metals to give permanent resistance to destructive influences due to wear, electrolytic decomposition, and contact with the weather or corrosive atmosphere.

Before metals can be coated it is necessary to prepare the surface properly for good adhesion. Parts should be cleaned by various methods, depending upon material, size, surface peculiarities, and the kind of coating to be applied. The basic methods used are mechanical, such as blasting or tumbling; chemical processes, such as by alkaline, acid, or organic agents; and electrolytic cleaning.

In general, the coating process is the application of a finite thickness of some material over the metal, or is the transformation of the surface by chemical or electrical means to an oxide of the original metal. A discussion of some of the important processes follows.

Metal plating. Electroplating has long served as a means of applying decorative and protective coatings to metals. For wear and abrasive resistance, the outstanding metal for plating metallic surfaces is chromium. Coatings are seldom less than 0.002 inch thick and may be considerably more. They are plated not on a soft base metal but directly onto the hard parent metal. If plated on a soft base metal, like copper or nickel, they would have greater corrosion-resisting power, but their resistance to abrasion and deformation would be much less. Hence, any measure of hardness or abrasive resistance is to some extent a function of the metal on which it is plated as well as of the chromium deposit itself.

The electrolytic process consists in passing an electric current from an anode to a cathode (the cathode being the object on which the metal is deposited) through a suitable chromium-carrying electrolytic solution in the presence of a catalyst. The catalyst does not enter into the electrochemical decomposition. A solution of chromic acid with a high degree of saturation is used as the electrolyte. The surfaces must be thoroughly polished and cleaned before operations start; and, since the rate of deposition is fairly slow, the work must remain in the tanks several hours for heavy plating.

Chromium has proved satisfactory for wear-resisting parts because of its extreme hardness, which exceeds most other commercial metals. According to the Brinell scale, the hardness of plated chromium ranges from 500 to 900. This wide variation is due not to the metal but to methods and equipment used.

Galvanizing. Galvanizing is a zinc coating used extensively for protecting low carbon steel from atmospheric deterioration. It offers a low cost coating that has reasonable appearance and good wearing properties. An improved appearance, known as the spangle effect, can be produced by small additions of tin and aluminum. Zinc baths are usually maintained at about 850 F. Rolls, agitators, and metal brooms are used to remove the excess zinc from the product. Continuous and automatic processes are used for sheet and wire coating. Zinc coatings may also be applied by *spraying* molten zinc on steel, by *sheradizing*, which is the tumbling of the product in zinc dust at elevated temperatures, and by *electroplating*.

Tin coating. Tin coatings are often applied to sheet steel to be used for food containers, tin can manufacturers using approximately 90% of the tin produced. Although many tin coatings are now applied by electrotinning, a process wherein parts are immersed in an electrolyte and a current passed from the electrode to the work, the hot dip method is still used considerably. Tin can be applied easily, without affecting the base metal, by dipping at temperatures of approximately 600 F. In most cases, the tin coating is about 0.0001 inch thick as compared to only about 0.00003 inch in electro-tinned sheets. Porosity is greater in plated tin coatings; and, when the containers are used for food, a lacquer seal is necessary.

Parkerizing. Parkerizing is a process for making a thin phosphate coating on steel to act as a base or primer for enamels and paints. In this process the steel is dipped in a heated solution (190 F) of manganese dihydrogen phosphate for about 45 minutes. *Bluing* is a process of dipping steel or iron in a 600 F molten bath of nitrate of potash (salt peter) for about 1 to 15 minutes. There are many salts that can be used to color brass and steel by dipping at elevated temperatures, but most of these have limited application and differing degrees of permanence.

Anodizing. Anodizing is an oxidation process developed for aluminum. An electrolyte of sulfuric, oxalic, or chromic acid is employed with the part to be anodized as the anode. Since the coating is produced entirely by oxidation and not by plating, the oxide coating is a permanent and integral part of the original base material. Although the coating is hard, it is porous, which is an advantage from a decorative point of view. The oxide coating enables organic coatings and dyes to be successfully applied to the surface of aluminum. Modern aluminum glasses and pitchers are examples of this process. Magnesium is anodized in a somewhat similar manner.

Calorizing. Calorizing is a process designed to protect steel from oxidation at high temperatures. Aluminum is diffused into the metal surface at elevated temperatures, forming a protecting film of aluminum oxide which prevents the underlying metal from oxidation. The process is used for treating parts for furnaces, oil refineries, driers, and kilns.

Hard surfacing. Hard surfacing is the application to a wearing surface of some metal or treatment that renders the surface highly resistant to abrasion. Such processes vary in technique. Some apply a hard surface coating by fusion welding; in others no material is added, and the surface metal is changed by heat treatment or by contact with other materials. With the development of the processes, many new hard-surfacing materials were discovered. The research for these hard materials has been especially keen during recent years, owing to the great demand of industry for longer-life products.

The several properties required of materials subjected to severe wearing conditions are hardness, abrasion resistance, and impact resistance. Hardness is easily determined by several known methods, and an accurate comparison of metals for this property can be obtained readily. Tests for wear or abrasion resistance have not been standardized, and it is difficult to obtain comparative results. In general, experience has shown that, to obtain proper results, wear testing must simulate the service conditions for each type of hard-facing material. The statement that "the wear resistance of a material is a function of the method by which it is measured" has been confirmed by both practical experience and research. All factors considered, hardness is probably the best criterion of wear resistance. Ability to withstand wear and abrasion usually increases as the hardness of the metal increases.

Table 13 is a classification of the various processes used for obtaining a hard surface. Obviously, there is a great difference in the hardness that can be obtained from these methods. The classification does not include heat-treating methods which produce a hard interior surface.

Where thick coatings of hard materials are required, it is necessary to use some form of welding. The hard-facing materials used as electrodes or filler rods are classified roughly as "overlay" and "diamond-substitute" types. The overlay materials include such metals as high-carbon steel, ferrous alloys of chromium and manganese, and numerous nonferrous alloys containing principally cobalt, manganese, and tungsten. The hardness of these materials varies considerably, ranging from around Rockwell C40 to 70. According to the Mohs' scale, the hardness seldom exceeds 8. The "diamond substitutes," materials which are among the hardest available, include tungsten, boron, tantalum carbides, and chromium boride. On the Mohs' scale they fall between 8.5 and 9.5. They cannot be applied by self-fusion but must be bonded to the parent metal with some lower-melting alloy.

High-carbon welding rod with a carbon content ranging from 0.9 to 1.1% is the most economical hard-facing material to apply from the standpoint of initial cost. Such rods form a tough surface of moderate hardness, ranging from Rockwell C30 to 45. Hardest surfaces are obtained by rapid quenching; and, as with all martensitic deposits, not much additional hardness can be obtained by cold working. Corrosion resistance is poor, but such coatings have a wide application where wear resistance is desired.

Increased hardness and wear resistance can be obtained by alloying steel with such elements as nickel, manganese, molybdenum, and chromium. The limit of hardness for such coatings is around Rock-

TABLE 13. Methods of Producing Hard Surfaces

I. Heat treatment
    A. Carburizing—heating in contact
        1. With solids as charcoal
        2. With liquids as KCN
        3. With gases as CO
    B. Special case-hardening processes
        1. Nitriding—contact with NH_3 gas
        2. Chapmanizing—contact with liquid containing N and C
        3. Dry cyaniding—contact with gases
        4. Ni-carbing—contact with gases
    C. Induction hardening—electric heating and rapid quenching
    D. Flame hardening—heating with torch and rapid quenching

II. Metal spraying—applying with air pressure
    A. High-carbon steel
    B. Stainless steel
    C. Other alloys

III. Metal plating—electrolytic deposit of chromium and other hard elements

IV. Fusion welding processes
    A. Overlay process—welding with
        1. Ferrous alloys
            (*a*) High-carbon steel
            (*b*) Steel alloys
        2. Nonferrous alloys—chiefly of chromium, cobalt, molybdenum, and tungsten
    B. Diamond substitutes
        1. Cemented, cast, or sintered carbides of tungsten and other elements
            (*a*) Inserts
            (*b*) Screen sizes in tubes
            (*c*) Screen sizes and binder cast into rods
            (*d*) Screen sizes, loose or with gelatin binder
            (*e*) "Sweat-on"—paste containing very fine hard particles
    C. Casting or spinning process—chiefly nickel borides

well C55, and, since many of the alloys result in austenitic deposits, their hardness can be increased by cold working. Corrosion resistance of most of these materials is good, as well as their resistance to impact, and no heat treatment is required after application.

In the nonferrous group are included all rods that are made up of elements other than iron, but in some cases small percentages of iron may be present. The principal elements in this group are tungsten, chromium, molybdenum, and cobalt. The average room-temperature hardness of this group is about the same as that of the ferrous-alloy group. A high percentage of this hardness is retained while the rods are at red heat, which adds greatly to their wear-resisting power. In severe abrasive work considerable heat is developed by friction, which acts on the minute areas of particles in contact. The effect of this heat is to soften the metal on these areas and cause them to wear away. If the metal in contact can retain a hardness at a relatively high temperature. it has a much greater resistance to wear than metals that do not have this property. In such cases the initial hardness is not a true criterion of the wear-resisting ability of the metal.

Both the electric-arc and oxyacetylene processes can be used in applying this material, the latter being preferred. Better control of the deposit is obtained, and there is less dilution of the rod with the parent metal. There is also no loss of the expensive rod material by volatilization and spattering. Practically any carbon or alloy steel can be hard-surfaced with this material, and it is especially adapted for coating surfaces subject to severe abrasion and impact, such as valve seats and oil-drilling tools.

The so-called diamond substitutes constitute the hardest materials that are available for hard surfacing. These materials, generally spoken of as cemented carbides, include tungsten carbide, tantalum carbide, titanium carbide, boron carbide, and chromium boride, or a combination of these and other carbides with a suitable cementing agent. In tungsten carbide, which is one of the most common of the group, the usual analysis by percentage is tungsten 81.4%, cobalt 12.7%, carbon 5.3%, and iron 0.6%. The cobalt serves as a binder and adds to the ductility of the carbide. It may vary in percentage from 5 to 13. Tantalum carbide is 87% TaC, with 13% of some binder. Usually the binder is either a combination of molybdenum and iron or of tungsten carbide and cobalt. Boron carbide contains about 78.2% boron and 21% carbon, with a trace of silicon and iron. It is usually known by the symbol B_4C. Many similar carbide materials, the composition of which are not generally known, are manufactured under special trade names.

Carbide material cannot be applied like other hard-surfacing materials because of its high melting temperature and is therefore furnished either in the form of small inserts or in screen sizes. Inserts can be applied by a brazing or sweating-on process or placed in melted or puddled metal and then surrounded by metal from a steel or hard-surfacing welding rod. Screened sizes of crushed carbide particles can be applied conveniently by putting the particles in steel tubes. The steel sheath melts like an ordinary welding rod and fuses to the metal. The carbide particles do not melt but are distributed through the molten metal and are held fast when the metal cools.

Screened sizes can also be applied by mixing the particles with a suitable binder and casting them into rods. These rods can be used conveniently like other hard-surfacing welding rods.

All these materials have hardnesses approaching that of a diamond, and on the Moh's scale they range from 9 to 9.5. This hardness is maintained to a large extent at a red heat. Because of their extreme hardness and brittleness, diamond substitutes do not have a high strength rating and are not suitable where severe shock and impact conditions exist. This difficulty is partially eliminated by the elements being properly supported with a tough binding material. Another characteristic of these surfacing materials is that they do not respond to heat treatment or cold working and retain their initial hardness under all conditions. They are not suitable for casting, although a few hard materials, principally boron alloys with an iron base, can be processed in this manner.

Metal Spraying

The spraying of molten metal, a comparatively recent development, is rapidly becoming an important process in industry. Any metal obtainable in wire form can be applied in this manner. The wire is fed into the spray gun at a definite rate, melted by an oxyacetylene flame, and then blown by compressed air to the surface being coated. A cross section of a metal-spraying gun is shown in Figure 3.

Because the bond between the sprayed metal and the parent metal is entirely mechanical, it is important that the surface of the metal be properly prepared before spraying. The usual method of cleaning and preparing the surface is by blasting with sharp silica sand or angular steel grit. Cylindrical objects may be prepared by machining small grooves on the surface followed by rolling over the tops of these grooves with a tool similar to a knurling tool.

Either of these methods roughens the surface and provides the necessary interlocking surfaces or keys to make the plastic metal adhere to the surface. The molten metal is blown with considerable force against the surface, causing it to flatten out and interlock with surface irregularities and the adjacent metal particles. The sprayed metal itself provides a suitable surface for successive coatings and permits building up a layer of considerable thickness.

The change in the physical properties of metal applied in this manner is an increase in porosity and a corresponding decrease in the tensile strength of the material. The reason for this is that the bond is mechanical and not fusile, as it is for welding. The compressive strength is high, and there is some increase in hardness. Stainless-steel and high-carbon deposits will develop a Scleroscope hardness of 70 to 75, which corresponds to a Brinell hardness of 500 to 550. The wearing quality of sprayed metal is good, as evidenced by its wide use in building up worn shafts and other moving parts. All

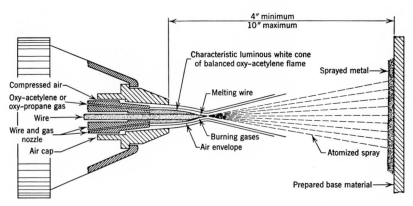

Fig. 3.   Cross section at nozzle of metal spray gun. (Courtesy Metallizing Engineering Company.)

deposits can be finished satisfactorily by usual machining or grinding methods, and the metals retain most of their original properties.

The success of this process is due largely to its economy and to the rapidity with which the metal can be applied. There is no distortion in the parts being surfaced, nor do internal stresses develop. Practically any metal can be applied to any other commercial metal and even to other base surfaces such as wood and glass.

REVIEW QUESTIONS

1. Name several products which can best be made by electroforming.
2. What are the limitations of the electroforming process?
3. What kind of metal structure is obtained by electrolytic deposition?
4. For what reasons are coatings applied to metals?
5. What metal coatings are best suited for wear resistance?
6. How does sheradizing differ from galvanizing?
7. How are tin cans coated?
8. What processes are designed to protect iron or steel from oxidation?
9. What materials are known as diamond substitutes?
10. How are hard-surfacing materials such as carbides applied to oil well drilling tools and similar instruments?
11. How should a surface be prepared for metal spraying?

REFERENCES

Begeman, M. L., "Hard-Surfacing Processes and Materials," *Mechanical Engineering*, Vol. 60, December 1938.

Bolz, R. W., *Production Processes*, Vol. 1, The Penton Publishing Company, 1949.

Lamb, V. A., and Wm. H. Metzger, Jr., "Electroforming," *The Tool Engineer*, Vol. 33, No. 2, August 1954.

Rice, H. D., "A New Look at Electroformed Parts," *Materials & Methods*, Vol. 42, No. 3, September 1955.

Shapiro, C. H., "Oxy-Acetylene Application of Hard Facing to Oil Well Drilling Bits," *Metal Progress*, Vol. 35, April 1939.

Tool Engineers Handbook, The American Society of Tool Engineers, McGraw-Hill Book Company, 1949.

Young, J. F., *Materials and Processes*, 2d edition, John Wiley and Sons, 1954.

CHAPTER 11

HOT WORKING
OF METAL

The mechanical working of metal is the shaping of metal in either a cold or a hot state by some mechanical means. This does not include the shaping of metals by machining or grinding, in which processes metal is actually machined off, nor does it include the casting of molten metal into some form by use of molds. In mechanical working processes, the metal is shaped by pressure—actually forging, bending, squeezing, drawing, or shearing it to its final shape. In these processes the metal may be either cold- or hot-worked. Although normal room temperatures are ordinarily used for cold working of steel, temperatures up to the recrystallization range are sometimes used. Hot working of metals takes place above the recrystallization or work-hardening range. For steel, recrystallization starts around 950 to 1300 F, although most hot work on steel is done at temperatures considerably above this range. There is no tendency for hardening by mechanical work until the lower limit of the recrystalline range is reached. Some metals, such as lead and tin, have a low recrystalline range and can be hot-worked at room temperature, but most commercial metals require some heating. Alloy composition has a great influence upon the proper working range, the usual result being to raise the recrystalline range temperature. This range may also be increased by prior cold working.

236

During all hot-working operations the metal is in a plastic state and is readily formed by pressure. In addition hot working has the following advantages:

1. Porosity in the metal is largely eliminated. Most ingots when cast contain many small blow holes. These are pressed together and eliminated by the high working pressure used.

2. Impurities in the form of inclusions are broken up and distributed through the metal.

3. Coarse or columnar grains are refined. Since this work is in the recrystalline range, it should be carried on until the low limit is reached in order to provide a fine grain structure.

4. Physical properties are generally improved, owing principally to the grain refinement. Ductility and resistance to impact are improved, strength is increased, and greater homogeneity is developed in the metal. The greatest strength of rolled steel exists in the direction of metal flow.

All hot-working processes present a few disadvantages which cannot be ignored. Because of the high temperature of the metal there is a rapid oxidation or scaling of the surface with accompanying poor surface finish. Tooling and handling costs are high, and close tolerances cannot be maintained. Hot working, however, is a rapid, economical process that is used on nearly all commercial metals.

The principal methods of hot-working metals are:

1. Rolling
2. Forging
   (a) Hammer or smith forging
   (b) Drop forging
   (c) Upset forging
   (d) Press forging
   (e) Roll forging
   (f) Swaging
3. Pipe welding
   (a) Butt welding of heated strips
   (b) Butt welding by electrical resistance
   (c) Lap welding
   (d) Hammer welding
4. Piercing
5. Drawing or cupping
6. Spinning
7. Extruding

Hot-working Processes

Ingot casting. Before metals can be mechanically worked, they must first be cast into ingot molds of suitable form, as shown in Figure 1. The mold may be rectangular, square, or round in cross

Fig. I. Steel being poured into molds to make ingots for subsequent rolling. (Courtesy Bethlehem Steel Company.)

section, the final casting varying in size from a few hundred pounds to several tons. The kind of metal cast and the product desired are the factors which determine the ingot size. Both rectangular and square section ingots have rounded corners, and the sides are corrugated. Rounding the corners reduces the tendency for columnar grains to meet and form a plane of weakness. Cooling is accelerated by corrugating the sides, a process which reduces the size of the columnar grains being formed.

The two types of ingot molds, shown in Figure 2, are used for top pouring. The big-end-down type shown at *A* is easy to strip from the ingot, but the loss in metal is high due to the shrinkage cavity (pipe) which is formed dur-
ing the cooling operation. This loss is lower when the big-end-up type shown at *B* is used. When an ingot is poured, the solidification is progressive, starting at the mold surface and progressing towards the center. During this period there is considerable shrinkage of the metal. As layer after layer solidifies, the volume of metal decreases, resulting

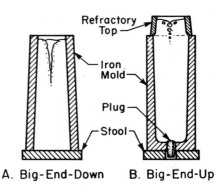

A. Big-End-Down   B. Big-End-Up

Fig. 2. Types of ingot molds.

in the formation of a pipe when solidification is complete. The rate of cooling is an important factor in the production of a sound ingot.

Ingots made in big-end-up molds have a large volume of hot metal available at the top of the mold during the cooling operation and when solidified show little loss of metal due to shrinkage cavities. Losses from pipe formation in ingots can be reduced by either adding metal during cooling or by using refractory risers. Metal in the riser remains molten until the ingot has solidified, and during the solidification period supplies the ingot with needed metal to compensate for shrinkage.

Several types of ingot structures are obtained by controlling or eliminating gas evolution in the metal during solidification. *Killed* steel has been deoxidized, and it evolves no gas during solidification. Such ingots have a minimum of segregation and are of good structure, but the loss due to pipe formation is high. The other extreme in ingot structure is known as *rimmed* steel, which is characterized by a semiboiling action in the ingot after it has been poured, due to rapid evolution of carbon monoxide gas during the solidification period. This causes the formation of a honeycomb structure which, if controlled, compensates for most shrinkage loss. These small blow holes do not constitute a defect, provided that they have not had contact with the outside atmosphere and are closed by pressure welding in the hot-working processes. Rimmed steel ingots have a good surface and there is little or no opportunity for pipes to form. Semikilled and other ingot structures are obtained by controlling the formation of gas during solidification.

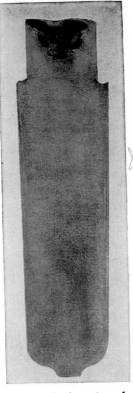

A longitudinal and a cross section of a medium-carbon killed-steel ingot are shown in Figure 3. The coarse dendritic crystalline structure, clearly indicated in the cross section, subsequently will be eliminated by the effect of hot working. The impurities in ingots tend to segregate in the shrink head during the process of solidification. Cutting off the end

Longitudinal section of steel ingot.

Cross section of medium-carbon killed-steel ingot showing crystalline structure. (Courtesy Drop Forging Association.)

Fig. 3.

of the ingot, either before the rolling starts or after, largely eliminates this defect.

Rolling. The steel remains in ingot molds until the solidification is about complete, at which time the molds are removed. While still hot, the ingots are placed in gas-fired furnaces called *soaking pits,* where they remain until they have attained a uniform working temperature (around 2200 F) throughout. They are then taken to the rolling mill. Because of the large variety of finished shapes to be made, ingots are first rolled into such intermediate shapes as blooms, billets, or slabs. A *bloom* has a square cross section with a minimum size of 6 by 6 inches. A *billet* is smaller than a bloom and may have any square section from 1½ inches up to the size of a bloom. Most primary rolling is done in either a two-high reversing mill or a three-high continuous rotating mill. In the two-high reversing mill (A in Figure 4), the piece passes through the rolls, which are then stopped and reversed in direction, and the operation is repeated. At frequent intervals the metal is turned 90 degrees on its side

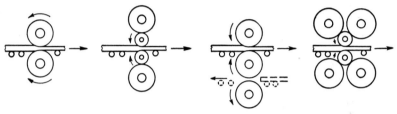

A. Two-High Mill-   B. Four-High Mill   C. Three-High Mill   D. Cluster Mill
   Continuous or   with backing-up   for Back-and-   using four
   Reversing.   Rolls for wide   Forth Rolling.   Backing-up
                        Sheets.   Rolls.

Fig. 4. Various roll arrangements used in rolling mills.

to keep the section uniform and to refine the metal throughout. About thirty passes are required to reduce a large ingot into a bloom. Grooves are provided on both the upper and the lower rolls to accommodate the various reductions in cross-sectional area. The two-high rolling mill is quite versatile, since it has a wide range of adjustment as to size of pieces and rate of reduction. It is limited by the length that can be rolled and by the inertia forces which must be overcome each time a reversal is made. These are eliminated in the three-high mill (*C* in Figure 4), but an elevating mechanism is required. Although there is some difficulty due to lack of correct speed for all passes, the three-high mill is less expensive to make and has a higher output than the reversing mill.

Billets could be rolled to size in a large mill used for blooms, but this is not usually done for economic reasons. Frequently they are rolled from blooms in a continuous billet mill consisting of about eight rolling stands in a straight line. The steel makes but one pass through the mill and emerges with a final billet size, approximately 2 by 2 inches, which is the raw material for many final shapes such as bars, tubes, and forgings. Figure 5 illustrates the number of passes and the sequence in reducing the cross section of a 4 by 4 inch billet to round bar stock.

Slabs may be rolled from either an ingot or a bloom. They have

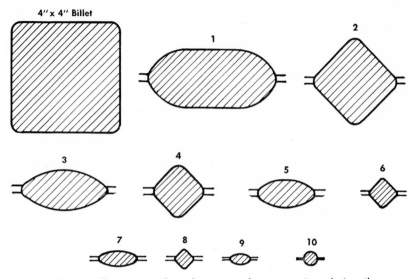

Fig. 5. Diagram illustrates number of passes and sequence in reducing the cross section of a 4-by-4-inch billet to round bar stock. (Courtesy Carnegie-Illinois Steel Corporation.)

a rectangular cross-sectional area with a minimum width of 10 inches and a minimum thickness of 1½ inch. From slabs are rolled plates, skelp, and thin strips.

Various arrangements of rolls used in rolling mills are shown in Figure 4. Those that have four or more rolls use the extra ones for backing up the two that are doing the rolling. In addition, many special rolling mills take intermediary rolled products and fabricate them into such finished articles as rails, structural shapes, plates, and bars. Such mills usually bear the name of the product being rolled and in appearance are similar to mills used for rolling blooms and billets.

As previously stated, one effect of hot-working is the grain refinement brought about by recrystallization. This is shown diagrammatically in Figure 6. The coarse structure is definitely broken up and elongated by the rolling action. Because of the high temperature, recrystallization starts in immediately and small grains start to form. These grains grow rapidly until recrystallization is complete, growth continuing at high temperatures, if further work is not carried on, until the low temperature of the recrystalline range is reached.

The arcs AB and $A'B'$ are the contact arcs on the rolls. The wedging action on the work is overcome by the frictional forces which act on these arcs and draw the metal through the rolls. The metal emerges from the rolls traveling at a higher speed than it enters. At a point midway between A and B the metal speed is the same as the roll peripheral speed. Most deformation takes place in thickness although there is some increase in width. Temperature uniformity is important in all rolling operations since it controls metal flow and plasticity.

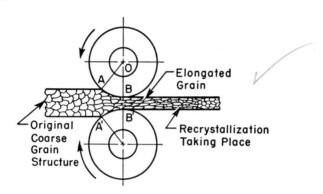

Fig. 6. Effect of hot rolling upon grain structure.

Hammer or smith forging. This type of forging consists of hammering the heated metal either with hand tools, or between flat dies in a steam hammer. Hand forging, as done by the blacksmith, is the oldest form of forging. It is largely used for repair or maintenance work and in the production of small parts such as hooks, crowbars, chisels, cutting tools, U bolts, and similar articles, where only small quantities are involved. The nature of the process is such that close accuracy is not obtained, nor can complicated shapes be made. Forgings ranging from a few pounds to over 200,000 pounds are made by smith forging.

Forging hammers are made in the single or open frame type for light work, while the double housing type is made for heavier service. A typical steam hammer is shown in Figure 7. The force of the blow is closely controlled by the operator, and considerable skill is required in the use of this machine.

Drop forging. Drop forging differs from smith forging in that closed-impression rather than open-face dies are used. The forging is produced by impact or pressure which compels the plastic metal to conform to the shape of the dies. In this operation there is drastic flow of the metal in the dies caused by the repeated blows on the metal. To insure proper flow of the metal during the intermittent blows, the operation is divided into a number of steps. Each step changes the form in a gradual fashion, controlling the flow of the metal until the final shape is obtained. The number of steps re-

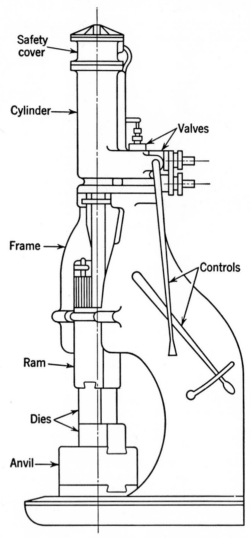

Fig. 7. Open-frame steam hammer. (Courtesy Chambersburg Engineering Company.)

quired varies according to the size and shape of the part, the forging qualities of the metal, and the tolerances required. For products of large or complicated shapes a preliminary shaping operation, using more than one set of dies, may be required.

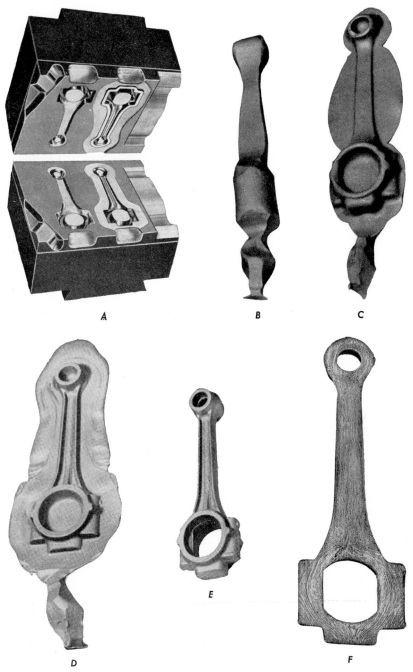

Fig. 8. Steps in drop forging a connecting rod. (Courtesy Drop Forging Association.)

The forging will have a thin projection of excess metal extending around it at the parting line. This excess metal is provided to insure complete filling of the dies and is removed in a separate trimming press immediately after the forging operation. Small forgings may be trimmed cold, though care must be taken in the trimming operation not to distort the part. The forging is usually held uniformly by the die in the ram and pushed through the trimming edges. Punching operations may also be done while trimming is taking place.

Steps in the forging of a connecting rod are illustrated in Figure 8. The first step in the manufacture of this part is to shear off bar stock to proper length and bring it up to forging temperature in a furnace adjacent to the forge. The dies used in this operation, shown at *A*, contain impressions for several operations. Preliminary hot-working first proportions the metal for forming the connecting rod; then the fillering operation, illustrated at *B*, reduces the cross-sectional area of the center while the edging gathers metal for the two ends of the rod. The blocking operation, which forms the rod into a definite shape, is shown at *C*.

The appearance of the connecting rod after several blows in the finishing die is shown at *D*. Flash around the edges of the finished forging is removed in a separate press by trimmer dies immediately after the finishing operation is completed. The completed connecting rod, ready for heat treatment, is shown at *E*. At *F* is a macro-etched cross section of a connecting-rod forging, showing the flow lines of the metal and the fiber structure obtained by the hammering action.

The two principal types of drop-forging hammers are the *steam hammer* and the *gravity drop* or *board hammer*. In the former the ram and hammer are lifted by steam, and the force of the blow is controlled by throttling the steam. These hammers, which work rapidly, obtain over 300 blows a minute. The capacities of steam hammers range from 500 to 50,000 pounds. They are usually of double-housing design, with an overhead steam cylinder assembly providing the power for actuating the ram. For a given weight ram, a steam hammer will develop twice the energy at the die as can be obtained from a board or gravity drop hammer.

In the gravity-type hammer the impact pressure is developed by the force of the falling ram and die as it strikes upon the lower fixed die. The gravity drop hammer, shown in Figure 9, is one type which has several hardwood boards attached to the hammer for lifting purposes. After the hammer has fallen, rollers engage the boards and lift

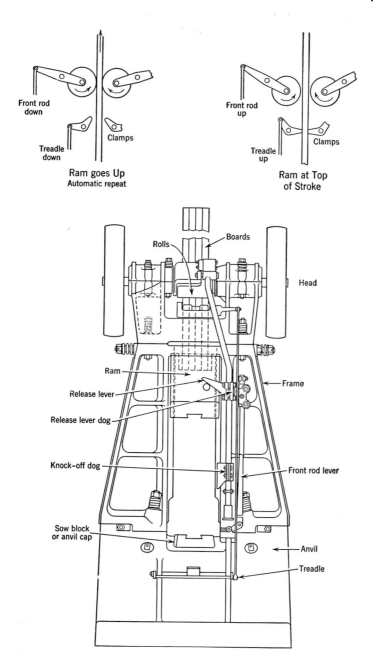

Fig. 9. Board drop hammer. (Courtesy Chambersburg Engineering Company.)

the hammer a desired amount (ranging up to 5 feet). When the stroke is reached, the rollers spread, and the boards are held by dogs until they are released by the operator. The force of the blow is entirely dependent upon the weight of the hammer which seldom exceeds 8000 pounds.

A modification of the board hammer is a design employing a single-acting compressed air or steam cylinder to lift the weight. This design eliminates frequent board replacement, has a quicker lifting speed, is less expensive, and requires less physical effort to operate. One feature of this hammer is that the stroke can be varied readily

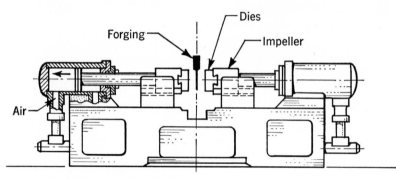

Fig. 10. Horizontal forging machine with opposing impellers. (Courtesy Chambersburg Engineering Company.)

to suit forging conditions. Hammers of this type are procurable from a ram weight of 500 pounds up to and including a 10,000-pound ram weight size. Both the board and air hammers find extensive use in industry for such articles as hand tools, scissors, cutlery, implement parts, and airplane parts.

A recent development in forging equipment is known as the *impacter forging hammer*. This machine, shown in Figure 10, has two opposing cylinders in a horizontal plane which actuate the impellers and dies toward each other. Stock is positioned in the impact plane in which the dies collide. Its deformation absorbs the energy, and there is no shock or vibration in the machine. With this process the stock is worked equally on both sides, there is less time of contact between stock and die, less energy is required than with other forging processes, and the work is held mechanically.

Upon completion, all forgings are covered with scale and must be given a cleaning operation. This can be done by pickling in acid, shot peening, or tumbling, depending on the size and composition of the forgings. If some distortion has occurred in forging, a sizing or straightening operation may be required. Controlled cooling is usually provided for large forgings; and if certain physical properties are necessary, provision is made for subsequent heat treatment.

Forging imparts fine crystalline structure to the metal, closes all voids, forms the metal to shape, and improves the physical properties of the metal. Defects which may occur with this process include misalignment of the dies, scale inclusions on the surface, and cracks in the forging caused by the metal folding over during the operation. These defects can be controlled. Forging is adapted to both carbon and alloy steels, wrought iron, copper-base alloys, aluminum alloys, and magnesium alloys.

Press forging. Press forging employs a slow squeezing action in deforming the plastic metal, as contrasted with the rapid-impact blows of a hammer. The squeezing action is carried completely to the center of the part being pressed, thoroughly working the entire section. These presses are the vertical type and may be either mechanically or hydraulically operated. The mechanical presses, which are faster operating and most commonly used, range in capacity from 500 to 10,000 tons.

For small press forgings closed impression dies are used, and only one stroke of the ram is normally required to perform the forging operation. The maximum pressure is built up at the end of the stroke which forces the metal into shape. Dies may be mounted as separate units, or all the cavities may be put into a single block. For small forgings individual die units are more convenient. There is some difference in the design of dies for different metals; copper-alloy forgings can be made with less draft than steel, consequently more complicated shapes can be produced. These alloys flow well in the die and are readily extruded.

In the forging press a greater proportion of the total work put into the machine is transmitted to the metal than in a drop hammer press. Much of the impact of the drop hammer is absorbed by the machine and foundation. Press reduction of the metal is faster, and the cost of operation is consequently lower. Most press forgings are symmetrical in shape, having surfaces which are quite smooth, and provide a closer tolerance than is obtained by a drop hammer. However, many parts of irregular and complicated shapes can be forged more economically by drop forging. Forging presses are often used for sizing operations on parts made by other forging processes.

Upset forging. Upset forging entails gripping a bar of uniform section in dies and applying pressure on the heated end, causing it to be upset or formed to shape. A large machine of this type is shown in Figure 11. Here rear-axle drive shafts with flanged ends are being forged from round stock. The heated bar of stock is placed

Fig. 11. Five-inch upset forging machine in operation—forging flanged rear-axle drive shafts. (Courtesy The Ajax Manufacturing Company.)

between a fixed and a movable die which grip the bar firmly when closed. A portion of the bar projects beyond the die for the upsetting operation by the header rams. The cavity impression on the end of the ram squeezes the plastic metal until it conforms to the die cavity. For some products the heading operation may be completed in one position, though in most cases the work is progressively placed into different positions in the die. The impressions may be in the punch, in the gripping die, or in both. In most instances the forgings do not require a trimming operation. Machines

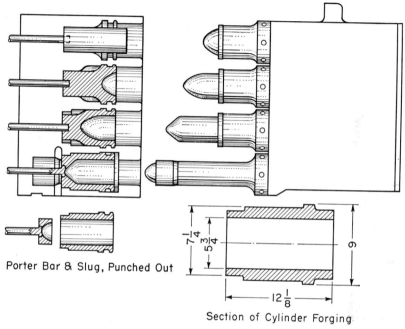

Porter Bar & Slug, Punched Out

Section of Cylinder Forging

Fig. 12. Sequence of operations for a cylinder forging used on upset forging machine. (Courtesy The Ajax Manufacturing Company.)

of this type are an outgrowth of smaller machines designed for cold heading nails and small bolts.

Progressive piercing, or internal displacement, is the method frequently employed on upset forging machines for producing parts such as artillery shells and radial engine cylinder forgings. The sequence of operations for a cylinder forging is shown in Figure 12. Round blanks of a predetermined length for a single cylinder are first heated to forging temperature. To facilitate handling the blank, a porter bar is pressed into one end. The blank is upset and is progressively pierced to a heavy bottom cup. In the last operation a tapered-nosed punch expands and stretches the metal into the end of the die, frees the porter bar, and punches out the end slug. Large

cylinder barrels weighing over 100 pounds can be forged in this manner. Parts produced by this process range from small to large
products weighing several hundred pounds. The dies, not limited
to upsetting, may also be used for piercing, punching, trimming,
or extrusion.

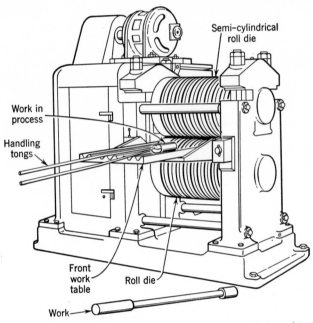

Fig. 13. Forging rolls producing automobile rear-axle drive shafts. (Courtesy The
Ajax Manufacturing Company.)

Roll forging. Roll forging machines are primarily adapted to
reducing and tapering operations on short lengths of bar stock. The
rolls on this machine, shown in Figure 13, are not completely circular
but have from 50 to 75% cut away to permit the stock to enter between the rolls. The circular portion of the rolls is grooved according to the shaping to be done. When the rolls are in open position
the operator places the heated bar between them, retaining it with
tongs. As the rolls rotate, the bar is gripped by the roll grooves and
pushed toward the operator. When the rolls open, the bar is pushed
back and rolled again, or is placed in the next groove for subsequent
forming work. By rotating the bar 90 degrees after each roll pass,
there is no opportunity for flash to form.

Roll forging is used on a wide variety of parts, including axles,
blanks for airplanes propellers, crowbars, knife blades, chisels, ta-

pered tubing, and ends of leaf springs. Parts made in this fashion have a smooth finished surface and tolerances equal to other forging processes. The metal is hot-worked thoroughly and has good physical properties. Because of the high cost of the rolls a large volume of production is necessary to amortize tooling expense.

In the rolling of wheels, metal tires, and similar items a roll mill of somewhat different construction is used. Figure 14 shows how a rough forged blank is converted into a finished wheel by the action of the various rolls about the circumference of the wheel.

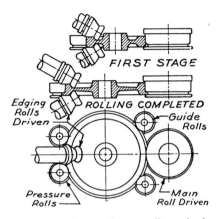

Fig. 14. Mill setup for hot-rolling wheels. (Courtesy Edgewater Steel Company.)

As the wheel rotates, the diameter is gradually increased while the plate and rim are reduced in section. When the wheel is rolled to its final diameter, it is then transferred to a press and given a dishing and sizing operation.

Pipe and Tube Manufacture

Butt welding. Pipe and tubular products may be made by either welding or piercing, the latter being a seamless process. In the butt welding processes both intermittent and continuous methods are

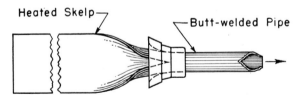

Heated Skelp

Butt-welded Pipe

Fig. 15. Producing butt-welded pipe by drawing skelp through a welding bell.

used. Heated strips of steel, known as *skelp*, which have the edges beveled slightly are used so that they will meet accurately when formed to a circular shape. In the intermittent process, one end of the skelp is trimmed to a V shape to permit it to enter the welding bell, as shown in Figure 15. When the skelp is brought up to welding heat, the end is gripped by tongs which engage a draw chain. As

the tube is pulled through the welding bell, skelp is formed to a
circular shape, and the edges are welded together. A final operation passes the pipe between sizing and finishing rolls to give it
correct size and to remove scale. Continuous butt welding of pipe
is accomplished by supplying the skelp in coils and providing means
for flash-welding the coil ends to form a continuous strip. As the

Fig. 16. Skelp emerging from furnace at right is formed into continuous butt-weld
pipe. (Courtesy Bethlehem Steel Company.)

skelp enters the furnace, flames impinge on the edges of the strip
to bring them to welding temperatures. Leaving the furnace, the
skelp enters a series of horizontal and vertical rollers as shown in
Figure 16, which form it into pipe. An enlarged view of the rollers,
showing how the pipe is formed and sized, is shown in Figure 17.
As the pipe leaves the rollers, it is sawed into lengths which are
finally processed by descaling and finishing operations. Pipe is made
by this method in sizes up to 3 inches in diameter.

Electric butt welding. Electric butt welding of pipe necessitates
cold forming of the steel plate to shape prior to the welding operation. The circular form is developed by passing the plate through
a continuous set of rolls which progressively change its shape, a
method known as roll forming. The welding unit, placed at the end
of the roll-forming machine, consists of three centering and pressure
rolls which hold the formed shape in position and two electrode
rolls which supply current to generate the heat. Immediately after
the pipe passes the welding unit, shown in Figure 18, the extruded
flash metal is removed from both inside and outside the pipe. Sizing
and finishing rolls then complete the operation by giving the pipe

accurate size and concentricity. This process is adapted to the manufacture of pipe up to 16-inch diameter, with wall thicknesses varying

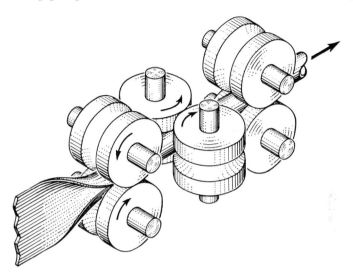

Fig. 17. Skelp being formed into continuous butt-weld pipe.

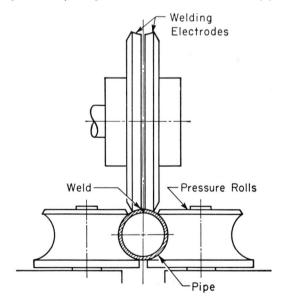

Fig. 18. Continuous resistance butt welding unit for making pipe.

from ⅛ to ½ inch. Pipes of larger diameter are usually fabricated
by submerged-arc welding after being formed to shape in large, spe-

cially constructed presses. Some large pipe is fabricated by hammer welding, which is essentially a forge-welding process.

Lap welding. In the lap welding of pipe, the edges of the skelp are beveled as it emerges from the furnace. The skelp is then drawn

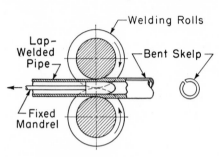

through a forming die, or between rolls, to give it cylindrical shape with the edges overlapping. After being reheated, the bent skelp is passed between two grooved rolls as shown in Figure 19. Between the rolls is a fixed mandrel of a size to fit the inside diameter of the pipe, the edges being lap-welded by pressure between the rolls

Fig. 19. Method of producing lap-welded pipe from bent skelp.

and the mandrel. Lap weld is mades in sizes ranging from 2 to 16 inches in diameter.

Piercing. To produce seamless tubing, cylindrical billets of steel are passed between two conical-shaped rolls operating in the same direction. Between these rolls is a fixed point or mandrel which assists in the piercing and controls the size of the hole as the billet is forced over it.

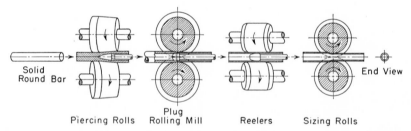

Fig. 20. Principal steps in the manufacture of seamless tubing. (Courtesy National Tube Company.)

The entire operation of making seamless tubing in this conventional process is shown in Figure 20. The solid billet is first center-punched and then brought to forging heat in a furnace before being pierced. It is then pushed into the two piercing rolls which impart both rotation and axial advance. The alternate squeezing and bulging of the billet open up a seam in its center, the size and shape of which are controlled by the piercing mandrel. As the thick-walled tube emerges from the piercing mill, it passes between grooved rolls over a plug held by a mandrel and is converted into a longer tube with specified wall thickness. While still at working temperatures, the tube passes through the reeling machine which further straightens and sizes it and, in addition, gives the walls a smooth surface. Final sizing and finishing are accomplished in the same manner as with welded pipe.

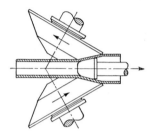

Rotary Rolling Mill

Fig. 21. Rotary seamless process for large tubing. (Courtesy National Tube Division, U.S. Steel Corp.)

This procedure applies to seamless tubes up to 6 inches in diameter. Larger tubes up to 14 inches in diameter are given a second operation on piercing rolls. To produce sizes up to 24 inches in diameter, reheated, double-pierced tubes are processed on a rotary rolling mill as shown in Figure 21 and are finally completed by reelers and sizing rolls, as described in the single-piercing process.

In the continuous method, shown in Figure 22, a 5½ inch round bar is pierced and conveyed to the nine-stand mandrel mill where a cylindrical bar or mandrel is inserted. These rolls reduce the tube diameter and wall thickness. The mandrel is then removed, and the

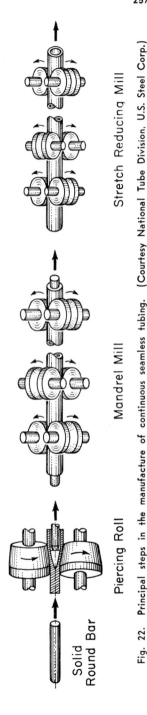

Stretch Reducing Mill

Mandrel Mill

Piercing Roll

Solid Round Bar

Fig. 22. Principal steps in the manufacture of continuous seamless tubing. (Courtesy National Tube Division, U.S. Steel Corp.)

tube reheated before it enters the twelve-stand stretch reducing mill. This mill reduces not only the wall thickness of the hot tube but also the tube diameter. Each successive roll is speeded up so as to produce a tension sufficient to stretch the tube between stands. The maximum delivery of this mill is 1300 fpm for pipe around 2 inches in diameter.

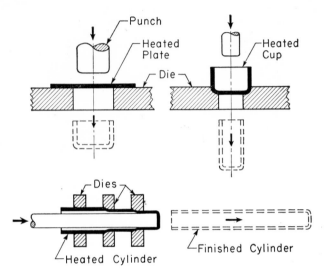

Fig. 23. Drawing thick-walled cylinders from heated plates. (Courtesy National Tube Division, U.S. Steel Corp.)

Drawing or cupping. Some thick-walled tubes or cylinders are produced by drawing circular heated plates through a die, as illustrated diagrammatically in Figure 23. The procedure consists of several two-step drawing operations, between which the cup-shaped cylinder must be reheated to provide the necessary plasticity for working. After about two drawing operations, the formed cup is pushed through a horizontal drawbench consisting of several dies, of successively decreasing diameter, mounted in one frame. The hydraulically operated punch forces the heated cylinder through the full length of the drawbench. For long thin-walled cylinders of tubes, repeated heating and drawing may be necessary. If the final product is to be a tube, the closed end is cut off and the balance is sent through finishing and sizing rolls, similar to those used in the piercing process. To produce closed-end cylinders, similar to those used for storing oxygen, the open end is swaged to form a neck or reduced by hot spinning.

Hot Spinning

Hot spinning of metal is used commercially to dish or form heavy circular plates to some shape over a rotating form, and to neck down or close the ends of tubes. In both cases a form of lathe is used to rotate the part rapidly. Shaping is done with a blunt pressure tool which contacts the surface of the rotating part and causes the metal to flow to some desired form. Once the operation is started, considerable frictional heat is generated which aids in maintaining the metal at a plastic state. Tube ends may be reduced in diameter, formed to some desired contour, or completely closed by the spinning action.

Extrusion

Any plastic material can be extruded to uniform, cross-sectional shape by the aid of pressure. The principle of *extrusion,* similar to the simple act of squirting toothpaste from a tube, has long been utilized in processes ranging all the way from the production of brick, hollow tile, and soil pipe, to the manufacture of macaroni. Some metals, notably lead, tin, and aluminum, may be extruded cold, whereas others require the application of heat to render them plastic or semisolid before extrusion. In the actual operation of extrusion, the processes differ slightly, depending on the metal and application, but in brief they consist of forcing metal (confined to a pressure chamber) out through specially formed dies. Rods, tubes, molding trim, structural shapes, brass cartridges, and lead-covered cables are typical products of metal extrusion.

Most presses used in conventional extruding of metals are of a horizontal type and hydraulically operated. Correct operating speeds, depending upon temperature and material, vary from a few feet a minute up to 900 fpm. Several variations of this process are in common use.

Direct extrusion. Direct extrusion is illustrated diagrammatically in Figure 24. A heated, round billet is placed into the die chamber and the dummy block and ram placed into position. The metal is extruded through the die opening until only a small amount remains. It is then sawed off next to the die and the butt end removed.

Indirect extrusion. Indirect extrusion, also shown in Figure 24, is similar to direct extrusion except that the extruded part is forced through the ram stem. Less force is required by this method since there is no frictional force between the billet and the container wall. The weakening of the ram when it is made hollow and the impossibility of providing adequate support for the extruded part constitute limitations of this process.

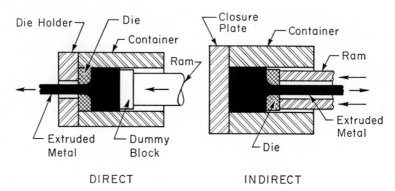

Fig. 24. Diagrammatic sketch illustrating direct and indirect extrusion.

Extruded sheathing. The coating of wire cable with lead sheathing, as illustrated in Figure 25, is an example of hot extrusion. Molten lead is poured into the cylinder above the die and allowed to solidify under slight pressure of the cylinder plunger. When the correct extruding temperature is reached (around 500 F), the

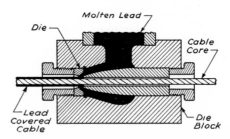

Fig. 25. Method of extruding lead sheathing on wire cable.

plunger, actuated by hydraulic means, forces the lead in two streams around the cable which weld together underneath. The lead is forced through the die, forming a uniform lead coating which grips the cable sufficiently to draw it through the die block. At the end of the stroke the plunger rises, more lead is added, and the cycle is repeated.

Impact extrusion. An interesting example of extrusion by impact is in the manufacture of collapsible tubes for shaving cream, toothpaste, and paint pigments. These extremely thin tubes are pressed out from slugs, as illustrated in the upper half of Figure 26. The punch strikes a single blow of considerable force, causing the metal to squirt up around the punch.

The outside diameter of the tube is the same as the diameter of the die, and the thickness is controlled by the clearance between the punch and die. The tube shown in the figure has a flat end, but

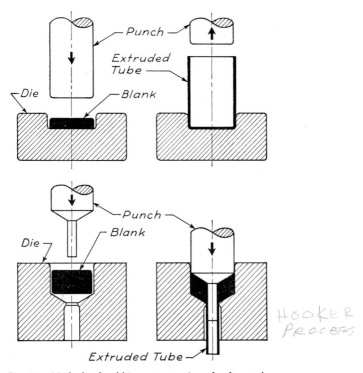

Fig. 26. Methods of cold-impact extrusion of soft metals.

any desired shape can be made by properly forming the die cavity and the end of the punch. On the upstroke, the tube is blown from the ram with compressed air. The entire operation is automatic, with a production rate of 35 to 40 tubes per minute. The tubes are then inspected, trimmed, enameled, and printed. Zinc, lead, tin, and aluminum alloys are worked in this fashion.

In the lower half of the figure is illustrated a variation of what is known as the Hooker process for extruding small tubes or cartridge cases. Small slugs or blanks are used as in the impact-extrusion process, but in this case the metal is extruded downward through the die opening. The size and shape of the extruded tube are controlled by the space between the punch end and die cavity wall. Copper tubes having wall thicknesses of 0.004 to 0.010 inch can be produced in lengths of about 12 inches. Impact extrusion is a cold-working process.

Tube extrusion. The usual method for extruding tubes is shown in Figure 27. It is a form of direct extrusion but uses a mandrel to shape the inside of the tube. After the billet is placed inside, the die containing the mandrel is pushed through the ingot as shown

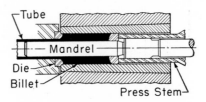

Fig. 27. Extruding a large tube from a heated billet. (Courtesy Hydropress Inc.)

in the diagram. The press stem then advances and extrudes the metal through the die and around the mandrel. The entire operation must be rapid, and speeds up to 10 feet per second have been used in making steel tubes. Low-carbon steel tubes can be extruded cold, but for most alloys the billet must be heated to around 2400 F.

REVIEW QUESTIONS

1. Distinguish between hot and cold working of steel.
2. List the various methods of hot-working metals mechanically.
3. What are the advantages gained by hot-working steel?
4. What is the difference between rimmed and killed steel?
5. How is the grain structure in steel affected by hot rolling?
6. What defects are found in ingots, and how are they eliminated?
7. Describe each of the following shapes used in connection with the rolling of steel: ingot, bloom, slab, and billet.
8. What is the usual temperature range for hot-working steel?
9. Show by sketch the various roll arrangements used in rolling mills.
10. Describe the process of drop forging.
11. What is a board hammer, and how does it operate?
12. What advantages does press forging have over drop forging?
13. Describe the impacter forging hammer.
14. What products are shaped by roll forging?
15. List the various methods used in producing pipe and tubular products.
16. What type of work is done by upset forging?
17. Describe the process of producing lap-welded pipe.
18. Describe the continuous method of making seamless tubing.

19. Show by sketch how wire is coated with lead.
20. How are collapsible tubes produced?
21. Describe the Hooker process of extrusion.

REFERENCES

Bolz, R. W., *Production Processes*, Vol. 1, Penton Publishing Company, 1949.
Camp, J. M., and C. B. Francis, *The Making, Shaping and Treating of Steel*, 5th edition, Carnegie-Illinois Steel Corporation.
Friedman, J. H., "Hot Press and Upset Forgings," *Transactions ASM*, Vol. 25, March 1937.
Fisher, D. A., *Steel Making in America*, United States Steel Corporation, 1949.
Impact Die Forging, Chambersburg Engineering Company, 1944.
Koenig, Philip, "Impact Extrusion and Cold Pressing of Airplane Parts," *Transactions SAE*, Vol. 51, November 1943.
Metals Handbook, 1948 edition, American Society for Metals.
Metal Quality, Drop Forging Association, 1953.
Nanjoks, W., and D. C. Fabel, *Forging Handbook*, American Society for Metals, 1939.
Pearson, C. E., and R. Genders, *The Extrusion of Metals*, John Wiley and Sons, 1944.
Teichert, E. J., *The Manufacture and Fabrication of Steel*, Vol. 2, McGraw-Hill Book Company, 1944.
Tool Engineers Handbook, The American Society of Tool Engineers, McGraw-Hill Book Company, 1949.
Wulff, J., H. E. Taylor, and A. J. Shaler, *Metallurgy for Engineers*, John Wiley and Sons, 1952.
Young, J. F., *Materials and Processes*, 2d edition, John Wiley and Sons, 1954.

CHAPTER 12

COLD WORKING
OF METAL

Although many of the operations used in hot working may also be
applied in cold working, the resulting effect upon the crystalline
structure and physical properties of the metal is different. Hot
work, performed on the metal in a plastic state, actually refines the
grain structure, whereas cold work merely distorts it and does little
towards reducing its size. Though temperatures up to the recrystalline range may be used, cold work is normally done at room
temperature.

Effects of Cold Working

To understand the action of cold working one must have some
knowledge of the structure of metals. All metals are crystalline in
nature and are made up of irregularly shaped *grains* of various sizes.
These may be seen clearly under the microscope if the metal has been
properly polished and etched. Each grain is made up of atoms in
an orderly arrangement known as a *lattice*. The orientation of the
atoms in a given grain is uniform but differs from that in adjacent
grains. When material is cold-worked the resulting change in material shape brings about marked changes in the grain structure.

Structural changes which occur are grain fragmentation, movement of atoms, and lattice distortion. _Slip planes_ develop through the lattice structure at points where the atomic bonds of attraction are the weakest, and whole blocks of atoms are displaced. When slip occurs, the orientation of the atoms is not changed. In cases where atoms are reoriented a phenomenon known as _twinning_ occurs. In twinning, the lattice on one side of a plane is oriented in a different fashion from the other, but the atoms have shape identical to adjacent atoms. Slip is the more common method of bringing about deformation in metal.

Much greater pressures are needed for cold working than for hot working. The metal, being in a more rigid state, is not permanently deformed until stresses exceeding the elastic limit are passed. Since there can be no recrystallization of grains in the cold-working range, there is no recovery from grain distortion or fragmentation. As grain deformation proceeds, greater resistance to this action is built up, resulting in increased strength and hardness of the metal. This method of hardening is known as _strain hardening_ and for some metals represents the only method imparting this property. Several possible theories have been advanced by metallurgists as to how this occurs. In general they all refer to resistance built up in the grains by atomic dislocation, fragmentation, or lattice distortion. It is quite possible that strain hardening is due to all three phenomena.

The amount of cold work that a metal will stand is dependent upon its composition, which controls possible ductility; the more ductility a metal possesses, the more it can be cold-worked. Pure metals can withstand a greater amount of deformation than metals having an addition of alloying elements which increase the tendency and rapidity of strain hardening.

When metal is deformed by cold work, severe stresses, known as _residual stresses,_ are set up inside the metal. These stresses are undesirable and to remove them the metal must be reheated below the recrystalline range temperature. In this range the stresses are rendered ineffective without appreciable change in physical properties or grain structure. Further heating into the recrystalline range eliminates the effect of cold working and restores the metal to its original condition. Sometimes it is desirable to have residual stresses in the metal. The fatigue life of small parts can be improved by shot peening which causes the metal surface to be in compression and the layer beneath in tension.

Advantages and limitations. Many products are cold-finished after hot rolling to make them commercially acceptable. Hot-rolled strips and sheets are soft, have surface imperfections, and lack dimensional accuracy and certain desired physical properties. The cold-rolling operation reduces size slightly permitting accurate dimensional control. No surface oxidation results from the process, a smooth surface is obtained, and strength and hardness are increased. In general, the same results are obtained from other forms of cold work. For metals that do not respond to heat treatment, cold work is a possible method used to increase hardness. The process is also useful in the forming of many articles by extrusion of ductile materials. Higher pressures and heavier equipment are needed for cold-working than for hot-working operations. As a shaping process it is limited to ductile materials. Brittleness results if the metal is overworked, and an annealing operation then becomes necessary.

In general cold working produces the following effects:

1. Stresses are set up in the metal which remain unless they are removed by subsequent heat treatment.
2. A distortion or fragmentation of the grain structure is created.
3. Strength and hardness of the metal are increased with a corresponding loss in ductility.
4. Recrystalline temperature for steel is increased.
5. Surface finish is improved.
6. Close dimensional tolerance can be maintained.

Cold-Working Processes

The effects just listed are not fulfilled by all cold-working processes. Operations involving bending, drawing, and squeezing metal result in grain distortion and changes in physical properties, whereas shearing or cutting operations change only form and size. The classification on p. 267 lists the various cold-working operations of metals, including press operations.

Tube drawing. Tubing which requires dimensional accuracy, smooth surface, and improved physical properties is finished by a cold-drawing operation. This method also produces tubes having smaller diameters or thinner walls than can be obtained by hot rolling. For large reductions in area several passes are required with intermediate annealing.

Hot-rolled tubing must first be treated by pickling and washing to remove all scale and then covered with a suitable lubricant. The drawing is done in a *drawbench,* shown diagrammatically in Figure 1. One end of the tube is reduced in diameter by a swaging operation to permit it to enter the die, and it is then gripped by tongs fastened to

Cold-Working Operations—Metal at Near Room Temperature

1. Drawing
   - (a) Blanks
   - (b) Tubes
   - (c) Embossing
   - (d) Wire
   - (e) Metal spinning
   - (f) Stretch forming

2. Squeezing
   - (a) Coining
   - (b) Cold rolling
   - (c) Sizing
   - (d) Swaging or cold forging
   - (e) Thread rolling and knurling*
   - (f) Riveting
   - (g) Staking

3. Bending
   - (a) Angle bending
   - (b) Roll forming

   - (c) Plate bending
   - (d) Curling
   - (e) Seaming

4. Shearing
   - (a) Blanking
   - (b) Punching
   - (c) Cutting off
   - (d) Trimming
   - (e) Perforating
   - (f) Notching
   - (g) Slitting
   - (h) Lancing
   - (i) Sharing

5. Extruding†
   - (a) Cold
   - (b) Impact

6. Shot peening

7. Hobbing

* See Chapter 18.
† See Chapter 11.

the chain of the drawbench. In this operation the tube is drawn through a die smaller than the outside diameter of the tube, the inside surface and diameter being controlled by a fixed mandrel over

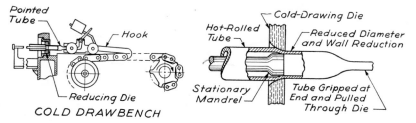

COLD DRAWBENCH

Fig. 1. Process of cold-drawing tubing. (Courtesy National Tube Company.)

which the tube is drawn. This mandrel may be omitted for small sizes or for larger sizes if the accuracy of the inside diameter is not important. Drawbenches require a pulling power ranging from 50,000 to 300,000 pounds and may have a total length of 100 feet. The operation of drawing a tube is very severe: the metal is stressed above its elastic limit to permit plastic flow through the die. The maximum reduction for one pass is around 40%. This operation increases the hardness of the tube so much that, if several reductions are desired, the material must be annealed after each pass.

Wire drawing. Wire is drawn by pulling a rod through several dies of decreasing diameter, as illustrated in Figure 2, until the final diameter is obtained. Rods from the mill, first cleaned in acid baths

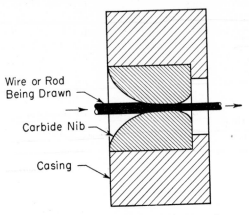

Wire or Rod
Being Drawn

Carbide Nib

Casing

Fig. 2. Section through die for drawing wire.

to remove scale and rust, are coated in various ways to prevent oxidation and to facilitate being drawn through the die. The dies are usually made of carbide materials, although diamonds may be used for small diameters.

Both single-draft or continuous-drawing processes may be used. In the first method a coil is placed on a reel or frame and the end of the rod pointed so that it will enter the die. The end is grasped by tongs on a drawbench and pulled through to such length as may be wound around a drawing block or reel. From there on, the rotation of the draw block pulls the wire through the die and forms it into a coil. These operations are repeated with smaller dies and blocks until the wire is drawn to its final size.

In continuous drawing, as shown in Figure 3, the wire is fed through several dies and draw blocks arranged in series. This permits drawing the maximum amount in one operation before annealing is necessary. The number of dies in the series will depend on the kind of metal or alloy being processed and may vary from four to twelve successive drafts.

Metal spinning. Metal spinning is the operation of shaping thin metal by pressing it against a form while it is rotating. The nature

Fig. 3. Section of continuous wire drawing machine. (Courtesy Bethlehem Steel Company.)

of the process limits it to symmetrical articles of circular cross section. This type of work is done on a speed lathe, which is like the ordinary wood lathe except that, in place of the usual tailstock,

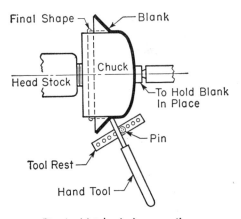

Fig. 4. Metal spinning operation.

it is provided with some means of holding the work against the form as shown in Figure 4. The forms are usually turned from hard wood and attached to the face plate of the lathe, although smooth steel chucks are recommended for production jobs. This type of chuck will not develop interior imperfection and is more economical where surface finish is to be considered.

Practically all parts are formed by the aid of blunt hand tools which press the metal against the form. The cross slide has a hand or compound tool rest in the front for supporting the hand tools and some means for supporting a trimming cutter or forming roll in the rear. Parts may be formed either from flat disks of metal or from blanks that have previously been drawn in a press. The latter method is used as a finishing operation for many deep-drawn articles. Most spinning work is done on the outside diameter as shown in the figure, although inside work is also possible.

Bulging work on metal pitchers, vases, and similar parts is done by having a small roller, supported from the compound rest, operate on the inside and press the metal out against a form roller. In an operation such as this one, the part must first be drawn, and possibly given a bulging operation beforehand, as spinning cannot be done near the bottom. Contact of the spinning tools can take place only next to the chuck.

Lubricants such as soap, beeswax, white lead, and linseed oil are used to reduce the tool friction. Of these, ordinary laundry soap proves very satisfactory, particularly for aluminum spinning. Since metal spinning is a cold-working operation, there is a limit to the amount of drawing or working the metal will stand, and one or more annealing operations may be necessary. Spinning lends itself to short-run production jobs, although it has many applications in quantity production work. Simple shapes can be formed from soft nonferrous metals up to $\frac{1}{4}$ inch in thickness and from low-carbon steel up to $\frac{3}{16}$ inch in thickness. Tolerances up to $+\frac{1}{32}$ inch can be easily maintained for diameters under 18 inches. This process is frequently used in the making of bells on musical instruments and also for light fixtures, kitchenware, reflectors, funnels, and large processing kettles.

Stretch forming. In the forming of large sheets of thin metal involving symmetrical shapes or double-curve bends, a metal stretch press can be used effectively. Hydraulically operated, it is of rather simple construction as shown in Figure 5. A single die mounted on a ram is placed between two slides which grip the metal sheet. The die has a movement in a vertical direction, and the slides have a horizontal movement. Large forces of 50 to 150 tons are provided for the die and slides. The process is a stretching one and causes the sheet to be stressed above its elastic limit while conforming to

,the die shape. This is accompanied by a slight thinning of the
sheet, and the action is such that there is little spring back to the
metal once it is formed.

Adapted to short-run jobs, inexpensive dies of wood, kirksite,
plastic, or steel can be used. Large double-curvature parts, difficult

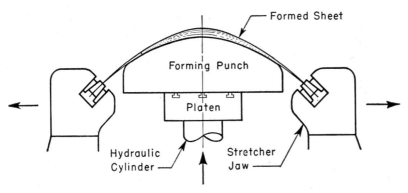

Fig. 5. Stretch forming press.

by other methods, are easily made with this process. Scrap loss is
fairly high since considerable material must be left at the ends and
sides for trimming, and there is a limitation to the shapes that can
be formed.

Swaging or cold forging. These terms refer to methods of cold
working by a compressive force or impact which causes the metal to
flow in some predetermined shape according to the design of the dies.
The metal conforms to the shape of the dies, but it is not restrained
completely and may flow at some angle in the direction to which
the force is applied. *Sizing,* the simplest form of cold forging, is the
operation of slightly compressing a forging, casting, or steel assembly
to obtain close tolerance and a flat surface. The metal is confined
only in a vertical direction.

Rotary swaging, as shown in Figure 6, is a means of reducing the
ends of bars and tubes by rotating dies which open and close rapidly
on the work, so that the end of the rod is tapered or reduced in size
by a combination of pressure and impact. Since swaging action is
rather severe, the metal hardens and an annealing operation is necessary if much reduction is desired.

The *cold heading* of bolts, rivets, and other similar parts, done
on a cold-header machine, is another form of swaging. Since the
product of the cold header is made from unheated material, the
equipment must be able to withstand the high pressures that de-

velop. Also, alignment of the upsetting tool with the dies must be accurate so that the work turned out will be free from defects. A solid die machine of this type is illustrated in Figure 7. The rod

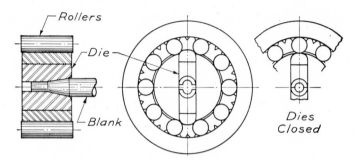

Fig. 6. Illustrating the operation of dies in a swaging machine.

is fed by straightening rolls up to a stop and is then cut off and moved into the header die as shown in Figure 8. The heading operation may be either single or double, and upon completion the part is ejected from the dies.

Fig. 7. Solid die cold-header. (Courtesy The National Machinery Company.)

Bolt-making machines are available which completely finish the bolt before it leaves the machine, the operations consisting of cutting off an oversize blank, extruding the shank, heading, trimming, pointing, and roll threading. All operations are carried on simultaneously, and outputs range from 50 to 150 pieces per minute.

Nails, rivets, and small bolts are made from coiled wire and forged cold, whereas large bolts require the end of the rod to be heated before the heading operation. Swaging may also be used to form small cams, gears, flanges, and other irregularly shaped parts.

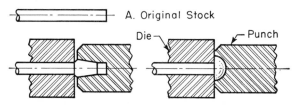

A. Original Stock

B. Preshaping Operation   C. Forming Operation

Fig. 8. Sequence of operations performed in a cold-header.

Hobbing. Mold cavities, such as shown in Figure 9, may be produced by forcing a hardened steel form or hob into soft steel. The hob, machined to the exact form of the piece to be molded, is heat-treated to obtain the necessary hardness and strength to withstand

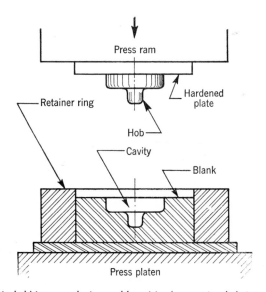

Fig. 9. Die hobbing—producing mold cavities by pressing hob into soft steel.

the tremendous pressures involved. Pressing the hob into the blank requires much care, and frequently several alternate pressings and annealings are necessary before the job is complete. During the hobbing operation the flow of metal in the blank is restrained from any appreciable lateral movement by a heavy retainer ring placed around it. The actual pressing is done in hydraulic presses having capacities ranging from 250 to 8000 tons.

The advantage of hobbing is that multiple, identical cavities can be produced economically. The surfaces of the cavities have a highly polished finish, and no machine work is necessary other than to remove surplus metal from the top and sides of the blank. This process is used a great deal in producing molds for the plastic and die-casting industries.

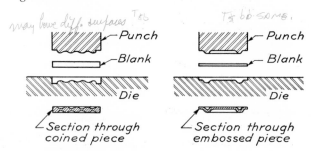

may have diff. surfaces Top   *Tf bb same.*

Fig. 10. Illustrating the difference between the processes of coining and embossing.

Coining and embossing. The operation of coining, shown in Figure 10, is performed in dies which confine the metal and restrict its flow in a lateral direction. Shallow configurations on the surfaces of flat objects, such as coins, are produced in this manner. Because special-type presses developing high pressures are required in this operation, its use is limited to fairly soft alloys.

Embossing is more of a drawing or stretching operation and does not require the high pressures necessary for coining. The punch is usually relieved so that it touches only the part of the blank that is being embossed. The mating die conforms to the same configuration as the punch so that there is very little metal squeezing in the operation and practically no change in the thickness of the metal.

Riveting and staking. Both these processes are used to fasten parts together, as illustrated in Figure 11. In the usual riveting operation, a solid rivet is placed through holes made in the parts to be fastened together, and the end is pressed to shape by a punch. Hollow rivets may have the ends secured by curling them over the edges of the plate.

Staking is a similar operation in that the metal of one part is upset in such a fashion as to cause it to fit tightly against the other part. A staking punch may have one or more projections on it as shown in the figure, or it may be in the form of a ring with sharp chisel-like edges. Both operations can be performed on small presses because not much pressure is required.

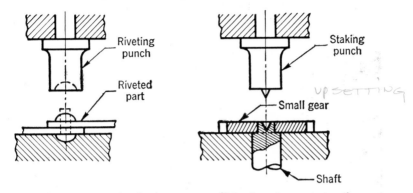

Fig. 11. Riveting and staking processes used for fastening parts together.

Fig. 12. Cold-roll tube-forming machine. Strip enters machine from coil (not shown) and is bent to tubular shape by 5 pairs of rolls before entering welder. (Courtesy The Yoder Company.)

Roll forming. Cold-roll-forming machines are constructed with a series of mating rolls which progressively form strip metal as it is fed continuously through the machine at speeds ranging from 50 to 300 fpm. Such a machine is shown in Figure 12, where tubular sections are being produced by five pairs of rolls. The tubular section enters a resistance welder after being formed and is con-

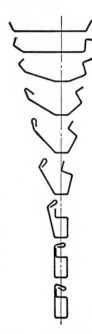

Assortment of shapes, cold-roll-formed from coiled strip. (Courtesy The Yoder Company.)

Sequence of forming operations for window screen section. (Courtesy The Yoder Company.)

Fig. 13.

tinuously welded as it passes through the machine. The number of roll stations depends on the intricacy of the part being formed; for a simple channel four pairs may be used, whereas for more complicated forms several times that number may be required. In addition to the mating horizontal rolls, these machines are frequently equipped with guide rolls mounted vertically to assist in the forming operation and straightening rolls to "true-up" the product as it emerges from the last forming pass.

Figure 13 shows a typical variety of parts that have been roll-formed, and in the figure adjacent to it, is shown a sequence of forming operations for the window screen section. In such a forming sequence the vertical center or pass line is first established so that the number of bends on either side is about the same. Forming usually starts at the center and progresses out to the two edges as the sheet moves through the successive roll passes. The amount of bending at any one roll station is limited. If the bending is too great it carries back through the sheet and affects the section at the preceding roll station. Corner bends are limited to a radius of the sheet diameter.

In terms of capacity for working mild steel, standard machines form strips up to 0.156 inch thick by 16 inches wide. Special units have been made for much heavier and wider strip steel. The process is rapid and is applicable to the forming of products having sections requiring a uniform thickness of material throughout their entire length. Unless production requirements are high, the cost of the machine and tooling cannot be justified.

Plate bending. Another method of bending metal plates and strips into cylindrical shapes is by means of a roll-bending machine as illustrated in Figure 14. This machine is made up of three rolls of the same diameter, two of them being held in a fixed position and one being adjustable. As a metal plate enters and goes through the rolls, its final diameter is determined by the position of the adjustable roll; the closer it is moved to the other rolls, the smaller will be the diameter. Machines of this type are made in capacities ranging from those that form small gage thicknesses to others that form heavy plates up to $1\frac{1}{4}$ inch in thickness.

Seaming. In the manufacture of metal drums, pails, cans, and numerous other products made of light-gage metal, several types of seams are used. The most common of these are shown in Figure 15. The *lock seam* used on longitudinal seams is adapted for joints that do not have to be absolutely tight. After the container is formed, the edges are folded and pressed together. The *compound seam,* sometimes called the Gordon or box seam, is much stronger and tighter than the lock seam and is suitable for holding fine materials. Both these joints may be formed and closed on either hand- or power-seaming presses.

Bottom seams, which are somewhat similar to the longitudinal seams, are made in either *flat* or *recessed styles.* Flat-bottom recessing is limited to one end of a container, as the container must be open to make the joint. Double seaming with recessed bottoms can be done on both ends of a container. Edge flanging, curling, and flattening, the operations necessary to make a recessed double seam, are shown in the figure.

Double-seaming machines may be hand-operated, semiautomatic,

or automatic. Semiautomatic machines must be loaded and unloaded by the operator, but the operation of the machine is automatic. In automatic machines the cans are brought to the machine
by conveyor, and ends are supplied by magazine feed. The cans are

Fig. 14. Plate bending rolls. (Courtesy Aluminum Corporation of America.)

fed from the conveyor to a star wheel, which transfers them to an
automatic delivery turret. The delivery turret feeds them into position with the seaming heads, and the closing seam is made.

Shot peening. This method of cold working has recently been
developed to improve the fatigue resistance of the metal by setting up
compressive stresses in its surface. This is done by blasting or hurling
a rain of small shot at high velocity against the surface to be peened.
As the shot strikes, small indentations are produced, causing a slight
plastic flow of the surface metal to a depth of a few thousandths of an

inch. This stretching of the outer fibers is resisted by those underneath, which tend to return them to their original length, thus producing an outer layer having a compressive stress while those below are in tension. In addition, the surface is slightly hardened and

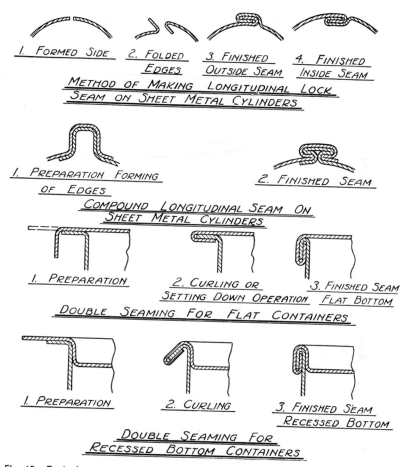

1. FORMED SIDE   2. FOLDED   3. FINISHED   4. FINISHED
                     EDGES   OUTSIDE SEAM   INSIDE SEAM
METHOD OF MAKING LONGITUDINAL LOCK
SEAM ON SHEET METAL CYLINDERS

1. PREPARATION FORMING   2. FINISHED SEAM
   OF EDGES
        COMPOUND LONGITUDINAL SEAM ON
            SHEET METAL CYLINDERS

1. PREPARATION   2. CURLING OR   3. FINISHED SEAM
                   SETTING DOWN OPERATION   FLAT BOTTOM
   DOUBLE SEAMING FOR FLAT CONTAINERS

1. PREPARATION   2. CURLING   3. FINISHED SEAM
                                             RECESSED BOTTOM
        DOUBLE SEAMING FOR
     RECESSED BOTTOM CONTAINERS

Fig. 15. Typical seams used in manufacture of light-gage metal containers. (Courtesy Niagara Tool & Machine Company.)

strengthened by the cold-working operation. Since fatigue failures result from tension stresses, having the surface in compression greatly offsets any tendency toward such a failure.

Shot peening is done by air blast or by some mechanical means. Figure 16 shows the unit from a machine that utilizes centrifugal force for hurling steel shot upon the work at a high velocity. This unit is similar to the one used in the machine shown in Figure 18, Chapter 3, for cleaning castings. Shot enters the funnel at A, which feeds it to the rotating wheel at G. The wheel then discharges the

Fig. 16. Unit from Wheelapeening machine utilizing centrifugal force for hurling shot upon work at high velocity. (Courtesy Wheelabrator Corp.)

Fig. 17. Surface character of 45 Rockwell-C Steel which has been shot peened with steel shot. A 19½-inch diameter Wheelabrator unit was used at a speed of 2250 rpm. (Courtesy Wheelabrator Corp.)

shot at a high velocity by its rotation. The surface obtained by this action is shown in Figure 17. The surface roughness or finish can be varied according to the size of shot used. Stress concentrations due to the roughened surface are offset for the reason that the indentions are close together and no sharp notches exist at the bottom of the pits.[1] Intense peening is not to be desired, for it may cause weakening of the steel.

This process adds increased resistance to fatigue failures of working parts and can be used either on parts of irregular shape or on local areas that may be subject to stress concentrations. Surface hardness and strength are also increased, and, in some cases, the process is used to produce a suitable commercial surface finish. However, it is not effective for parts subjected to reversing stresses, nor is its effect appreciable on heavy sections.

REVIEW QUESTIONS

1. What is meant by strain hardening?
2. How are residual stresses removed from cold-worked metal?
3. What are the effects of cold working?
4. Why is shafting usually cold-rolled?
5. Describe the operation of tube drawing.
6. How is wire made?
7. Describe the metal spinning process.
8. For what type of work is stretch forming used?
9. What is meant by swaging and how is it done?
10. Describe the process of putting heads on small bolts and rivets.
11. How does coining differ from embossing?
12. Distinguish between riveting and staking.
13. For what type of work is roll forming used?
14. Describe the operation of a plate-bending machine.
15. For what purposes is shot peening used?
16. How is die hobbing done?
17. Describe how the fatigue resistance of metal can be improved by cold working.

REFERENCES

Campbell, J. S., Jr., *Casting and Forging Processes in Manufacturing*, McGraw-Hill Book Company, 1950.
Kent's Mechanical Engineers' Handbook, 12th edition, John Wiley and Sons, 1950.
Sachs, G., *Fundamentals of the Working of Metals*, Interscience Publishers, 1954.
Shot Peening, American Wheelabrator and Equipment Company, 1947.

[1] H. F. Moore, *Shot Peening and the Fatigue of Metals*, American Foundry Equipment Company, 1944.

Tool Engineers Handbook, American Society of Tool Engineers, McGraw-Hill Book Company, 1949.

Turnbull, D. C., "Fatigue Life of Stressed Parts Increased by Shot Peening," *American Machinist,* August 31, 1941.

Young, J. F., *Materials and Processes,* 2d edition, John Wiley and Sons, 1954.

CHAPTER 13

PRESS WORK

The machine used for most cold-working operations is known as a *press*. It consists of a machine frame supporting a bed and a ram, a source of power, and a mechanism to cause the ram to move in line with and at right angles to the bed. The illustrations in this chapter show numerous typical designs of press equipment.

A press in itself is not sufficient as a production machine but must be equipped with tools commonly called *dies* and *punches,* designed for certain specific operations. Although some presses are better adapted for certain types of work than others, most of the forming, punching, and shearing operations can be performed on any standard press if the proper dies and punches are used. This versatility makes it possible to use the same press for many different jobs and operations, which is a desirable feature for short-run production.

Presses are capable of rapid production, since the actual time of operation is only the time necessary for one stroke of the ram plus the time necessary to feed the stock. Accordingly, production costs may be kept very low. Any product that can be fabricated from thin metal and does not require extreme accuracy in dimensional tolerances can be economically made on this type of machine. Its special adaptability to mass-production methods is evidenced by its wide application in the manufacture of automotive and aircraft parts, hardware specialties, toys, and kitchen appliances.

Types of Presses

A classification of press machines is difficult to make, as most presses are capable of varied types of work. Hence, it is not entirely correct to call one press a *bending press,* another an *embossing press,* and still another a *blanking press,* since all three types of operations can be done on one machine. However, some presses, especially designed for one type of operation, may be known by the operation name, as for example, a *punch press,* or a *coining press.* The simplest classification would be according to source of power—either manually operated or power-operated. Many manually operated machines are used for thin sheet-metal work, particularly in jobbing work, but most production machines are power-operated. Other ways of grouping presses would be according to number of rams or method of operating the rams. Most manufacturers name them according to the general design of the frame, although in many cases they are designated according to the power-transmitting arrangement or the main purpose for which the press will be used. If this method of classification is used, most presses can be listed under the following headings:

Types of Presses

A. According to design of frame:

1. Bench	3. Gap	6. Horn
2. Inclinable	4. Arch	7. Pillar
	5. Straight side	

B. According to method of applying power to ram:

1. Crank	4. Power screw	7. Hydraulic
2. Cam	5. Rack and pinion	8. Toggle
3. Eccentric	6. Knuckle joint	9. Pneumatic

C. According to purpose of press:

1. Squaring shears	6. Seaming	10. Transfer
2. Circle shears	7. Straightening	11. Knibbler
3. Brake	8. Forcing	12. Stretching
4. Punching	9. Coining	13. Turret
5. Extruding		14. Forging

In the selection of the type of press to use for a given job, a number of factors must be considered. Among these are the kind of operation to be performed, size of the part being worked upon, power required, and speed of operation. For most punching, blanking, and trimming operations, crank or eccentric-type presses are generally used. In these presses the energy of the flywheel may be transmitted to the main shaft either directly or through a gear train. For coining, squeezing, or forging operations, the knuckle-joint press is ideally suited. It has a short stroke and is capable of exerting a tremendous force. Presses for drawing operations normally operate at slower speeds than for operations such as blanking, and hydraulically operated presses are especially desirable for this work. The standard practice is not to exceed 65 fpm when working mild steel; however, aluminum and other nonferrous metals may be worked at speeds up to 150 fpm. Hydraulic presses may also be used for forging, straightening, sizing, and similar operations.

Fig. I. Open-back, single-action, inclinable press, capacity 200 tons. (Courtesy Clearing Machine Corp.)

Inclined press. A single-action, single-crank inclinable press is shown in Figure 1. The inclined frame of the machine aids in the discharge of the work and scrap from the press. Parts can slide by gravity into a tote box, or material may be fed by chute into the dies. Most presses of this type are adjustable and vary from a vertical to a rather steep angle position. For diversified press work this arrangement is preferred, since many jobs are done best with the press in a vertical position, particularly if the parts are discharged through the die. Inclinable presses are often used in the production of small parts involving bending, punching, blanking and similar operations.

Gap press. Gap or C-frame presses are so named because of the open throat arrangement of the press frame. Figure 2 shows four of the common types of presses from the standpoint of press frame design, including a gap press. This design provides excellent clearance around the dies and permits the press to be used for long or wide parts. The usual stamping operations may be performed on a gap press, and frequently the inclinable feature is used.

Arch press.   The arch press, also illustrated in Figure 2, is named for the peculiar shape of its frame. The lower part of the frame near the bed is wide to permit the working of large-area sheet metal; the upper part is narrow. The crankshafts are small in relation to the area of the slide and press bed, as these presses are not designed for heavy work. They are used for blanking, bending, and trimming in the manufacture of large paint cans and numerous other sheet metal products. Other applications include the forming of shovels, the embossing of letters on metal panels, and the manufacture of kitchenware.

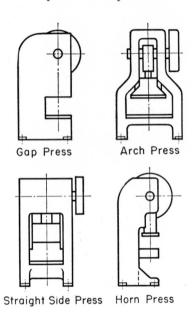

Gap Press   Arch Press

Straight Side Press   Horn Press

Fig. 2.   Typical frame designs used in presses.

Straight-side press.   As the capacity of a press is increased, it becomes necessary to increase the strength and rigidity of the frame. Straight-side presses accomplish this because loads imposed on the die are taken up in a vertical direction by the heavy side frame, and there is little tendency for punch and die alignment to be affected by the strain.

Presses of this type are made with various means of supplying power and different methods of operation. For the smaller presses a single crank or eccentric usually furnishes the power, but as the size of the work increases, additional cranks are needed to distribute the load on the slide uniformly. Double-acting presses, used a great deal in drawing operations, have an outer ram which precedes the punch and clamps the blank before the drawing operation. The outer ram is usually driven by a special link motion or cams, whereas the inner ram carrying the punch is crank-driven.

A large straight-side enclosed, double-acting toggle press is shown in Figure 3. Pressure is applied on the slide in four places. This is a distinct advantage in large-area presses because such construction prevents tilting of the slide with unbalanced loads. The *toggle* mechanism in this machine is for the purpose of controlling the motion of the blank holder. "A toggle mechanism may be described

Fig. 3. Turret top completely formed with one stroke of enclosed toggle press after being removed from die. (Courtesy E. W. Bliss Company.)

as a grouping of cranks, levers, and slides with the necessary connecting links so arranged that the train of movement may contain several dead-center positions at approximately the same time. If the motion is so controlled that the several points pass through dead center a little way, and back through it again in returning, the effective dwell period may be extended within certain limits."[1] The dwell

[1] E. V. Crane, *Plastic Working of Metals and Non-Metallic Materials in Presses,* John Wiley and Sons, 1944, p. 302.

period is the interval of time during which there is no motion of the blank holder. This is necessary for blank holding on drawing operations, and it is frequently advisable to have a slight dwell on the punch to allow the metal to adjust itself properly under pressure.

Straight side frames are also used on hydraulic presses where heavy loads are encountered such as the forming of heavy gage material, press forging, coining, and deep drawing.

Horn press. Horn presses, also illustrated in Figure 2, are usually provided with a heavy shaft projecting out from the machine frame instead of the usual bed. Where a bed is furnished, provision is made to swing it to one side when the horn is used. This press is used principally on cylindrical objects involving seaming, flanging edges, punching, riveting, and embossing.

Knuckle-joint press. Presses designed for coining, sizing, and heavy embossing must be quite massive to withstand the large concentrated loads imposed upon them. The press shown in Figure 4 is designed for this purpose and is equipped with a *knuckle-joint mechanism*

Fig. 4. Knuckle-joint press. (Courtesy E. W. Bliss Company.)

for actuating the slide. The upper link or knuckle of this point is hinged at the upper part of the frame at one end and fastened to a wrist pin at the other. The lower link also is attached to the same wrist pin and the other end to the slide. A third link is fastened to the ends of the wrist pin and acts in a horizontal direction to move the joint. As the two knuckle links are brought into a straight-line position, tremendous force is exerted by the slide. The press shown in the figure has a capacity of 150 tons.

This type of press has always been widely used in the striking of coins. According to tests made at the United States Mint in Phila-

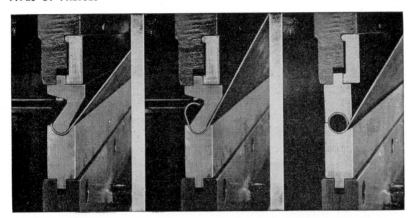

Fig. 5A. Progressive forming of bead on press brake. (Courtesy The Cincinnati Shaper Company.)

Fig. 5B. Corrugating light-gage metal with press brake. (Courtesy The Cincinnati Shaper Company.)

delphia a pressure of 98 tons is required to bring out clear impressions on silver half dollars made in a closed die.

Aside from striking coins, many other parts, such as medals, key blanks, car tokens, license plates, watch cases, and silverware are cold-pressed in this type of machine. Sizing, cold heading, straightening, heavy stamping, and similar operations can also be performed. As the stroke of this type of press is short and slow, it is not adapted to some of the usual press operations.

Press brake. A press brake, arranged for corrugating light-gage metal, is shown in Figure 5B, and Figure 5A above illustrates die setups for the progressive forming of a large bead on the edge of a long plate of steel. This figure illustrates the adaptability of this machine for processing large sheets of relatively thin metal. Aside from the usual brake or forming operations, a press of this type may be used for corrugating, seaming, embossing, trimming, and multiple punching. These presses are made in lengths ranging from 4 to 20 feet, with metal thickness ranging from light gage to $\frac{5}{8}$ inch.

The pressure capacity of a press brake required for a given material is determined by the length of work it will take, the thickness of the metal, and the radius of the bend. The minimum inside radius of a bend is usually limited to a radius equal to the thickness of the material; however, the thickness rating of a press can be increased slightly if a larger radius is used. For bending operations the required pressure varies directly in proportion to the tensile strength of the material. Press brakes have short strokes and are generally equipped with an eccentric-type drive mechanism.

Squaring shears. This machine is used entirely for shearing sheets of steel and is made in both manual and power-operated sizes. Figure 6 shows a large shear capable of shearing sheets up to a width of 10 feet. Hydraulic hold-down plungers are provided every 12 inches to prevent any movement of the sheet during the cutting. In operation the sheet is advanced on the bed so that the line of cut is under the shear. When the foot treadle is depressed, the hold-down plungers descend, and the shearing blade cuts progressively across the sheet.

Turret press. The principal features of the press shown in Figure 7 are the upper and lower turrets designed for carrying the different-size punches and dies. The two turrets are geared together and, when operating, are securely locked in position for exact alignment. The table, shown in front of the machine with its cross slide, offers an accurate and convenient means of locating the sheet under

Fig. 6. Metal shear—capacity ¼ inch × 10 feet. (Courtesy The Cincinnati Shaper Company.)

Fig. 7. Turret punch press in operation. (Courtesy Wiedemann Machine Company.)

the punching station. When a number of identical parts are to be made, a fixed template is prepared and, if the template is followed with the movable stylus, all holes are accurately positioned. The large hand wheel just below the table is used for rotating the turret. Other machines of this general type have gaging tables which accurately position the work under the turret by turning two hand wheels in front of the operator.

These punches are designed to handle short-run production and jobbing work in an efficient manner. Aside from ordinary metal punching, these machines can also be set up for slotting, embossing, notching, and louver operations.

Power screw or percussion press. Figure 8 shows a percussion press for applications where a hard end pressure is required. The friction drive accelerates the flywheel gradually on the down stroke, and all its energy is utilized as it comes to a stop, striking the work. Regulation of the blow is obtained by raising or lowering the position of the die. If the die is raised, the flywheel is stopped at a higher point and has less force, since its speed is less. For a given setting the blows are the same, and overloading is impossible. Since all the force of the blow is absorbed in the frame of the machine, expensive foundations are unnecessary.

Small machines of this type are used for striking medals and signet rings, stamping and embossing jewelry, and for similar processes. Larger machines can be used for cold-stamping and pressing small metal parts as well as for hot-pressing brass and other forgeable metals. The largest of these machines, exerting 50,000 foot-pounds per stroke, can be used to replace drop-forging operations. The hot pressing of brass (60% copper and 40% zinc) has proved very satisfactory with this type of press.

Hydraulic press. Hydraulic presses have longer strokes than mechanical presses and develop full tonnage throughout the entire stroke. However, the capacity of these presses is readily adjustable, and only a fraction of the tonnage may be used. Also the length of the strokes may be adjusted to whatever is needed. The presses are especially adapted to deep-drawing operations because of their slow, uniform motion. They are also used for numerous other press operations requiring heavy tonnage such as briquetting powdered metals, extruding, laminating, plastic molding, and press forging. They are not recommended for heavy blanking and punching operations as the break-through shock is detrimental to the press. Maintenance is higher than for mechanical presses even though the operation of the press is much slower. Small hydraulic presses are similar in appearance to straight-side presses. For large area work the post or four-column-type construction is used.

The three special hydraulic presses in Figure 9 progressively form 40-foot skelp into large tubes up to 26 inches in diameter. The skelp

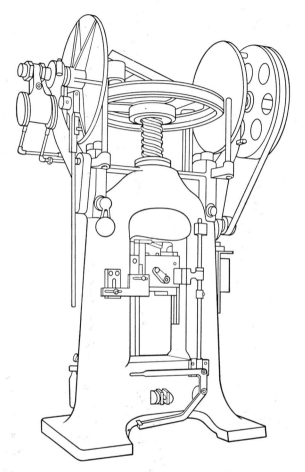

Fig. 8. Percussion power press. (Courtesy Zeh and Hahnemann Company.)

is formed to a U shape in the first press and to a near tubular section in the second and closed to a tubular form in the third. The joint is closed by flash welding, after which the flash is removed, the ends are faced, and the pipe is sized, straightened, and tested. Other methods of forming pipe are discussed in a previous chapter.

Transfer press. Transfer presses, being fully automatic, are capable of performing consecutive operations simultaneously. Mate-

Fig. 9. Special presses form a tube out of flat steel in three operations. (Courtesy A. O. Smith Corporation.)

rial is fed to the press by rolls or as blanks from a stack feeder. In operation the stock is moved from one station to the next by a mechanism synchronized with the motion of the slide. Each die is a separate unit and is provided with a punch which may be independently adjusted from the main slide.

The economic use of transfer presses is dependent upon quantity production, as their usual production rate is 500 to 1500 parts per hour. Products made on this equipment include headlight bodies, brake-drum shells, ice-cube trays, refrigerator doors, and stove parts.

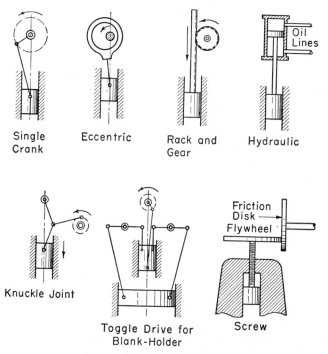

Fig. 10. Various drive mechanisms used on presses.

Drive Mechanisms Used in Presses

Most of the drive mechanisms used in presses for transmitting power to the slide are shown in Figure 10. The most common drive is the *single crank,* which gives a movement to the slide approaching simple harmonic motion. On a down stroke the slide is accelerated. Reaching its maximum velocity at midstroke, it is then decelerated. Most press operations occur near the middle of the stroke, at maximum slide velocity. The *eccentric drive* gives a motion like that of a crank and is often used where a shorter stroke is required. Some proponents of this drive claim for it greater rigidity and less tendency for deflection than a crank drive might have. *Cams* are used where some special movement is desired, such as a dwell at the bottom of the stroke. This drive has some similarity to the eccentric drive, except that roll followers are used to transmit the motion to the slide.

Rack and gear presses are used only where a very long stroke is needed. The movement of the slide is much slower than in crank presses, and uniform motion is attained. Such presses are provided with stops to control the stroke length and may be equipped with some quick-return feature to raise the slide back to starting position. The common arbor press is a familiar example of this type.

Hydraulic drive is used in many presses for a wide variety of work. It is especially adapted to large pressures and slow speeds in forming, pressing, and drawing operations.

In the *screw* drive, the slide is accelerated by means of the friction disk engaging the flywheel; and, as the flywheel moves down, greater speed is applied to it. From beginning to end of the stroke, the slide motion is an accelerated one. At the bottom of the stroke the entire amount of stored energy is absorbed by the work. The action resembles that of a drop hammer, but it is slower and there is less impact.

Several link mechanisms are used in press drives, either because of the type of motion they have or because of the mechanical advantage they develop. The *knuckle joint* is very commonly used, because it has a high mechanical advantage near the bottom of the stroke when the two links approach a straight line. Because of the high load capacity of this mechanism, it is used for coining and sizing operations. Eccentric or hydraulic drives may be substituted for the crank shown in the figure. *Toggle mechanisms,* used primarily as a means of holding the blank on a drawing operation, are made in a variety of designs. The auxiliary slide in the figure is actuated by a crank, but eccentrics or cams may be used. The principal aim of this mechanism is to obtain a motion having a suitable dwell so that the blank may be held effectively.

Feed Mechanisms

Safety is a paramount consideration in press operation, and every precaution must be taken to protect the operator. Wherever possible, material should be fed to the dies by some means that eliminates any chance of the operator having his hands near the dies. In long-run production jobs such features can be worked out economically in various ways. Feeding devices are best applied to medium-sized and small presses and have the advantage of rapid, uniform machine feeding in addition to the safety features.

One of the common types of feeding mechanisms is the double-roll feed, operating in connection with coiled stock and scrap reels as illustrated in Figure 11. The operation of the feed rolls is controlled by an eccentric on the crankshaft through a linkage to a ratchet wheel which pulls the material across the die from right to

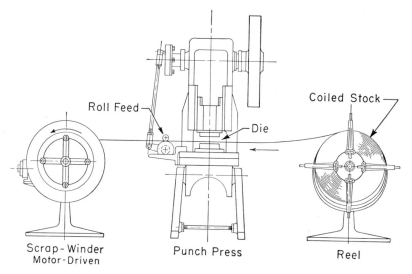

Fig. 11. Diagrammatic illustration of roll feed for press. (Courtesy F. J Littell Machine Company.)

left. Each time the ram moves up, the rolls turn and feed the proper amount of material for the next stroke. By providing the machine with a variable eccentric, the amount of stock fed through the rolls can be varied easily. The rolls are relieved before the stroke to permit proper alignment of the stock. For heavy material, straightening rolls can be used which also act as feeding rolls.

Another type of feeding device is the dial-station feed. This method is designed to take care of single parts previously blanked or formed in some other press. Again the indexing is controlled by an eccentric on the crankshaft through a suitable link mechanism to the dial. Each time a stroke is made, the dial indexes one station. All feeding by the operator takes place at the front of the machine away from the dies.

Light parts can be stacked in a magazine and placed in position by a suction device. A blank is lifted off the top of the stack by suction fingers and placed against a stop gage on the die. Magazine feeds may also be used with a reciprocating mechanism which feeds blanks from the bottom of the stack. Gravity feed is sometimes used on inclined presses, the blank sliding into a recess at the top of the die.

Press Operations and Tools Used

The tools used in most presses come under the general heading of punches and dies. The punch refers to that part of the assembly which is attached to the ram of the press and is forced into the die cavity; the die is usually stationary and rests on the press bed. It has an opening to receive the punch, and the two must be in perfect alignment for proper operation. Punches and dies are not interchangeable, but must work together as a unit. A single press may do a large variety of operations, depending on the types of dies used.

Dies may be classified according to either the type of press operation performed or their construction. A simple classification including most dies is as follows:

Types of Dies

A. According to type of press operation:
  1. Shearing—blanking, punching, notching, perforating, trimming, shaving, slitting, and lancing
  2. Bending—angle bending, curling, folding, forming, and seaming
  3. Drawing—forming flanges, tubes, embossing, bulging, cupping, and reducing
  4. Squeezing—coining, sizing, flattening, swaging, cold forging, riveting, upsetting, extruding, and hot pressing

B. According to construction or method of operation:
  1. Simple   4. Transfer
  2. Compound   5. Hydraulic
  3. Progressive   6. Rubber

Shearing. The cutting of metal involves stressing it in shear above its ultimate strength between adjacent sharp edges as shown in Figure 12. As the punch descends upon the metal, the pressure first causes a plastic deformation to take place as at b in the figure. The metal is highly stressed adjacent to punch and die edges, and fractures start on both sides of the sheet as the deformation progresses. When the ultimate strength of the material is reached, the fracture progresses; and, if the clearance is correct and both edges are of equal sharpness, the fractures meet at the center of the sheet as shown at *c*. The amount of clearance, which plays an important part in die design, depends upon the hardness of the material. For steel it should

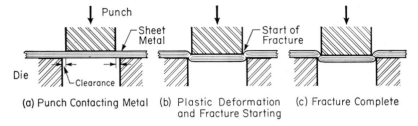

(a) Punch Contacting Metal   (b) Plastic Deformation   (c) Fracture Complete
and Fracture Starting

Fig. 12. Process of shearing metal with punch and die.

be 5 to 8% of the stock thickness per side. If improper clearance is used, the fractures do not meet and cross the entire sheet thickness, using more power.

Flat punches and dies as shown in the figure require a maximum of power. To reduce the shear force the punch or die face should be made at an angle so that the cutting action is progressive. This distributes the shearing action over a greater length of the stroke and

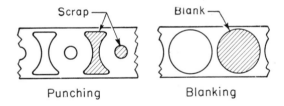

Punching   Blanking

Fig. 13. Illustrating the difference between punching and blanking operations.

materially reduces the power required. The angle given the punch or die ranges from one fourth to full thickness of the sheet, which amount will reduce the power required by about 50%.

Blanking, as shown in Figure 13, is the operation of cutting out flat areas to some desired shape and is usually the first step in a series of operations. In this case the punch should be flat and the die given some shear angle so that the finished part will be flat. *Punching* or *piercing* holes in metal, *notching* metal from edges, or *perforating* are all similar operations, but the metal removed per punch is usually much smaller than that removed by blanking. For these operations the shear angle is on the punch and the metal removed is scrap. *Trimming* is the removal of "flash" or excess metal from around the edges of a part and is essentially the same as blanking. *Shaving* is similar except that it is a finishing or sizing process in which less metal is removed. *Slitting* is the making of incomplete cuts in a sheet as illustrated in Figure 14. If a hole is partially

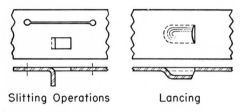

Slitting Operations   Lancing

Fig. 14.   Examples of slitting and lancing operations.

punched and one side bent down as a louver, it is called *lancing*. All these operations may be done on presses of the same type and differ little except in the dies that are used.

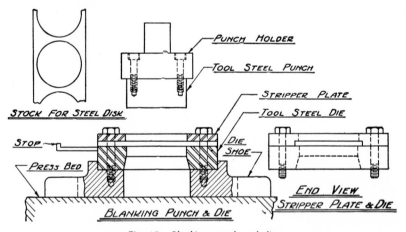

Fig. 15.   Blanking punch and die.

A simple blanking punch and die are shown in Figure 15. The parts that do the cutting are made of tool steel and are built in as inserts. The punch is made up of a holder having a shank and a tool-steel punch. The shank of the punch fits into the press slide or a punch plate attached to the slide. The die is supported on a cast-steel die shoe, which, in turn, is fastened to the bolster plate on the press bed. The die shown in the figure is designed for blanking disks from strip metal. Steel is fed into the opening at one end of the die up to a stop provided at the other end. The steel plate over the stock is called a stripper plate, since it holds the blanked strip in place as the punch moves up to its starting position. Blanks, which have been sheared by the punch, drop through it to a container underneath the press.

Bending and forming. Bending and forming may be performed on the same equipment as that used for shearing, namely, crank, eccentric, and cam-operated presses. Where bending is involved, the metal is stressed in both tension and compression at values below the ultimate strength of the material without appreciable change in

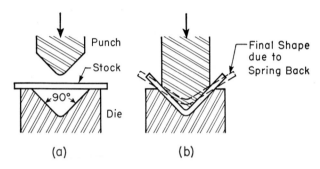

Fig. 16. Spring back in bending operations.

its thickness. As in a press brake, simple bending implies a straight bend across the sheet of metal. Other bending operations such as curling, seaming, and folding are similar, though the process is slightly more involved.

In designing a rectangular section for bending one must determine how much metal should be allowed for the bend, since the outer fibers are elongated and the inner ones shortened. During the operation the neutral axis of the section is moved in toward the compression side which throws more of the fibers in tension. The entire thickness is slightly decreased, with the width being increased on the compression side and narrowed on the other. Though correct lengths for bends can be determined by empirical formulae, they are influenced considerably by the physical properties of the metal. Metal which has been bent retains some of its original elasticity and there is some elastic recovery after the punch is removed, as shown in Figure 16. This is known as *spring back*. The fibers in compression expand slightly and those in tension contract, the combined action resulting in a slight opening up of the bend. Spring back may be corrected by overbending an amount such that when the pressure is released the part will return to its correct shape. Spring back is more

pronounced in large bend radii. The minimum bend radius varies
according to the ductility and thickness of the metal.

A forming die, designed to bend a flat strip of steel to a U shape,
is shown in Figure 17. As the punch descends and forms the piece,
the knockout plate is pressed down, compressing the spring at the

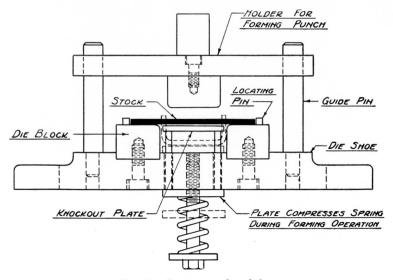

Fig. 17. Forming punch and die.

bottom of the die. When the punch moves up, the plate forces the
work out of the die with the aid of the spring. Such an arrangement
is necessary in most forming operations because the metal presses
against the walls of the die, making its removal difficult. Parts that
tend to adhere to the punch are removed by a knockout pin which
is engaged on the up stroke.

Drawing. Three types of bent flanges are shown in Figure 18.
The first one, shown at *A,* is the simple straight bend. The stretch
flange and shrink flange, shown at *B* and *C,* respectively, involve a
plastic flow of metal which does not take place in a straight bend
flange. This plastic flow or adjustment of metal is characteristic of all
drawing operations. Stresses are involved which exceed the elastic
limit strength of the metal so as to permit the metal to conform to
the punch. However, these stresses cannot exceed the ultimate
strength without developing cracks. If the stretch flange at *B* is considered to be a section of a circular depression that has been drawn,
the metal in arc *aa* must have been stretched to *a'a'* in the operation.

The action is a thinning one and must be uniform to avoid cracks. In the shrink flange at c the action is just the opposite, and the metal in the flange is thickened. Most drawn parts start with a flat plate of metal. As the punch is forced into the metal, severe tensile stresses are

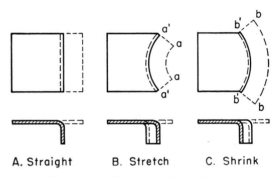

A. Straight   B. Stretch   C. Shrink

Fig. 18. Possible types of bent flanges.

induced into the sheet being formed about the punch. At the same time the outer edges of the sheet which have not engaged the punch are in compression and undesirable wrinkles tend to form. This must be counteracted by a blankholder or pressure plate which holds the flat plate firmly in place.

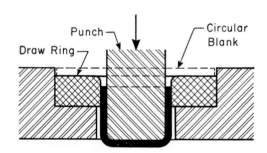

Fig. 19. Arrangement of punch and die for simple drawing operation.

In a simple drawing operation of relatively thick plates, the plate thickness may be sufficient to counteract wrinkling tendencies and may be done in a single-acting press as shown in Figure 19. Additional draws may be made on the cup-shaped part, each one elongating it and reducing the wall thickness.

Most drawing, involving the shaping of thin metal sheets, requires the use of double-acting presses in order that the sheet may be held in place as the drawing progresses. Presses of this type vary considerably in performance, but usually two slides are provided, one within the other. One slide, controlling the blank holding rings, moves to the sheet ahead of the other to hold it in place. This action is illustrated in Figure 20. The motion of the blank holding

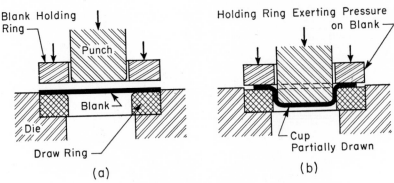

Fig. 20. Action of blank holder and punch in a drawing operation.

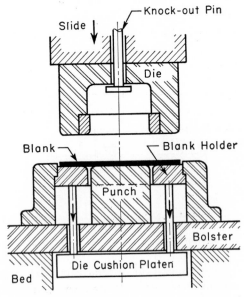

Fig. 21. Drawing operation using an inverted punch.

slide is controlled by a toggle or cam mechanism in connection with the crank. Hydraulic presses are well adapted for drawing because of their relatively slow action, close speed control, and uniform pressure. Figure 21 shows a sectional diagram of an inverted drawing die. The punch is stationary, being mounted on the bed of the press. As the die descends, the blank is contacted; and then, as its downward movement continues, the blank holding ring maintains contact with the blank during drawing. By the use of a die cushion to control the holder the pressures on the blank can be increased and controlled easily.

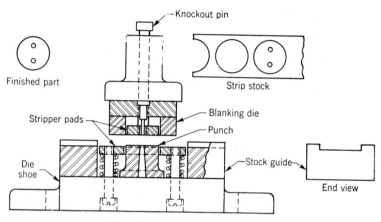

Fig. 22. Compound punch and die.

Special Dies and Forming Processes

Dies. The die sets shown in Figures 16 and 18 are classified as *simple* dies, only one operation being performed at each stroke of the ram. *Compound* dies are those that combine two or more operations at one station such as the punch and die illustrated in Figure 22. Here strip stock is progressively moved through the die, two holes are punched each time the press slide descends, and the piece is blanked. When the operations are not similar, as in the case of a blanking and forming operation, dies of this type are frequently known as combination dies.

A *progressive* die set is one that performs two or more operations simultaneously, but at different stations. A punch and die set of this type is shown in Figure 23. As the strip enters the die, the small square hole is punched first. The stock is then advanced to the next station where it is properly positioned by the pilot as the blanking punch descends to complete the part. This general type of design is simpler than the compound dies since the respective operations are not crowded together. Regardless of the number of operations to be performed, the finished part is not separated from the strip block until the last operation. A progressive die set which performs

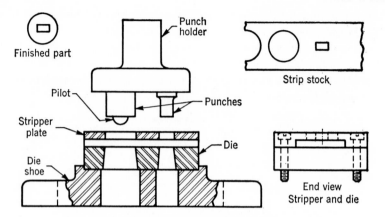

Fig. 23. Progressive punch and die.

fifteen operation on a can opener, completing one at each stroke, is shown in Figure 24. Production is rapid, but close tolerances are difficult to maintain.

Fig. 24. Progressive die set which performs 15 operations on can openers and completes one at each stroke. (Courtesy Verson Allsteel Press Company.)

Misalignment of punch and die causes excessive pressures, shearing or chipping of die edges, or actual breaking of the tools. Such action may occur through shifting, even though the setup is originally correct. To prevent such occurrences, proper alignment is insured by providing guide rods at two or four corners of the die which fit into holes provided in the punch holder. Such dies are known as *pillar dies.* This arrangement of having the punch and die always held in proper alignment greatly facilitates the setting up of the tools. A similar arrangement, known as a *subpress die* (occasionally used on small work), employs a punch and die mounted in a small frame so that accurate alignment is always maintained. Pressure is applied by a plunger which extends out of the top of the assembly.

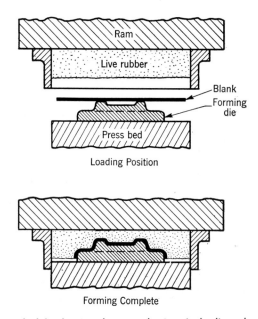

Loading Position

Forming Complete

Fig. 25. Method for forming sheet metal using single die and rubber pad.

Guerin process. This process greatly reduces the cost of dies in the blanking and forming of thin sheet required for aircraft manu-facture. In place of expensive steel-mating dies, it employs a single die of low-cost material and a thick pad of rubber which adapts itself to the die while under pressure. Sheet metal placed between the resilient pad and the die can be cut or formed to shape readily.

Rubber has proved satisfactory in this work because of its similarity to a fluid when properly restrained. Thick pads are mounted on the moving platen of the press and held in a container which extends about one inch past the pad. On the bed of the press is mounted a pressing block which fits into the container recess and upon which are mounted the cutting and forming dies. As the platen moves down and the rubber is confined, the force of the ram is exerted evenly in all directions, resulting in the sheet metal being pressed against the die block as illustrated in Figure 25. Cutting die blocks are merely steel templates of the required parts and need not be over $\frac{3}{8}$ inch thick. Forming dies may be made of Masonite, wood, aluminum, and magnesium, as well as of steel.

The Guerin process is limited in the cutting of soft aluminum to sheet thickness up to 0.051 inch. For bending and forming, the usual limit is around $\frac{3}{16}$ inch thick. Thin gages of stainless steel may also be fabricated, and magnesium alloys may be hot-formed. In the latter application heater plates are mounted on the loading table, and the form blocks are maintained at the correct temperature.

The advantages of this process include simplicity of tooling, low tooling cost, use of gang setups, minimum material waste, uniform pressure on the metal, and adaptability to various press operations.

Marform process.[2] This process is somewhat similar to the one just described and represents a further development in forming technique which permits the deep drawing and forming of irregularly shaped parts without certain defects heretofore present in these operations. A confined rubber pad is used on the movable platen of the press, and a stationary punch is located below, as shown in Figure 26. In the operation shown, a metal cup is in the process of being formed. At the start of the operation, a flat piece of metal is placed on the blank holder plate which is then flush with the top of the punch. As the movable platen descends, the rubber pad contacts the blank and clamps it securely against both the top of the punch and surrounding plate. As the downward movement continues, the blank is formed over the end of the punch, and at the same time sufficient pressure is exerted over the unformed portion so that no wrinkling of the metal occurs. In this respect the process is superior to the Guerin process, since in the latter the pressure on the blank at the start of the draw does not build up to the point where wrinkles are prevented. During the drawing operation, the downward movement of the blank holding plate is opposed by pressure pins which are hydraulically operated and can be controlled to exert the pressure desired. Any tendency for tearing around the top of the drawn piece is materially decreased because the rubber locks the drawn metal against the punch as the operation continues.

A complete Marform unit is mounted in the four-column hydraulic press shown in Figure 27. This unit may be removed if the press is to be used for other operations. Advantages claimed for this process are deeper draws than are possible in one operation by other meth-

[2] Developed by the Glenn L. Martin Company.

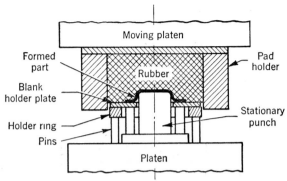

Fig. 26. Arrangement of the Marform components in a forming operation. (Courtesy Hydropress.)

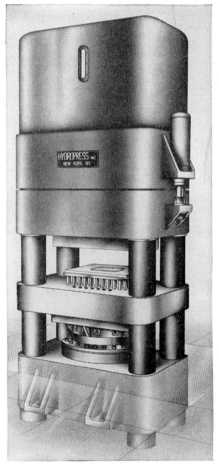

Fig. 27. Hydraulic four-column press arranged for Marforming. (Courtesy Hydropress.)

ods, low tooling costs, no damage to surface finish, and the possibility
of forming tapered and other difficult shapes economically. Shearing
is also possible by providing undercuts in the punch or blank holder
plate. In the forming of aluminum, sheets ranging from 0.010 to
0.675 inch thickness have been processed.

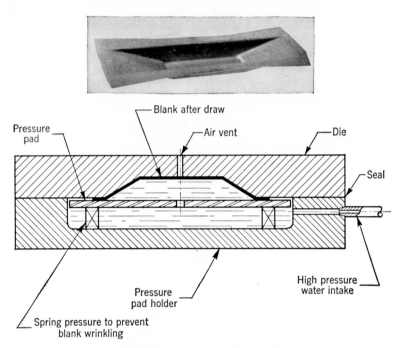

Fig. 28. Dies used in hydrodynamic process for forming tapered part shown above.
(Courtesy S. B. Whistler & Sons.)

Hydrodynamic process.[3]   This process is designed for shallow
forming and embossing operations of thin metal by hydraulic means.
The die arrangement used in the process is shown in Figure 28.
When in actual operation, it is mounted on a hydraulic press, the
pressure-pad holder and forming die being attached, respectively, to
the lower and upper platens.   The cycle of operation consists of laying
a blank upon the pressure pad, closing the dies, and turning on the
high-pressure water.   A uniform fluid pressure (acting as the punch)
is exerted on the entire blank area, and there are no localized strains
involved.   Many odd-shaped and tapered pieces can be readily
formed to shape in one operation by this process, as illustrated by the
tapered part shown in the figure.

[3] Covered by U. S. Patents 2,066,085, 2,399,775, and 2,156,889.

REVIEW QUESTIONS

1. List the various operations that can be done with press equipment.

2. What advantages does an inclined press have over one with a rigid frame?

3. Describe an arch press, and state the type of work for which it is designed.

4. How does a double-acting press operate, and for what type of work is it used?

5. What type of work is a press brake used for?

6. Describe the operation of a screw or percussion press.

7. Show by sketches how a knuckle-joint mechanism operates. On what type of press is it used?

8. For what type of press work do you recommend the use of hydraulically operated presses?

9. What is a transfer press, and for what type of work is it used?

10. List and describe briefly five types of press drives.

11. What is the correct clearance between a punch and die in shearing operations? Why is it important?

12. Briefly describe the following press operations: blanking, punching, shaving, slitting, and lancing.

13. How may spring back in bending operations be corrected?

14. Distinguish between the Guerin and Marform Processes.

15. Describe the hydrodynamic process of forming.

16. What is a compound die?

17. Illustrate the use of a progressive die by some part that can be made in this manner.

18. What type of press do you recommend for each of the following jobs: forming steel tops for automobiles, stamping coins, making corrugated iron siding, forming stiffening ribs for airplane wings, and drawing brake drums for automobile wheels?

REFERENCES

Brootzkoos, S. D., *The Selection of Presses,* Dryden Press, 1941.

Campbell, J. S., Jr., *Casting and Forming Processes in Manufacture,* McGraw-Hill Book Company, 1950.

Camp, J. M., and C. B. Francis, *The Making, Shaping and Treating of Steel,* 5th edition, Carnegie-Illinois Steel Corporation.

Crane, E. V., *Plastic Working of Metals and Nonmetallic Materials in Presses,* 3d edition, John Wiley and Sons, 1944.

Die Design Handbook, American Society of Tool Engineers, McGraw-Hill Book Company, 1955.

Hinman, C. W., *Die Engineering Layouts and Formulas,* McGraw-Hill Book Company, 1943.

Hinman, C. W., *Press Working of Metals,* 2d edition, McGraw-Hill Book Company, 1950.

Jevons, J. D., and W. W. Swift, *The Metallurgy of Deep Drawing and Pressing,* John Wiley and Sons, 1942.

Le Grand, R., *American Machinist Handbook,* McGraw-Hill Book Company, 1955.

Sachs, G., *Fundamentals of the Working of Metals,* Interscience Publishers, 1954.

Schulze, R. B., "Deep and Tapered Stampings Without Wrinkles," *Metal Progress,*
June 1950.
Stanley, F. A., *Punches and Dies,* McGraw-Hill Book Company, 1937.
Tool Engineers Handbook, American Society of Tool Engineers, McGraw-Hill Book
Company, 1949.
Young, J. F., *Materials and Processes,* John Wiley and Sons, 1954.
Wulff, J., H. F. Taylor, and A. J. Shaler, *Metallurgy for Engineers,* John Wiley and
Sons, 1952.

CHAPTER 14

INSPECTION—
MEASURING INSTRUMENTS
AND GAGES

Mass production requires that all parts be made according to rigid specifications and working drawings. No matter how carefully these drawings and specifications are prepared, they lose their value unless they are adhered to by the production department. It is the function of inspectors to see that the standards established by the engineering department are maintained in the shop.

Inspection

Since inspection departments in companies demand close quality control of their product, they are separate from the production department. Because it is the aim of the production department to produce goods as fast as possible, there is some tendency to lower quality standards if maintaining quality means lowering the output. For this reason it is advisable to place the inspection department in a position on the organization chart that will insure it sufficient authority to act independently and for the best interest of quality control. Frequently it is directly responsible to the engineering department, since it is from this department that the drawings originate.

The inspector occupies a very important place in an organization. He should have personal qualities that warrant placing him in an authoritative position; ability, tact, impartiality, and thoroughness are all essential qualities. To understand the problems of the operator, he must have a knowledge of materials, manufacturing processes, and tools. Avoiding arbitrary methods of inspection at all times, he must accept or reject work entirely on merit and on established specifications.

The amount of inspection given to the product will vary according to the nature of the product, the degree of accuracy required, and the type of equipment used. When greater accuracy is demanded in the product, more inspection is necessary. A watch factory may use one inspector for seven to ten workmen, whereas a foundry requires only one inspector for thirty to forty workmen. After being set up, certain types of machines, particularly presses for blanking, punching, and forming, require very little attention from the inspector. The tools and first parts produced are carefully inspected at the start, and, from then on, periodic inspection (aside from the attention given the machines by the operator) is sufficient. Automatic screw machines and other similar automatic equipment can be handled in the same way. Once the machine is set up, the change in the product due to wear of the tools is so slight that the periodic inspection given by a roving inspector is sufficient.

A system of inspection known as *sampling* is used on most bulk materials such as coal, batch materials, and foundry sand. It is used also in the dimensional inspection given parts in machine shops. If a proper sample can be determined readily, this method offers a means of reducing inspection costs. The frequency or method of sampling must be such that there is no possibility of producing a large number of defective parts before an error is discovered.

Many parts that require accurate machine work should be given 100% inspection to eliminate any possibility of performing expensive operations on defective parts. Crankshafts, bearing races, and gears are typical parts that should be treated in this manner. In many cases 100% inspection is necessary at several points in the manufacturing cycle as well as at completion. In any event, a final inspection should always be given before assembly operations.

Types of Fits

The term "interchangeable manufacture" implies that the parts which go into the assembly of the machine can be selected at random from a large number of parts. In such a system of manufacture, selective fitting is unnecessary except possibly for special close-working parts. To make this possible, manufacturing methods must be standardized and limits of accuracy specified on details. Extreme accuracy is not always necessary or desirable since manufacturing costs increase greatly as working limits become closer. In many cases, on modern production machines, it is possible to maintain, with no added expense, a limit of accuracy in excess of that required by the part. However, no part should be made with any greater degree of accuracy than is required by its use in a given mechanism or machine. A balance must be established between cost of manufacture and ease of assembly.

The fact that there is a need for various types of fits in manufacturing work is clearly evident. A given industry may require only a few; others will maintain that a large number are necessary. In general, there are but three types of fits: a *clearance fit,* a *tight fit,* and an *interference fit.* It is quite obvious that these three conditions will not satisfy all needs since the amount of clearance or interference of the mating parts is also an important factor. Hence, it becomes necessary to subdivide these classifications further to include those fits most commonly used in manufacturing work. Any such classification or standard will probably not satisfy all manufacturers, but it should include the general needs of all industry.

According to the American Standards Association,[1] fits are classified as follows:

CLASS 1 (Loose Fit—Large Allowance) : This fit provides for a large allowance giving considerable freedom and is used where accuracy is not essential (on a 1-inch size, an allowance of 0.003 inch).

CLASS 2 (Free Fit—Liberal Allowance) : For running fits with speeds of 600 rpm or over, and journal pressures of 600 psi or over (on a 1-inch size, an allowance of 0.0014 inch).

CLASS 3 (Medium Fit—Medium Allowance) : Used on parts revolving easily. For speeds under 600 rpm and with journal pressures less than 600 psi. This is also applied to sliding parts and is the largest allowance for freedom consistent with accuracy (on a 1-inch size, an allowance of 0.0009 inch).

CLASS 4 (Snug Fit—Zero Allowance) : This is the closest fit that can be assembled by hand without appreciable pressure. It will not rotate easily, and no shake is permissible. A snug fit is not intended to move freely under a load (on any size an allowance of 0.000 inch).

CLASS 5 (Wringing Fit—Zero to Negative Allowance) : This is a

[1] ASA B4a–1925, *Tolerances, Allowances, and Gages for Metal Fits,* superseded in part by ASA B4.1–1947.

metal-to-metal contact. It allows for no movement and is assembled with slight pressure. Wringing fits are not usually interchangeable (on a 1-inch size, an allowance of −0.0004 inch).

CLASS 6 (Tight Fit—Slight Negative Allowance) : Light pressure is required to assemble these fits, and the parts are permanently assembled. It is used in automotive, ordnance, and general machine manufacturing (on a 1-inch size, an allowance of −0.0009 inch).

CLASS 7 (Medium Force Fit—Negative Allowance): Considerable pressure is required to assemble these fits, and the parts are considered permanently assembled. The fit is the tightest possible for cast iron or parts where internal stress will be detrimental (on a 1-inch size, an allowance of −0.0011 inch).

CLASS 8 (Heavy Force and Shrink Fit—Considerable Negative Allowance) : These fits are used for steel holes where the metal can be highly stressed without exceeding its elastic limit. They are used where heavy force fits are practical, as on locomotive wheel tires. Parts united by heavy force fits form one unit without other means of holding. In most cases the outer part is expanded by heat before assembly (on a 1-inch size, an allowance of −0.0016 inch).

Tolerance and Allowance

In dimensioning a drawing, the figures placed in the dimension lines represent *nominal sizes* which are only approximate and do not represent any degree of accuracy unless so stated by the designer. To specify a degree of accuracy, it is necessary to add *tolerance* figures to the dimension. Tolerance is the amount of variation permitted in the part of the total variation allowed in a given dimension. A shaft might have a nominal size of 2½ inches, but for practical reasons this figure could not be maintained in manufacture without great cost. Hence, a certain tolerance would be added; and, if a variation of ±0.003 inch could be permitted, the dimension would be stated 2.500 ± 0.003. Where dimensions are given close tolerances, the reason is that the part must fit properly with some other part. Both must be given tolerances in keeping with the type of fit and allowance desired.

Allowance, which is sometimes confused with tolerance, has an altogether different meaning. It is the minimum clearance space intended between mating parts and represents the condition of tightest permissible fit. Figures 1 and 2 illustrate exaggerated conditions for clearance and interference fits. The tolerances for shaft and hole are indicated by the black bars. In the figure showing a clearance fit, the allowance is the difference between the largest shaft size and the smallest hole size indicated as 0.002 inch. This value represents the minimum allowable clearance space, and 0.008 inch represents the maximum. All shafts and mating parts have tolerances, which, if maintained, will give clearances between these two extremes. Figure 2, representing an interference fit, has tolerances limiting the inter-

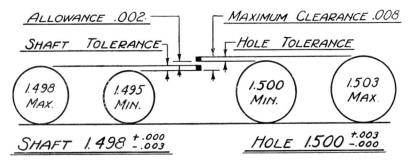

Fig. I. Loose or clearance fit.

ference to values between 0.001 and 0.005 inch. In both cases there is probably one clearance or interference value that is best, but for manufacturing reasons a variation is necessary. To obtain the best value, selective or assembly fitting would have to be resorted to.

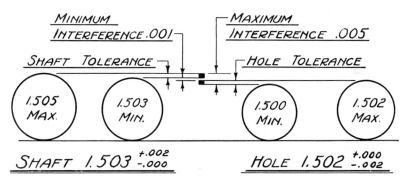

Fig. 2. Tight or interference fit.

Tolerances may be either *unilateral* or *bilateral*. Unilateral tolerance means that any variation is made in only one direction from the nominal or basic dimension. Referring again to Figure 1, we see that the hole is dimensioned 1.500 $+0.003_{-0.000}$, which represents a unilateral tolerance. If the dimensions were given as 1.500 $\pm$ 0.003, the tolerance would be bilateral; that is, it would vary both over and under the nominal dimension. The majority of manufacturing concerns in the United States use the unilateral system. The reason for this can be determined by reference to Figure 3, which illustrates the use of both types of tolerance. The unilateral system permits changing the tolerance while still retaining the same allowance or type of

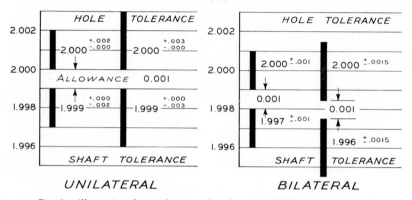

Fig. 3. Illustrating the application of unilateral and bilateral tolerances.

fit. With the bilateral system this is not possible without also changing the nominal size dimension of one or both of the two mating parts. In mass production, where mating parts must be interchangeable, unilateral tolerances should always be used.

MEASURING INSTRUMENTS

Standard of Measurement

The standard of measurement in the United States is the *meter*. This standard, adopted by Congress in 1866, has reference to the international meter at the International Bureau of Weights and Measures at Sèvres, France. Our legal *yard* is defined as $\frac{3600}{3937}$ of the length of the meter at a temperature of 68 F, from which 1 meter is equal to 39.37 inches. The British standard yard is slightly different, 1 meter being equal to 39.370113 inches. An inch under this system is equal to about 25.39998 mm, whereas the United States inch is equal to about 25.40005 mm. Although this difference does not seem to be of any great importance in ordinary shopwork, it is noticeable in accurate measurements. In 1933 these values were changed in both countries to permit the use of a uniform ratio: 1 inch equals 25.4 mm.[2] This change makes it possible to convert readily

[2] American Standard B48.1–1933, *Inch-Millimeter Conversion for Industrial Use*, and British Standard BS350–1930, *Conversion Tables*.

from one system to the other and eliminates any possible confusion.

The standard of angular measurement is the *degree* which is obtained by dividing a circle into 360 parts. A degree is further divided into 60 minutes, and each minute is divided into 60 seconds. This standard of measurement is universal.

Classification of Measuring Instruments

A measuring instrument is any device that may be used to obtain a dimensional or angular measurement. Some instruments, such as a steel rule, may be read directly; others, like the caliper, are used for transferring or comparing dimensions. Also, various principles are employed in obtaining measurements. A micrometer, for example, utilizes a different principle from a steel rule or a vernier caliper. Here are a number of the common measuring instruments listed according to use:

Measuring Instruments

1. Linear measurement
   (*a*) Steel rule
   (*b*) Micrometer
   (*c*) Vernier caliper
   (*d*) Depth gage
   (*e*) Vernier height gage
   (*f*) Calipers
   (*g*) Dividers
   (*h*) Telescopic gages
   (*i*) Combination square
   (*j*) Measuring machine:
      (1) Mechanical
      (2) Optical

2. Angular measurement
   (*a*) Adjustable bevel
   (*b*) Bevel protractor
   (*c*) Sine bar
   (*d*) Square
   (*e*) Angle gage blocks
   (*f*) Dividing head

3. Plane-surface measurement
   (*a*) Level
   (*b*) Straight edge
   (*c*) Surface gage
   (*d*) Profilometer
   (*e*) Optical flat

Linear Measuring Instruments

Rule. The most common measuring device in the shop is the steel *rule*—made of tempered steel, carefully ground, and accurately graduated on both sides. Usually one side is graduated in eighths and sixteenths and the other in thirty-seconds and sixty-fourths, although numerous other graduations in both metric and English systems are used. This tool is very satisfactory for rough machine work, layout work, checking dimensions, and many other shop applications. Mechanics with considerable skill and experience can attain a high degree of accuracy in measuring with a rule and calipers.

Combination set. A combination set (see Figure 4) consists of a steel rule or blade on which is mounted a *square head, a center head,* and a *bevel protractor*. Although a set includes all three accessories, only one is used at a time. With the square head mounted on the blade, it serves as both try and miter squares; and it can be adjusted

Fig. 4. Combination set including square, center head, protractor, and scale. (Courtesy The Lufkin Rule Company.)

to be used as a marking gage. Placing it on the end converts the tool into a height gage. The head alone may be used as a level. When the center head is mounted on the blade, centers of all cylindrical work can be determined. The bevel protractor, used in connection with the blade, permits the measurement, layout, and checking of angles.

Depth gage. As shown in Figure 5, narrow steel scales are frequently mounted in a head which has a straight edge at right angles to the scale. This forms a depth gage, with a scale that can be adjusted and clamped so as to extend a given amount below the straight edge. Similar gages are made with micrometer adjustments.

Caliper. The caliper is used for approximate measurements, both external and internal. It does not measure directly, but must be set to size, with a steel rule or some form of gage being used. Most shop calipers, known as *spring calipers*, consist of two legs with a flat spring head plus a nut and screw to hold

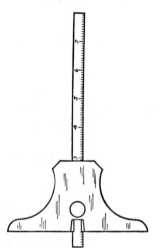

Fig. 5. Rule depth gage.

them in position. The legs on outside calipers curve outward so that the caliper may pass over cylindrical work, while on inside calipers the legs are straight with the ends turned outward. *Hermaphrodite* calipers are used principally for locating centers and layout work. They have one leg similar to the leg on an outside caliper while the other is a straight point. In layout work the curved leg rests against the edge of the work while the other leg is used as a scriber.

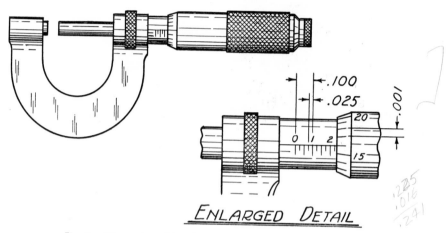

Fig. 6. Micrometer with enlarged view showing graduations.

Divider. A divider is similar in construction to a caliper except that both legs are straight with sharp hardened points at the end. This tool is used for transferring dimensions, scribing circles, and doing general layout work.

Micrometer caliper. The *micrometer* is used for quick, accurate measurements to the thousandth part of an inch. This tool illustrates the use of an accurate screw thread as a means of obtaining a measurement. The screw is attached to a spindle and is turned by movement of a thimble at the end. The barrel, which is attached to the frame, acts as a nut to engage the screw threads, which are very accurately made with a pitch of 40 threads per inch. Each revolution of the thimble advances the screw $\frac{1}{40}$ of an inch, or 0.025 inch. The outside of the barrel is graduated in 40 divisions, and any movement of the thimble down the barrel can be read next to its beveled end. When the spindle is in contact with the anvil on a 1-inch micrometer, the zero readings on barrel and thimble should coincide.

The scale on the barrel and thimble edge can best be understood by reference to the enlarged view of Figure 6. On the beveled edge of the thimble are 25 divisions, each division representing 0.001 inch. To read the micrometer, the division on the thimble coinciding with the line on the barrel is added to the number of exposed divisions on

Fig. 7. Supermicrometer for accurate measurements up to 0.0001 inch. (Courtesy Pratt & Whitney—Division Niles-Bement-Pond Company.)

the barrel, converted into thousandths. Thus, the reading shown in Figure 6 is made up of 0.200 plus 0.025 on the barrel, or 0.225 inch, to which is added 0.016 on the thimble to give a total reading of 0.241 inch.

Since a micrometer reads only over a 1-inch range, in order to cover a wide range of dimensions several micrometers are necessary. The micrometer principle of measurement is also applied to inside measurements and depth reading, and to the measurements of screw threads.

For accurate shop measurements to 0.0001 inch a supermicrometer, as shown in Figure 7, may be used. This machine is set to correct size by precision-gage blocks, and readings may be made directly from the dial on the headstock. Constant pressure is maintained on all objects being measured. Standard measuring machines are similar in appearance but may be read to an accuracy of 0.00001 inch.

Direct readings are obtained by electrolimit pressure control on the tailstock.

Vernier caliper. In Figure 8 is shown a *vernier caliper,* which may be used for taking both inside and outside measurements over a wide range of dimensions. It consists of a main scale graduated in inches and an auxiliary scale having 25 divisions. Each inch on the main scale is divided into tenths and each tenth into four divi-

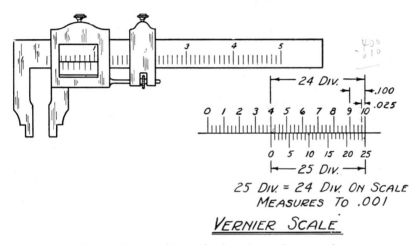

25 Div. = 24 Div. On Scale
Measures To .001

Vernier Scale

Fig. 8. Vernier caliper and enlarged view showing scale.

sions, so that in all there are 40 divisions (each 0.025 inch) to the inch. The 25 divisions on the auxiliary or sliding scale correspond to the length of 24 divisions on the main scale and are equal to $2\frac{4}{40}$ of an inch. One division would be equal to $\frac{1}{25}$ times $2\frac{4}{40}$, or $2\frac{4}{1000}$ inch, which is $\frac{1}{1000}$ inch less than a division on the main scale. Hence, if the two scales were on zero readings, the first two lines would be 0.001 inch apart, the tenth lines 0.010 inch apart, and so on.

In actual use, the reading on the main scale is first observed and converted into thousandths, and to this figure is added the reading on the vernier. The vernier reading is obtained by noting which line coincides with a line on the main scale. If it is the fifteenth line, 0.015 inch is added to the main scale. These scales are shown in some detail in the enlarged view of the vernier scale. As shown, the vernier reads exactly 0.400 inch.

Outside measurements are taken with the work between the jaws; inside measurements with the work over the ends of the two jaws. This method of measurement is not so rapid as a micrometer but has the advantage of having a wider range with equal accuracy. It also has some use on protractors for angular measurement.

Vernier height gage. An application of the vernier scale to a *height gage* is shown in Figure 9. This tool differs from a vernier caliper in that it rests on a heavy base and has a beveled pointer on the movable jaw. In using this instrument the work is placed on a surface plate, and distances are measured above this reference eleva-

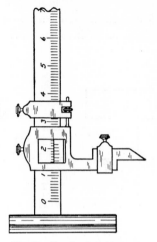

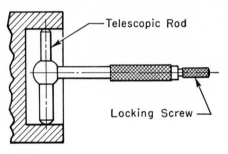

—Telescopic Rod

Locking Screw —

Fig. 9.   Vernier height gage.   Fig. 10.   Telescopic gage.

tion. The reading of the scale is identical with that of a vernier caliper. This measuring tool is used principally for accurate measurements and scribing lines in layout work.

Telescopic gage. The *telescopic gage,* shown in Figure 10, is used for measuring the inside size of slots or holes. This is much quicker than other methods. The gage consists of a handle and two plungers, one telescoping into the other and both under spring tension. The plungers may be locked in any position by the knurled screw at the end of the handle. In using the telescopic gage, the plungers are first compressed and locked in position. Next, the plunger end is inserted into the hole and the screw released, allowing the plungers to expand to the hole size. Finally, the plungers are locked in place and removed, after which the overall length of the plungers is measured with an outside micrometer.

Toolmakers' microscope. Because of their extreme accuracy and ability to measure parts without pressure or contact, numerous optical instruments have been devised for inspecting and measuring. A microscope for toolroom work is shown in Figure 11. An object viewed is greatly enlarged, and the image is not reversed as in the ordinary microscope. To be measured, a part is first clamped in proper position on the cross-slide stage. The microscope is focused and the part to be measured brought under the crossline seen in the microscope. The micrometer screw is then turned until the other extremity is under the crossline, the dimension being obtained from

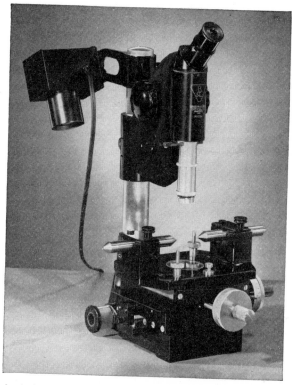

Fig. 11. Toolmaker's microscope with centering stage and illuminator. (Courtesy Bausch & Lomb Optical Company.)

the difference in the two readings. The micrometer screws operate in either direction and read to an accuracy of 0.0001 inch. In the illustration the microscope is shown with a screw-measuring attachment in position for checking the lead of the screw.

Angular Measurements

As previously stated, the basic unit of angular measurement is the *degree*. This unit is defined as the angle formed by two radii subtending an arc $\frac{1}{360}$ of the circumference of a circle. Although degrees may be further subdivided by fractions, the usual smaller subdivisions are minutes and seconds. Common angular measuring instruments read the degrees directly from a circular scale scribed on the dial or circumference. There are also devices that require the aid of other measuring instruments and calculations to obtain the result. Some few, such as the ordinary square, measure only a single angle and are not adjustable. Fixed instruments of this type are more correctly classified as gages.

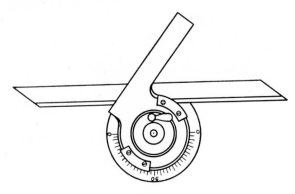

Fig. 12. Vernier bevel protractor.

Bevel protractor. The plain or universal *bevel protractor* measures directly in degrees and is adapted to all classes of work where angles are to be laid out or established. The universal protractor, shown in Figure 12, is graduated in degrees and, in addition, is provided with a vernier scale for fine measurements. Protractors ordinarily read to 5 minutes or one-twelfth of a degree.

Adjustable bevel. An instrument known as an *adjustable bevel* or a bevel gage is widely used for checking or transferring angles. This tool consists of two blades, which can be set and locked in relation to each other. No direct reading is obtained, and the angle must be set or checked from some other angular measuring device.

Sine bar. A *sine bar* is a simple device used either for accurately measuring angles or for locating work to a given angle. Mounted on the center line are two buttons of the same diameter and at a known distance apart, the distance on most sine bars being either 5 or 10 inches. For purposes of accurate measurement the bar must be used in connection with a true surface.

The operation of the sine bar is based on the trigonometric relationship that the sine of an angle is equal to the opposite side divided by the hypotenuse. Hence, if the hypotenuse is known, the angle may be determined by measuring the height of the opposite side, dividing it by the known figure, and referring to trigonometric tables.

Measurement of the unknown side is accomplished by the use of a height gage or precision blocks.

In Figure 13 is shown a sine bar set to check the angle on the end of a machined part. In this case

$$\text{Sine } \theta = \frac{h_1 - h_2}{L}$$

where L is a known distance, either 5 or 10 inches, depending on the size bar used. The heights h_1 and h_2 are built up to correct amounts with precision gage blocks, and their difference in elevation over L gives the sine of the angle θ being checked.

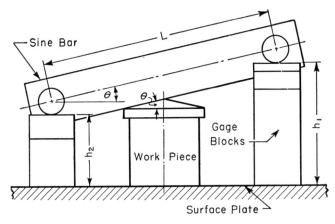

Fig. 13. Sine bar set up on gage blocks for measuring workpiece.

When work is set up to be machined at a given angle, the operation is reversed. The bar is then set at the proper angle, which in turn acts as a gage to position the work correctly. Various designs of the sine bar have been worked out, but the method of measuring the angle is the same in all cases.

Angle gage blocks. A quick and convenient means of measuring angles is by means of angle gage blocks made with the usual accuracy of standard gage blocks. A set of 16 angle blocks will permit the measuring of some 356,400 angles in steps of one second. In Figure 14 is shown a revolving magnetic chuck being set to an angle of 38 degrees. Three blocks are assembled with a parallel, and an indicator is used to tell if the setting is correct. Such an operation can be quickly performed and does not require the calculation necessary when a sine bar is used.

Dividing heads. Index or *dividing heads* were originally developed for use on milling machines, but their use has been extended to inspection work for checking angles about a common center. The head is made up of a worm and worm-gear set having a ratio of 40 to 1. Hence, one turn of the crank will turn the spindle one-

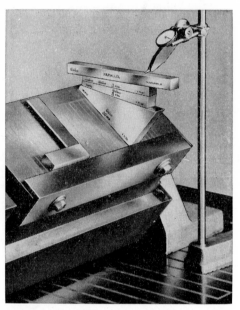

Fig. 14. Angle gage block used to set universal magnetic chuck to a precise desired angle. (Courtesy Webber Gage Company.)

fortieth of a revolution or 9 degrees. By using index plates with the head, a desired angle can be obtained with close accuracy. The operation of this device is discussed in the chapter on milling machines. For inspectional work it is used in connection with a surface plate for checking parts already machined.

Surface Measurements

Surface checking instruments are for the purpose of obtaining some measure of the accuracy of a surface or the condition of a finish. Much of this type of work is done on a flat, accurately machined casting known as a *surface plate.* It is the base upon which parts are laid out and checked with the aid of other measuring tools. These plates are very carefully made and should be accurate to within 0.001 inch from the mean plane any place on the surface. Small plates, known as *toolmakers' flats,* are lapped to a much greater degree of accuracy. Their field of application is limited to small parts, and in most cases they are used with precision gage blocks.

Straightedge. This tool is a bar of steel having either one or two straight edges. It is used for the inspection of surfaces for straightness, checking flat surfaces before straightening, and for accurately scribing straight lines. The ordinary shape is rectangular, but for accurate work one edge is beveled or formed into a knife edge. When one is working to a close tolerance, a feeler gage should be used to check the surface variations.

Surface gage. The *surface gage,* shown in Figure 15, is used to check the accuracy or parallelism of surfaces and, in addition, finds much use in layout work and in transferring measurements by scribing them on a vertical surface. When in use, it is set in approximate position and locked. Fine adjustment of the spindle can be made by turning the knurled nut which controls the rocking bracket. When used with the scriber, it is a line-measuring or locating instrument. If the scriber is replaced by a dial indicator, it then becomes a precision instrument for checking surfaces.

Optical flat. Measurements to the millionth part of an inch are made by interferometry, the science of measuring with light waves. Measurement by this principle is made with a small instrument known as an *optical flat.* Optical flats are usually made from natural quartz because of its hardness, low coefficient of

Fig. 15. Surface gage. (Courtesy The Lufkin Rule Company.)

expansion, and resistance to corrosion. They are flat lenses having very accurately polished surfaces with light-transmitting quality. The usual optical-flat set consists of two lenses 2 inches in diameter and ⅝ inch thick, although they may be obtained in various sizes and shapes up to 5 inches. It is not necessary that the two surfaces of a flat be absolutely parallel. A light having a single color (monochromatic light) is used, because it gives interference bands that are complete and dark in color.

One of the common uses for optical flats is the testing of plane surfaces. The optical flat is placed on the flat surface to be tested, and light is reflected both from the optical flat and the surface being tested through the very thin layer of air between the two surfaces. If the thickness of the air layer measures one half a wavelength of light or more an interference effect occurs. The interference between the rays reflected from the bottom of the flat and from the top of the work causes dark bands (Newton's rings) or areas to

Fig. 16. The straight interference fringes shown by this optical flat indicate that the gage block is flat. (Courtesy Pratt & Whitney—Division Niles-Bement-Pond Company.)

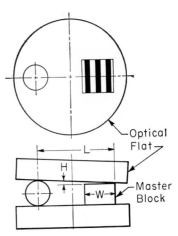

Fig. 17. Illustrating method of measuring a sphere using an optical flat and gage block.

appear. If the surface is irregular, the appearance is similar to a contour map. The position and number of lines show the location and extent of the irregularities. When bands are straight, evenly spaced, and parallel to the line of contact as shown in Figure 16, the surface is perfectly flat. Since we know the wavelength of the light source, any deviation from this pattern indicates an error in the surface, the amount of which can be measured. For ordinary daylight, the difference between bands is ten-millionths of an inch (one-half wavelength). Fluorescent helium light, which is often used, has a separation in one-half wavelengths equal to 11.6 millionths of an inch.

When used for comparison measurements, differences in height from a master block can be determined by the number of interference lines. In Figure 17 are shown two optical flats, being used in connection with a gage block of known size to check the height of a steel ball. The gage block is wrung to the lower flat and the upper flat is placed on top with the ball in position. The position of the two may be controlled by fitting a cardboard template over them. If the parts are not the same size, the upper flat will be tilted slightly, and parallel interference lines will appear on the top surface of the gage block. The difference in height can be determined from the number of bands that appear and may be calculated by the following formula:

$$H = 11.6 \times N \times (L/W)$$

where N = number of bands appearing on width of block,
L = distance between contact points,
W = width of precision block,
11.6 = 0.0000116 millionths of an inch.

Surface roughness. Several devices have been developed that have as their purpose the measurement of surface roughness. The need for some measurement of surface finish for various machining operations is brought about by the necessity of having smooth bearing surfaces in high-speed machinery. In order that surface roughness can be measured or specified, special measuring instruments have been devised using the *microinch* (0.000001) as the unit of measurement. The simplest procedure is a visual comparison with some established standard. Other methods include microscopic comparison, direct measurement of scratch depth by light interference, and the measurement of the magnified shadows cast by scratches of a surface. The usual procedure is to employ a diamond stylus to trace over the surface being investigated and record a magnified profile of the irregularities. This procedure for measuring roughness is used by both the *profilometer* and the *brush surface analyzer*.

In order to measure roughness and other surface characteristics it was first necessary to establish certain standards for measuring. Such a standard has been developed by the American Standards Association (ASA B46.1–1955) which deals with those surface irregularities as height, width, and direction of the surface pattern. These surface irregularities are shown in Figure 18 and above the figure is given the symbol for specifying surface roughness on a drawing.

One type of instrument, the profilometer, used in making surface roughness measurements is shown in Figure 19. This is a direct reading instrument which measures average roughness height in microinches by passing a fine tracing point over the surface. The unit consists of a tracer which converts the vertical movements of the tracing point into a small fluctuating voltage that is related to the

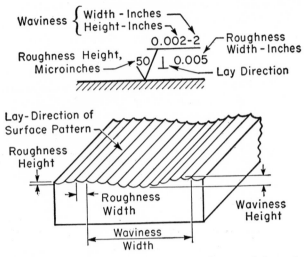

Fig. 18. Surface characteristics and symbols for indicating their maximum values. (From ASA B46.I—1955, The American Society of Mechanical Engineers.)

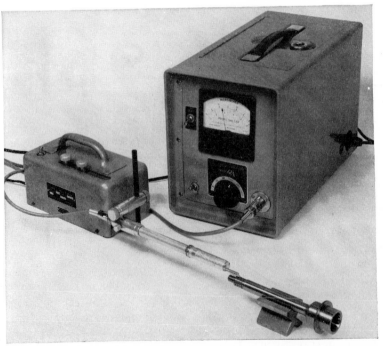

Fig. 19. Profilometer set up for measuring roughness of production parts using Mototrace and tracer. (Courtesy Micrometrical Manufacturing Company.)

height of the surface irregularity; a motor-driven device (*mototrace*) for operating the tracer; and the *amplimeter*. The amplimeter receives the voltage from the tracer, amplifies and integrates it, so that it may be read directly on the micro-inch meter or put in curve form on a recorder. The process is a continuous one, and the instrument shows the variation in average roughness from a reference line as illustrated in the magnified profile of a surface in Figure 20. Readings may be either *arithmetical* or *root-mean-square* (rms)

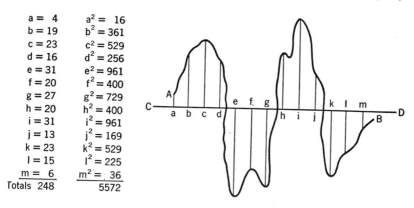

a = 4	a^2 = 16
b = 19	b^2 = 361
c = 23	c^2 = 529
d = 16	d^2 = 256
e = 31	e^2 = 961
f = 20	f^2 = 400
g = 27	g^2 = 729
h = 20	h^2 = 400
i = 31	i^2 = 961
j = 13	j^2 = 169
k = 23	k^2 = 529
l = 15	l^2 = 225
m = 6	m^2 = 36
Totals 248	5572

$$\text{Arithmetical average} = \frac{248}{13} = 19.1 \text{ microinches}$$

$$\text{Root mean square average} = \sqrt{\frac{5572}{13}} = 20.7 \text{ microinches rms}$$

Fig. 20. The relationship between arithmetic average and rms values used in determining surface roughness.

average deviation height from the reference line *CD*. The difference in result of the two methods of calculation are indicated in the example worked out in connection with the figure. The rms average is to be preferred as it gives more weight to the larger deviations from the reference line and is slightly larger than the arithmetical average. The profilometer or other surface analyzing instruments may be operated either manually or mechanically, and readings can be taken on both plain and curved surfaces. Surface roughnesses available by common production methods are indicated in Figure 21.

Production work requires speed as well as accuracy in measuring parts. Measuring instruments, such as those just described, can be used for this type of work, but many of them are more elaborate than necessary and require adjustments for each individual reading. Consequently, they are used only on short-run jobs where the expense of fixed gaging equipment is unwarranted. To attain the quick measurements required in production work, a measuring device that has a fixed shape or size is used. It represents a standard with which the manufactured parts are compared. Since its use is limited to one dimension and no adjustments are required, the operation of inspecting a part requires a minimum of time. Much gaging is done by operators in the shop while their equipment is in operation, with no loss of production time.

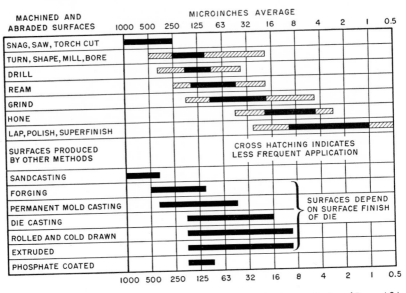

Fig. 21. Surface roughness available by common production methods. (From ASA B46.1–1955, The American Society of Mechanical Engineers.)

Classification of Gages

Numerous kinds of gages are used, varying widely in shape and size. Gages are classified, by the Ordnance Department of the Army and many industries as well, as *inspection gages* and *manufacturing gages*. Inspection gages are those used by inspectors in the final acceptance of the product. They are to insure that the product is made in accordance with the tolerance specification on the working blueprints. Manufacturing or working gages are those used by the machine operators in the actual production of parts. These gages are frequently made to slightly smaller tolerances than the inspection gages, the idea being to keep the size near the center of the limit tolerance. Parts, then, made around limit sizes may still pass the inspector's gage. In addition to these, a third type of gage, known as a *master gage,* is sometimes used. Such a gage is merely a reference gage with which inspection gages are periodically compared. Most industries have abandoned this type of gage and have adopted precision measuring instruments and methods. The equipment used consists of such tools as precision-gage blocks, measuring machines, optical flats, microscopes, and projecting equipment.

The following gages represent those most commonly used in production work. The classification is principally according to the shape or purpose for which each is used. A complete classification would require more subdivisions under the various headings.

Gages

1. Plug
2. Ring
3. Snap
4. Length
5. Form
   (*a*) Screw thread
   (*b*) Fillet
   (*c*) Center
   (*d*) Drill point
   (*e*) Angle
   (*f*) Gear tooth
   (*g*) Special contour, etc.
6. Thickness
   (*a*) Precision gage blocks
   (*b*) Feeler
   (*c*) Wire, etc.
7. Indicating
8. Air-operated
9. Projecting

Gage materials

The true value of a gage is measured by its accuracy and service life, which, in turn, depends on the workmanship and materials used in its manufacture. Since all gages are continually subject to abrasive wear while in use, the selection of the proper material is of great importance. High-carbon and alloy tool steels have been the principal materials used for many years. These materials can be accurately machined to shape, and they respond readily to heat-treating operations which increase their hardness and abrasive resistance. Objections to steel gages are that they are subject to some distortion because of the heat-treating operation and that their surface hardness is limited.

These objections are largely overcome by the use of chrome plating or cemented carbides as the surface material. Chrome plating permits the use of steels having inert qualities, since wear resistance is obtained by the hard chromium surface. This process also is widely used in the reclaiming of worn gages. Cemented carbides, applied on metal shanks by powder-metallurgy technique, provide the hardest wearing surface obtainable. Although the cost is several times that of a steel gage, their life is much greater, and the additional cost is more than justified.

Description of Gages

Plug gages. A plain plug gage is an accurate cylinder used as an internal gage for the size control of holes. It is provided with a suitable handle for holding and is made in a variety of styles. These

Fig. 22. Plug-type "Go—Not-Go" gages. (Courtesy Taft Peirce Manufacturing Company.)

gages may be either single- or double-ended, as shown in Figure 22. Double-ended, plain gages have "go" and "not-go" members assembled on opposite ends, whereas progressive gages have both gaging sections combined on one end.

Three separate designs have been recommended for adoption by the American Standards Association.[3] One is known as the taper-lock design and is the same as those shown in Figure 22. This design applies to all gages from 0.059 inch to and including 1.510 inches. For diameters varying from 1.510 to 8.010 inches, the trilock design with reversible gaging members is used. This gage has three wedge-shaped prongs on the handle which are forced into three locking

[3] Commercial Standard CS8–41, American Gage Design Committee, National Bureau of Standards.

grooves in the gaging cylinder by means of a through screw. When it becomes worn the cylinder may be reversed, thus prolonging the life of the gage. Large gages, ranging from 8.101 to 12.010 inches, are made in the form of a rim with reinforcing web. Holes are drilled and tapped in the web to receive two ball handles. The annular design has proved satisfactory for large gages, because they are light in weight and easily handled. These same designs are recommended for thread, taper, and special-form plug gages.

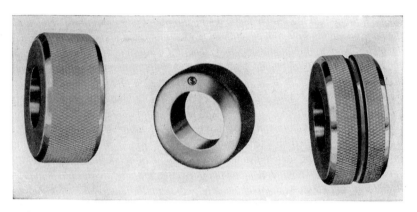

Fig. 23. Plain ring gages. (Courtesy Sheffield Gage Corporation.)

Ring gages. Plain ring gages are standardized in construction and general proportion. The three shown in Figure 23 are typical of gages up to 1.510 inches. A plain, knurled surface indicates a "go" gage, whereas a "not-go" gage is identified by an annular groove on the periphery. Above 1.510 inches all gages are flanged to reduce weight and facilitate handling. Large gages are provided with ball handles. Details of construction, with dimensions of all sizes, have been worked out by the Standards Committee.

Taper gages. Taper gages are made in both the plug and ring styles and, in general, follow the same standard construction as plain and ring gages. Two taper plug gages are shown in Figure 24. Taper gages are not dimensional gages but rather a means of checking in terms of degrees or inches per foot. Their use in testing is a matter of fitting rather than of measuring. If size is involved, "go" and "not-go" tolerances are indicated on the end of the gage by grooves or by milling off a portion of the gage. This type of gage is widely used in checking the standard tapers and sockets used on tools and production machines.

Thread gages. In Figure 25 are shown standard plug and ring gages for inspecting threads. Both these gages are standardized with size variations in the same manner as provided for plain plug and

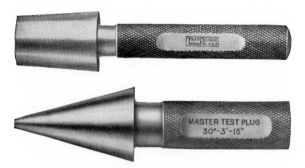

Fig. 24.   Special taper plug gages.   (Courtesy Taft Peirce Manufacturing Company.)

ring gages. Double-ended plug gages have the "go" and "not-go" feature according to the tolerances desired. All ring gages are of the adjustable type, as shown in the figure, with effective means for locking the adjusting screw in position. This feature is desirable, as it is very difficult to measure internal threads accurately in a blank

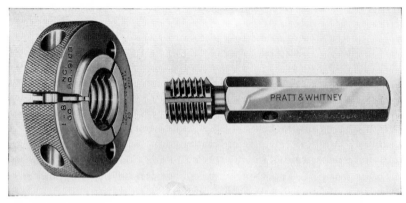

Fig. 25.   Thread ring and plug gage.   (Courtesy Pratt & Whitney—Division Niles-Bement-Pond Company.)

during its manufacture. After completion, they are set to correct size by means of a threaded plug of exact dimensions.

A simple method of approximate checking of the pitch of screws is by means of a small screw-pitch gage made up of a consecutive number of blades, each having a profile of one standard pitch thread.

A quick-acting indicating device for checking threads is shown in Figure 26. Initially the dial is set at zero with a standard threaded plug, and subsequent readings indicate any deviation from the original setting. In operation, the upper roll is raised by depressing a lever, and the work piece is placed between the three rolls. Errors in lead, angle, and pitch diameter are read cumulatively on the dial.

Snap gages. A snap gage, used in the measurement of plain external dimensions, consists of a U-shaped frame having jaws equipped with suitable gaging surfaces. A plain gage has two parallel jaws or anvils which are made to some standard size and cannot be adjusted. This type of gage is largely being replaced by adjustable gages to provide means of changing tolerance settings or adjusting for wear. Most gages are provided with the "go" and

Fig. 26. Tri-roll thread comparitor. (Courtesy Pratt & Whitney—Division Niles-Bement-Pond Company.)

"not-go" feature in a single jaw, and this design is both satisfactory and rapid. A wide variety of snap gages has been developed by various companies, although it is recognized that some disadvantage results from this lack of standardization. Four types, standardized by the American Gage Design Committee, are:

Model A Employing 4 gaging pins.
Model B Employing 4 gaging buttons, either square or round.
Model C Employing 2 gaging buttons, either square or round, and a single block anvil.
Model MC A miniature snap gage with 2 gaging buttons, either square or round, and a single block anvil.[4]

The model-B gage is shown in Figure 27, and the model-C is shown in Figure 28. Model-A gages are similar to the model-B design, except that straight pins are used in place of buttons as the gaging members. The model-MC is similar to the model-C gage, except that

[4] Commercial Standard CS8–41.

it is in miniature and is used only in gaging diameters up to 0.760 inch.

The general design shown in Figures 27 and 28 has been selected because it incorporates most of the advantages of all similar gages

Fig. 27. Adjustable-type snap gage (AGD Model B).

Fig. 28. Snap gage equipped with square buttons (AGD Model C). (Both photos courtesy Taft Peirce Manufacturing Company.)

now in use. It is light in weight, sufficiently rigid, easy to adjust, and provided with suitable locking means, and is designed to permit interchangeability of as many of the parts as possible.

Precision gage blocks. These blocks, of hardened steel, are square or rectangular in shape, having two parallel sides very accurately lapped to some size. Blocks up to 1 inch are made to size within five- to eight-millionths of an inch per block and per inch of length on larger blocks. Laboratory sets may be obtained with a guaranteed accuracy within two-millionths of an inch per block. These blocks are used mainly for reference in setting gages, for accurate measurements in tool, gage, and die manufacture, and as master laboratory standards for control of measurement in manu-facturing.

In Figure 29 is shown a set of 81 gage blocks which include the following:

One ten-thousandth series	0.1001–0.1009 in., inclusive 9 blocks
One thousandth series	0.101 –0.149 in., inclusive 49 blocks
Fifty thousandths series	0.050 –0.950 in., inclusive 19 blocks
Inch series	1.000 –4.000 in., inclusive 4 blocks

Fig. 29. Set of 81 precision gage blocks. (Courtesy Taft Peirce Manufacturing Company.)

With this set it is possible to obtain practically any dimension in increments of 0.0001 inch from 0.100 to over 10 inches by combining blocks of the proper size.

Precision gage blocks are assembled by a wringing process. The blocks must first be thoroughly cleaned. One is placed on the other centrally and oscillated slightly. It is then slid partially out of en-gagement, and they are wrung together under slight pressure. A slight liquid film between the surfaces of the gages causes them to adhere firmly. Gage blocks put together in this fashion should not be so assembled for more than a few hours.

Many interesting applications of gage blocks can be made with the aid of special holders and base blocks. The holders secure the blocks in one rigid accurate unit for such uses as height gages, snap gages, etc. Built-up gages of this type can be assembled quickly for accurate inspection of short-run jobs.

Thickness or feeler gage. This gage consists of a number of thin blades which are held together in a thin case. The blades usually vary in thickness from 0.001 to 0.015 inch but may be obtained in

Fig. 30. Dial indicating gage with permanent-magnet base. (Courtesy Brown & Sharpe Manufacturing Company.)

any thickness range. They are used in checking clearances and for gaging in narrow places.

Dial indicator. A dial indicator is composed of a graduated dial having a hand connected to a test point with suitable means for supporting or clamping it firmly. The dial is graduated in thousandths of an inch, the number depending on the accuracy desired. Most indicators have a spindle travel equal to 2½ revolutions of the hand. Between the test point and the hand is interposed an accurate multiplying mechanism which greatly magnifies on the dial any movement of the point. This tool may be considered either a measuring device or a gage. As a measuring device, it is used to measure inaccuracies in alignment, eccentricity, and deviations on surfaces supposed to be parallel. In gaging work, it gives a direct reading of tolerance variations from the exact size.

A dial test indicator equipped with a permanent-magnet base is shown in Figure 30. This base operates in the same fashion as the permanent-magnet chuck described on page 589. With the handle in the base turned to the "on" position, the indicator is held securely on the horizontal, vertical, or overhead, flat surface of any machine. Other methods of support are a suitable clamp or a heavy base as used on a surface gage.

Comparator or visual gage. A visual gage giving direct plus or minus readings to close tolerance is shown in Figure 31. This gage employs a feed mechanism in connection with a light beam to obtain high magnification of any movement of the gaging point. The magnification in this instrument is 5000 to 1, and the range on the 5-inch scale is only

Fig. 31. Visual gage, amplification 5000 to 1. (Courtesy The Sheffield Corporation.)

0.001 inch. Each graduation on the scale represents 0.000025 inch. This gage is used for checking inspection gages and for toolroom work, as well as for routine production work requiring close size control.

Projecting comparators. Projecting comparators are designed on the same principle as the ordinary projection lantern. An image is placed before a light source, and the shadow of the profile is projected on the screen at some enlarged scale. Usual magnifications are $\times 20$ and $\times 50$, although others up to $\times 100$ can be used.

The path of light in a different type of projector is shown diagrammatically in Figure 32. The object to be inspected is supported at 6 in the figure, and, as the light beam passes by the contour of the object, it enters the projection lens at 7 and is reflected to the screen. Contour inspection is of great value in processing

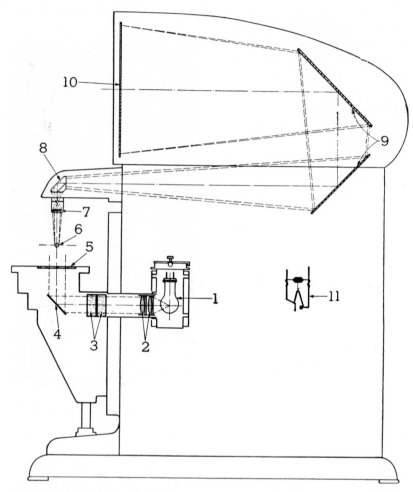

Fig. 32. Path of light in Bausch and Lomb contour measuring projector. (Courtesy Bausch & Lomb Optical Company.)

many tools, dies, gages, and formed products. It is employed in the inspection of many small parts such as needles, saw teeth, threads, forming tools, taps, and gear teeth. Since it checks work to definite tolerances, it can be used for studying wear on tools or distortion caused by heat treatment. Its limitations are based on the size of the object and the number of magnifications required.

Multiple - electric - contact gages.

In quantity production it is frequently advisable to check a number of dimensions simultaneously. This can be done both accurately and rapidly by means of specially constructed contact gages. Each dimension to be checked is provided with pairs of red and green lights which tell the operator whether the dimension is below or above the specified tolerance. Such a gage is made up for simultaneous checking of a number of dimensions. The part being checked is within the tolerance if all red and green lights go out. Master parts are used for setting the gage to the correct limits for the dimension in question. Multiple-type gages, operating electrically, with air, or mechanically, are widely used for the economical inspection of many parts.

Air gages.

Gaging with the aid of compressed air is accomplished by either measuring the back pressure of the air as it comes out of the gage or metering its flow. A dial-type machine, using the latter principle for air-gaging holes, is shown in Figure 33. The air spindle, shown

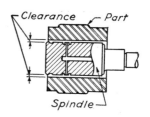

Typical air spindle for internal checking.

Fig. 33. Column-type Precisionaire for air-gaging holes. (Courtesy The Sheffield Corporation.)

above, has two small, diametrically opposed holes through which the air flows. The amount of air flow is controlled by the size of the spaces between the air spindle and the work. This change in flow is registered on the dial which is calibrated to read in fractions of a thousandth of an inch. The relationship between the rate of flow and the size of hole is true only for small clearances, and the maximum range is around 0.003 inch. High amplification permits reading in fractions of a tenth of a thousandth if very accurate readings are necessary.

Gages of this kind can be used for both internal and external checking, and, if desired, multiple checking of several dimensions can be done simultaneously. Advantages claimed for this type of gaging include low wear on gaging spindle, quick indication of true measurement, and little skill required for the operation of the instrument. In addition, air gages will also reveal taper, out-of-round, and tool gouges, which are difficult to detect with the usual plug gage.

Statistical Quality Control

The statistical approach to inspection utilizes a sampling procedure rather than a 100% inspection, which would be slow and costly and in the end would not completely eliminate all defective parts. Mass inspection tends to be careless; operators become fatigued; and inspection gages become worn or out of adjustment. The risk in passing defective parts is variable and of unknown magnitude, whereas in a planned sampling procedure the risk can be calculated.

The *control chart,* which is the important aid, or tool, in statistical quality control, is based upon the theory that variability exists in all repetitive processes. In any machining operation there is some variation from piece to piece which is inherent to the process or tooling method used. Two kinds of variations exist, those due to *chance causes* and those due to *assignable causes.* Variations due to chance causes are inevitable in any process or product; those due to assignable causes can be eliminated. Assignable causes include such factors as poor lighting, improper tooling, wrong material, or poorly trained workers. The control chart accepts the normal dispersion of chance variation but eliminates entirely the errors due to assignable causes.

A control chart, such as the one shown in Figure 34, is made by plotting the inspected dimension of a part against time. Four parts are measured every two hours and the average dimension plotted. The chart then is a record of the variation of an inspected dimension over a period of time. Normally the data fall in random fashion if the assignable causes of error have been eliminated. As long as the data fall in this manner and within the established control limits, it can be assumed that the product is made correctly 99.8% of the time. Two out of 1000 pieces would be passed that were not correct. So long as the points fall between the control lines, no adjustment or changes are made. However, when points fall out of control, then the cause must be located and corrected immediately. On the figure it can be noted that the inspection tolerance is larger than the control limits, permitting the operator frequently to regain control before parts are rejected.

If all of the dimensions taken over a long period of time were plotted according to the frequency with which each size appears, a curve similar to Figure 35 would be obtained. Since the variations

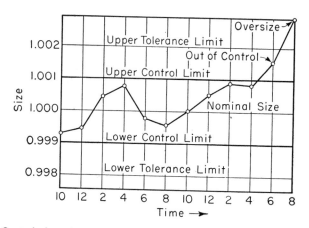

Fig. 34. Control chart showing variation of inspected dimension of a part with time.

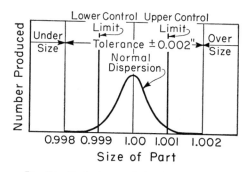

Fig. 35. Typical normal distribution curve.

plotted are chance variations, the curve appears bell shaped, with the *mode* or most frequently recurring element being at the center. Such a curve is known as a *normal distribution curve*. The upper and lower control limits of a series of samplings is a geometric average of how far the samples deviate from their average size. This is the root-mean-square deviation of the observed dimensions from their average and is called the *standard deviation*. It can be computed that for ±1 standard deviation about two-thirds of the occurrence will fall within the limits and for ±3 standard deviations, the number within limits is 99.8%. Experience has proved that few chance-caused deviations fall above or below 3 standard deviations. For this reason control limits are usually set at ±3 standard deviations. Sampling size depends upon the laws of chance, and the development of a good sampling procedure involves the mathematics of probability.

Statistical quality control is now widely used in the inspection of mass-produced parts and has reduced inspection costs materially. It keeps management informed as to how things are progressing and permits prompt remedial action to be taken when the equipment gets out of control.

REVIEW QUESTIONS

1. What is meant by interchangeable manufacture?

2. Distinguish among free fit, snug fit, and shrink fit.

3. Define tolerance. Why is unilateral tolerance usually specified on production drawings?

4. A bearing is dimensioned at 2.750 plus 0.003 minus 0.000. The shaft which runs in the bearing is 2.749 plus 0.0005 minus 0.0015. What is the allowance?

5. What is the standard of measurement in the United States? What is the standard relationship between inches and millimeters?

6. What is a combination set? State the use of each part.

7. How does a caliper differ from a divider in both construction and use?

8. Show by sketch a micrometer reading for 0.419 inch.

9. Explain the principle used on a vernier caliper.

10. How would you measure the lead of a small screw, using a toolmaker's microscope?

11. Explain the use of a telescopic gage in measuring the diameter of a hole.

12. What is the basic unit of angular measurement? List five ways an angle can be measured.

13. A 2-inch gage block is set up under one end of a 5-inch sine bar. What height would have to be used on the other end to check an angle of 15 degrees 30 minutes?

14. Explain the use of a surface plate. How does it differ from a toolmaker's flat?

15. What is an optical flat, and how is it used?

16. If the diameter of a hole is specified as 1.875 plus 0.003 minus 0.001, what should be the diameters of the gaging members of a "go" and "not-go" plug gage?

17. What is the purpose of a projecting comparator? Is it possible to check for dimensional tolerance with this instrument?

18. For what type of work are snap gages used?

19. What use does an inspector make of gage blocks? To what degree of accuracy are they made?

20. Explain how a dial indicator may be used for either measuring or gaging.

21. How does an air gage operate?

22. How is surface roughness measured with a profilometer?
23. Briefly discuss the procedure followed in quality control.
24. Explain how the height of a part can be checked with an optical flat.

REFERENCES

American Machinist's Handbook, McGraw-Hill Book Company, 1955.

American Standard B4a—1925, *Tolerances, Allowances, and Gages for Metal Fits*, American Standards Association, 1925.

American Standard B4.1—1947, *Limits and Fits for Engineering and Manufacturing*, American Standards Association, 1947.

Buckingham, E., *Dimensions and Tolerances for Mass Production*, The Industrial Press, 1954.

Cole, C. B., *Tool Making*, American Technical Society, 1939.

Fullmer, Irvin H., "Fundamentals of Mechanical Dimensional Control," *Mechanical Engineering*, Vol. 57, no. 12, 1935.

Gages, Pratt and Whitney, No. 12, 1954.

Kennedy, Clifford W., *Inspection and Gaging*, The Industrial Press, 1951.

Kent's Mechanical Engineers Handbook, 12th edition, John Wiley and Sons, 1950.

Kurtz, H. F., "Optical Projection," *Mechanical Engineering*, Vol. 60, no. 6, 1938.

Michelon, L. C., *Industrial Inspection Methods*, Harper and Brothers, 1949.

Precision Measuring in the Metal Working Industry, International Business Machine Company, Syracuse University Press, 1952.

Production Handbook, Ronald Press Company, 1957.

Surface Roughness, Waviness and Lay, ASA B46.1—1955, The American Society of Mechanical Engineers, 1955.

The Science of Precision Measurement, The DoALL Company, 1952.

CHAPTER 15

METAL CUTTING

In the manufacture of all products it is important that the processes involved be efficient and capable of producing parts of desired quality. After they have been refined, metals are changed by some primary process to shapes and sizes suitable for commercial use. Final products are obtained by machining these primary shapes to correct size. It is therefore important that metal-cutting operations be well understood and economical in their application. These operations, which produce parts of accurate dimension, include turning, planing, milling, drilling, and all the other processes performed by machine tools. Parts are produced by removing metal in the form of small chips. The cutting tool which removes these chips is the work center for these machines.

Metal-Cutting Tools

The simplest form of cutting tool is the single-point tool such as is used in lathe and shaper work. Multiple-point cutting tools are merely two or more single-point tools arranged together as a unit. The milling cutter and broaching tool are good examples of this type. The discussion in this chapter will be limited to orthogonal, single-point cutting in which the cutting edge is perpendicular to the direction of the cut and there is no lateral flow of metal. This form of cutting is illustrated in Figure 1. In actual cutting the chip is severed from the workpiece by a shearing action across the plane *AB* and is forced up against the face of the tool. The deformed chip is in compression against the face of the tool, resulting in the development of a high frictional force. The work of

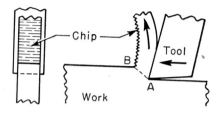

Fig. 1. Schematic diagram of chip formation with tool cutting edge perpendicular to the direction of the cut.

making the chip must overcome both the shearing force and the frictional force.

Cutting forces. The shearing force and the angle of the shear plane are definitely affected by the frictional force of the chip against the tool face. The frictional force, in turn, is dependent upon a number of factors, including the smoothness and keenness of the tool, whether or not a coolant is used, materials in the tool and workpiece,

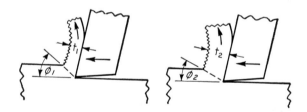

Fig. 2. Relationship between shear angle size and chip thickness.

cutting speed, and the shape of the tool. A large frictional force results in a thick chip having a low shear angle, as illustrated in Figure 2, whereas the reverse is true if the frictional force is low. Most efficient cutting is done when the latter situation prevails, and a thin chip is obtained. A vectorial analysis of these forces may be made by measuring the forces acting on the tool with some form of a dynamometer.

Mechanical and strain-gage dynamometers are most commonly used. Mechanical dynamometers measure deflection on the tool holder by the use of sensitive dial indicators, while flat, bonded strain gages, cemented to the holder, measure strain by the resistance change in the gage. The latter type is more accurate and is in general use. To measure the resultant force on the end of a tool at least two principal force components must be measured using the dynamometer. The forces acting on a tool are indicated in Figure 3. They are, respectively, the longitudinal, tangential, and radial forces—all of which may be measured by dynamometers. In most machining operations the tangential force is the largest and most significant one of the three.

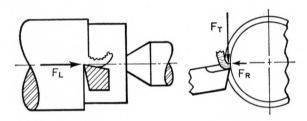

Fig. 3. Forces acting on end of lathe tool—longitudinal, tangential, and radial.

The magnitude of these forces is influenced considerably by the geometry of the tool. As the side-cutting-edge angle is increased, the longitudinal force drops, and the radial force is increased. The same is true for a given side-cutting-edge angle with increasing nose radius. The tangential force increases, with an increase in chip size. Tool forces are not affected by changes in cutting speed. The size of the cut is the variable that has the greatest influence over the cutting forces. These forces increase in direct proportion to an increase in either feed or depth of cut.

Tool shapes and angles. In order to understand the cutting action of a single-point tool as applied to a lathe, refer to Figure 4. The view at the upper left shows a cross section of the tool near its cutting end. The tool has been ground wedge-shaped, the included angle being called the *lip* or *cutting angle.* The *side-clearance* angle between the side of the tool and the work is to prevent the tool from rubbing. The angle is small, usually 6 to 8 degrees for most materials. The top angle, known as the *side-rake angle,* varies with the lip angle, which in turn depends on the type of material being cut. The view to the right center is a side view of the tool with similar angles indicated. If the tool is supported in a horizontal position, the *back-rake angle* is obtained by grinding. However, most tool holders are designed to hold the tool in approximate position for correct back rake. *End clearance* is also necessary to prevent a rubbing action on the flank of the tool. The complete nomenclature of the various parts of a tool is labeled on the finishing tool at the lower part of the figure.

In grinding tools it should be noted that the lip or cutting angle varies with the kind of material being cut. A properly selected cutting angle will have the cutting edge supported well enough to withstand heavy cuts and be capable of carrying away the heat gener-

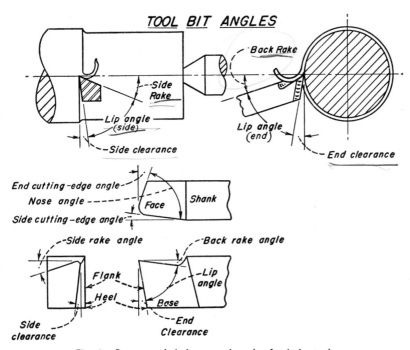

Fig. 4. Recommended shapes and angles for lathe tools.

ated, yet keen enough to cut well without requiring too much power. A compromise is necessary, and in general it is based on the hardness of the material. Hard materials require a cutting edge of great strength with a capacity for carrying away heat. Soft materials permit the use of smaller cutting angles, around 22 degrees for wood tools. Soft and ductile metals, such as copper and aluminum, require larger angles, ranging up to 47 degrees, whereas brittle materials, where chips crumble or break easily, require still larger angles. An interesting variation in tool angles is that recommended for brass and duralumin. These materials work best with practically zero rakes, the cutting action being a scraping one. Because of the high ductility, the tool will dig in and tear the metal if a small cutting angle is used. Table 14 lists suggested high-speed steel-tool angles and cutting speeds for various materials.

TABLE 14. Tool Angles and Cutting Speeds for High-Speed Steel Tools

Material	Side Clearance Angle, degrees	Side Rake Angle, degrees	Back Rake Angle, degrees	Front Clearance Angle, degrees	Cutting Speed, ft/min
Mild steel 1020	12	14	16	8	80
Medium carbon steel 1035	10	14	16	8	70
Medium carbon steel 1090	10	12	8	8	50
Screw steel × 1112	12	22	16	8	150
Cast iron	10	12	5	8	50
Aluminum	12	15	35	8	350
Brass	10	0	0	8	200
Monel metal	15	14	8	12	120
Plastics	12	0	0	8	120
Fiber	15	0	0	12	80

Carbide tools require slightly greater cutting angles than those shown in the figure because of the brittleness of the material. *Side-cutting-edge angles* of 5 to 20 degrees are recommended for these cutters. As the tool starts a cut, the load is not on the end but at a point back of the tip where the tool is stronger as illustrated in Figure 5. Also, at the end of the cut there is a gradual reduction of the load. With the cutting edge at an angle, the length of the cutting edge is increased and the pressure per unit length decreased. An *end-cutting-edge angle* of 8 to 15 degrees with a small nose radius is recommended.

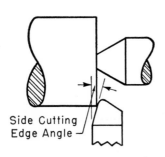

Side Cutting Edge Angle

Fig. 5. With side-cutting edge, angle tip of tool is protected at start of cut.

This shape is a compromise between a point contact, which is apt to break, and a large nose radius, which results in a thin chip, excessive tool wear, and chatter.

Recent experience in rough turning has demonstrated that carbide-tipped turning tools, having a 5-degree negative side and back rake, provide longer tool life. This is particularly true on roughing cuts, where materials are rough, scaly, or slightly eccentric, because with negative rake the surface irregularities strike the cutting edge of the tool back from the tip where the tool is much stronger. Naturally more heat is generated than by conventional turning; so an adequate coolant supply must be provided.

Machinability. The *machinability*,[1] or ease with which a given material can be cut, is greatly influenced by the kind and shape of cutting tool used. It must be recognized, however, that machinability is a relative term and is expressed only in such factors as length of tool life, power required to make the cut, cost of removing a certain amount of material, or surface condition obtained. Tests must be conducted under standardized conditions if results are to be comparable. These tests indicate the resistance of the material being cut, and the results are affected by its composition, hardness, grain size, microstructure, work hardening characteristics, and size. Other influencing factors include type and rigidity of equipment, coolant properties, feed and depth of cut, and the kind of tool used. Tests conducted should simulate actual machining operations.

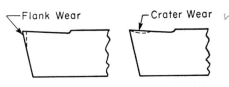

Fig. 6. Wear positions on single-point tools.

Tool life. The life of a tool is an important factor in production work since considerable time is lost whenever a tool is ground and reset. Tool life is a measure of the length of time a tool will cut satisfactorily and, like machinability, may be measured in a number of ways. On a tool, wear is evident in two places. See Figure 6. One is on the flank of the tool where a small land, extending from the tip to some distance below, is abraded away. On high-speed tools a failure is considered to have taken place if this land has worn 0.062 inch, and for carbide tools when the wear land has reached 0.030 inch. Wear also takes place on the face of the tool in the form of a small crater or depression behind the tip. This is because of the abrading action of the chip as it passes over the tool face. Since tool life decreases as the cutting speed is increased, tool life curves are plotted as tool life in minutes against cutting speed, in feet per minute, or in cubic inches of metal removed. In some cases the life is determined by surface finish measurements. It is well to consider the following reasons for tool failure so that preventive measures can be taken where possible.

1. IMPROPER GRINDING OF TOOL ANGLES. Cutting angles depend upon

---

[1] For discussion of this subject see "Machinability of Steel," O. W. Boston, *Metals Handbook*, A.S.M., p. 360.

the material to be cut, their values being well established in handbooks, manufacturers' literature, and other sources.

2. LOSS OF TOOL HARDNESS. Brought about by excessive heat generated at the cutting edge, this situation is relieved by the use of coolants or by reducing the cutting speed.

3. BREAKING OR SPALLING OF TOOL EDGE. This may be caused by taking too heavy a cut or by having too small a lip angle.

4. NATURAL WEAR AND ABRASION. All tools will gradually become dull by abrasion. In some cases this is accelerated by the development of a crater just back of the cutting edge. As the crater increases in size, the cutter edge becomes weaker and breaks off. This can be avoided by the proper selection of tool material.

5. FRACTURE OF TOOL BY HEAVY LOAD. This condition will be reduced materially if the cutting tools are rigidly supported with a minimum of overhang.

Tool life can be prolonged by careful selection of tool angles, feed, cutting speed, and depth of cut, and by the use of proper coolant when the job is originally set up. Frequently a tool failure is caused by disregard of one or more of these factors.

Tool materials. Present-day production practices make rather severe demands on machine tools. To accommodate the many conditions imposed upon them, a wide variety of tool materials have been developed. No one of these materials is superior in all respects, but rather each has certain characteristics which limits its field of application. The selection of the proper tool material therefore depends on the type of service to which the tool will be subjected. Obviously the best material to use for a certain job is the one that will produce the machined part at the lowest cost. Desirable properties for any tool material include the ability to resist softening at high temperatures, a low coefficient of friction, good abrasive resisting qualities, and sufficient toughness to resist fracture. The principal materials used in cutting tools are as follows:

1. HIGH-CARBON STEELS. For many years, before the development of high-speed tool steels, carbon steels were used entirely for all cutting tools. Their carbon content ranging from 0.80% to 1.20%, these steels have good hardening ability and, with proper heat treatment, attain as great a hardness as any of the high-speed alloys. At maximum hardness the steel is quite brittle, and, if some toughness is desired, it must be obtained at the expense of hardness. Depth-hardening ability (*hardenability*) is poor, limiting the use of this steel to tools of small size. Because of the tendency of these tools to

lose hardness at around 600 F, they are not suitable for high speeds and heavy-duty work, their usefulness being confined to work on soft materials such as wood. As a production-tool material for metal cutting, these steels are obsolete.

2. HIGH-SPEED STEELS. High-speed steels are high in alloy content, have excellent hardenability, and will retain a good cutting edge up to temperatures of around 1200 F. The ability of a tool to resist softening at high temperatures is known as *red hardness* and is a most desirable quality. The first tool steel that would hold its cutting edge to almost a red heat was developed by Frederick W. Taylor and M. White in 1900. This was accomplished by adding 18% tungsten and 5.5% chromium to steel as the principal alloying elements. Present-day practice in the manufacture of high-speed steels still uses these two elements in nearly the same percentage. Other common alloying elements are vanadium, molybdenum, and cobalt. Although there are numerous high-speed steel compositions, they may all be grouped in the following three classes:

(a) *18-4-1 high-speed steel.* This steel, containing 18% tungsten, 4% chromium, and 1% vanadium, is considered to be one of the best all-purpose tool steels. In some steels of similar composition the percentage of vanadium is increased slightly in order to obtain better results in heavy-duty work.

(b) *Molybdenum high-speed steel.* Many high-speed steels use molybdenum as the principal alloying element since one part will replace two parts of tungsten. Molybdenum steels such as 6-6-4-2 containing 6% tungsten, 6% molybdenum, 4% chromium and 2% vanadium have excellent toughness and cutting ability. For many applications, particularly drilling and tapping operations, molybdenum high-speed steels are better and cheaper than other types.

(c) *Superhigh-speed steels.* Some high-speed steels have cobalt added to them in amounts ranging from 2% to 15%, since this element increases the cutting efficiency, especially at high temperatures. One analysis of this steel contains 20% tungsten, 4% chromium, 2% vanadium, and 12% cobalt. Because of the greater cost of this material it is used principally for heavy cutting operations which impose high pressures and temperatures on the tool.

3. CAST NONFERROUS ALLOYS. A number of nonferrous alloys, containing principally chromium, cobalt, and tungsten, with smaller percentages of one or more carbide-forming elements like tantalum, molybdenum, or boron, are excellent materials for cutting tools. These alloys are cast to shape and have a high red hardness, being able to maintain good cutting edges on tools at temperatures up to

1700 F.   Compared with high-speed steels, they can be used at twice their cutting speeds and still maintain the same feed.   However, they are more brittle, do not respond to heat treatment, and can be machined only by grinding.   Intricate tools can be formed by casting into ceramic or metal molds and then finished to shape by grinding. Their final properties are largely determined by the degree of chill given the material in casting.   The range of elements in these alloys is 12% to 25% tungsten, 40% to 50% cobalt, and 15% to 35% chromium.   In addition to one or more carbide-forming elements, carbon is added in amounts of 1% to 4%.   These alloys have good resistance to cratering and can resist shock loads much better than carbides.   As a tool material they rank midway between high-speed steels and carbides for cutting efficiency.

4. CARBIDES.   Carbide cutting-tool inserts are made only by powder-metallurgy technique; the metal powders of tungsten carbide and cobalt are pressed to shape, semisintered to facilitate handling and forming to final shape, sintered in a hydrogen atmosphere furnace at 2800 F, and finished finally with a grinding operation.   Carbide tools containing only tungsten carbide and cobalt (approximately 94% WC and 6% Co) are suitable for machining cast iron and most other materials except steel.   Steel cannot be satisfactorily machined by this composition because the chips tend to stick or weld to the carbide surface and soon ruin the tool.   To eliminate this difficulty titanium and tantalum carbides are added in addition to increasing the cobalt percentage.   A typical analysis of a carbide suitable for steel machining is 82% tungsten carbide, 10% titanium carbide, and 8% cobalt.   This composition has a low coefficient of friction and, as a result, has little tendency toward top wear or cratering.   Since variation in composition alters the properties of carbide materials, several grades are available to accommodate the various types of work to be done.

Carbide tools are made by brazing or silver-soldering the formed inserts on the ends of commercial steel holders.   The red hardness of carbide tool materials is superior to any other tool materials, since it will maintain a cutting edge at temperatures over 2200 F.   In addition, it is the hardest manufactured material and has extremely high compressive strength.   However, it is very brittle, has low resistance to shock, and must be very rigidly supported to prevent cracking. Grinding is very difficult and can be done only with silicon carbide or diamond wheels.   Clearance angles should be held to a minimum. Carbide tools permit cutting speeds two to three times that of cast alloy tools, but at such speeds a much smaller feed must be used.

From an economic point of view, carbide tools should always be used if possible. However, machines using carbide tools must be rigidly built, have ample power, and a range of feeds and speeds suitable to the material.

5. DIAMONDS. Diamonds used as single-point tools for light cuts and high speeds must be rigidly supported because of their high hardness and brittleness. They are used either for hard materials, difficult to cut with other tool materials, or for light, high-speed cuts on softer materials where accuracy and surface finish are important. Diamonds are commonly used in the machining of plastics, hard rubber, pressed carbon, and aluminum with cutting speeds from 1000 to 5000 fpm. Diamonds are also used for dressing grinding wheels, for small wire-drawing dies, and in certain grinding and lapping operations.

6. CERAMIC TOOLS. A recently developed process in the field of tool materials utilizes aluminum oxide, in the form of small inserts, as a cutting tool. Aluminum oxide powder is mixed with certain other oxides and a binder and is then processed by hot-pressing or by forming and sintering. The resulting material has an extremely high compressive strength but is quite brittle. Because of this the inserts are given a 5- to 7-degree negative rake to strengthen their cutting edge, and are well supported by the tool holder. Heat conductivity is very low, and hence the tools are generally used without a coolant. Tests run on ceramic tools indicate that they will withstand much higher cutting speeds than other tool materials because of their ability to withstand high temperatures and to resist abrasion.

Chip shape and formation. Much research has been done in studying the mechanics and geometry of chip formation, and the relationship of chip shape to such factors as tool life and surface finish. Ernst[2] has classified tool chips into three types as shown in Figure 7. Type 1, a discontinuous or segmental chip, represents a condition in which the metal ahead of the cutting tool is fractured into fairly small pieces. This type of chip is obtained in machining most brittle materials, such as cast iron and bronze. As these chips are produced, the cutting edge smooths over the irregularities, and a fairly good finish is obtained. Tool life is reasonably good, and failure usually occurs as a result of abrading action on the contact surface of the tool. Discontinuous chips can also be formed on some ductile materials if the coefficient of friction is high. However, such

[2] H. Ernst, "Physics of Metal Cutting," *Machining of Metals*, American Society of Metals, 1938.

chips on ductile materials are an indication of poor cuttting conditions.

An ideal type of chip, from the standpoint of tool life and finish, is the simple continuous (type 2), which is obtained in cutting ductile materials having a low coefficient of friction. In this case the metal is continuously deformed and slides up the face of the tool without

A. Type I. Discontin-   *B.* Type 2. Continuous   *C.* Type 3. Continuous
uous or segmental chip.   chip without built-up edge.   chip with built-up edge.

Fig. 7. Basic chip types. Photomicrographs of cross sections taken through partially formed chips obtained, under various conditions, in machining operations such as turning, milling, planing, and broaching (according to Ernst). (Courtesy Cincinnati Milling Machine Company.)

being fractured. Chips of this type are obtained at high cutting speeds and are quite common when cutting is done with carbide tools. Because of their simplicity, they can be easily analyzed from the standpoint of the forces involved.

Type 3 chip is characteristic of those machined from ductile materials that have a fairly high coefficient of friction. As the tool starts the cut, some of the material (because of its high friction coefficient) builds up ahead of the cutting edge. As the cutting proceeds, the chips flow over this edge and up along the face of the tool. Periodically a small amount of this built-up edge separates and leaves with the chip or is embedded in the turned surface. Because of this action the surface smoothness is not as good as with the type 2 chip. The built-up edge remains fairly constant during cutting and has the effect of slightly altering the rake angle. However, as the cutting speed is increased, the size of the built-up edge decreases, and the surface finish is improved. This phenomenon is also decreased by either reducing the chip thickness or increasing the rake angle, although on many of the ductile materials it cannot be eliminated entirely.

Chip control. In high-speed production turning, the control and disposal of chips is important to protect both the operator and the tools. The *chip breaker* curls and highly stresses the chips so that they break into short lengths for easy removal from the machine. Various means can be provided to accomplish this. See Figure 8.

1. Grinding on the face of the tool along the cutting edge a small flat to a depth of 0.015 to 0.030 inch. This is known as a step-type

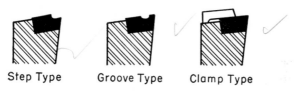

Step Type   Groove Type   Clamp Type

Fig. 8. Chip breakers used on single-point tools.

chip breaker, and it may be either parallel with the edge or at a slight angle. The width varies according to the feed and depth of cut and may range from $\frac{1}{16}$ to $\frac{1}{4}$ inch.

2. Grinding a small groove about $\frac{1}{32}$ inch behind the cutting edge to a depth of 0.010 to 0.020 inch. The correct dimension for both the land distance and depth depend upon the feed and should be increased slightly as the feed is increased.

3. Brazing or screwing a thin carbide-faced plate or clamp on the face of the tool. As the chip is formed, it hits the edge of the plate and is curled to the extent that it breaks in short pieces.

4. Proper selection of tool angles controlling the direction of the curled chip. They force the chip into some obstruction and stress the chip to its breaking point.

Coolants. Improvement in cutting action may be accomplished by the use of solids, liquids, emulsions, or gases in the cutting process. In all forming and cutting operations high temperatures will develop as the result of friction; and, unless temperatures and pressures are controlled, there is a tendency for the metal surfaces to adhere to one another. It is therefore important that the friction coefficient between contact surfaces such as the tool and the chip be kept as low as possible. This is done effectively by the use of various type coolants, which, in addition, perform the following useful functions:

1. Reduce the temperature of the tool and work.
2. Wash away chips.
3. Improve the surface finish.
4. Increase tool life.
5. Reduce the power required.
6. Reduce possible corrosion on both the work and machine.

Solids, which improve cutting ability, include certain elements in the work material as well as those injected into the tool-chip interface with liquids. Liquids are principally in the form of water-base or oil-base solutions having in them certain additives to increase their effectiveness. Gases include water vapor, carbon dioxide, and compressed air. Most coolants are in liquid form, because in this form they may be directed on the tool at the proper place and are readily recirculated. Any coolant used should be subjected to certain specifications since there are a number of desirable properties that a coolant should have. Among these are:

1. It should be free from undesirable odors.
2. It should not be injurious to the skin of the operator.
3. It should not corrode either the work or the machine.
4. It should be stable and should not volatilize, smoke, or foam easily.
5. It should have a high flash temperature.

Many kinds of coolants are used, depending primarily on the kind of material being machined and the type of operation being performed. Typical coolants used for several of the common materials are:

CAST IRON. Compressed air, soluble oil, or worked dry. The use of compressed air necessitates an exhaust system to remove the dust caused by blowing the fine particles of iron.

ALUMINUM. Kerosene lubricant, soluble oil, or soda water. Soda water consists of water with a small percentage of some alkali which acts as a rust preventive.

MALLEABLE IRON. Dry or water-soluble oil lubricant. The latter coolant consists of a light mineral oil held in suspension by caustic soda, sulfurized oil, soap, and other ingredients which form an emulsion when mixed with water.

BRASS. Worked dry, paraffin oil, or lard oil compounds.

STEEL. Water-soluble oil, sulfurized oil, or mineral oil.

WROUGHT IRON. Lard oil or water-soluble oil.

In addition to these listed, many other coolants are used, the selection depending on the type of work being done. For example, lard oil would be satisfactory for a tapping operation on steel, whereas, for high-speed cutting of the same steel on a turret lathe, a water-soluble oil emulsion would be better. Grinding operations use a water solution with some alkali such as soda or sodium carbonate to act as a rust preventive, a little oil being added to keep the soda in suspension.

Grinding coolants should not only cool efficiently but also keep the wheel clean. A poor coolant often contributes to wheel loading or glazing, resulting in the ineffective cutting action of abrasive particles. Coolants for grinding should be used in considerable volume and should not contain too much oil or gumming material.

The water-soluble oil emulsions, resembling milk in appearance, are widely used for all forms of operations. They are inexpensive, have high cooling properties, and have low viscosity which permits the oil to separate readily from the chips. In addition to the coolants mentioned, there is a wide variety of compounded mineral, fixed, and sulfurized oils that are used as cutting fluids.

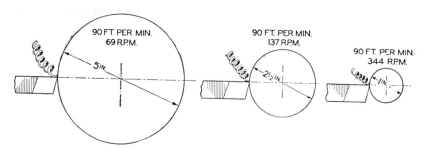

Fig. 9. Relation of rpm to surface speeds on different diameters. (Courtesy Warner & Swasey Manufacturing Company.)

Cutting Speeds and Feeds

Cutting speed is expressed in feet per minute and on a lathe is the surface speed or rate at which the work passes the cutter. It may be expressed by the simple formula: $CS = \pi DN$, where D is the diameter of the work in feet and N is the revolutions of the work per minute. The cutting speed in this expression is seldom unknown, since cutting speeds for various materials may be found in many textbooks and handbooks. In lathe work the unknown factor is the speed of the work, or the term N. Referring to Figure 9 we may note that, to maintain a recommended cutting speed of 90 fpm, it is necessary to increase the work revolution materially, as the diameter is decreased from 5 inches to 1 inch.

The term *feed* is used to express the distance that the tool moves for each revolution of the work and is sometimes expressed as chip thickness. Since so many factors must be given consideration, it is difficult to state definitely what the speed and feeds for a given material should be. In cutting steel, the color of the chip and the general feed of the machine are important indications, a blue chip indicating too much speed or feed. Vibration of the machine or rapid dulling of the tool also indicates that the tool is overloaded. In general, the speed and feed are determined by the following factors:

1. Kind of material being cut. Materials vary greatly in hardness and other physical properties which affect the cutting speed and life of the tool.

2. Kind of material in the cutter. Carbon-steel cutters can take about one-half the cutting speed of a high-speed tool-steel cutter. Stellite and carbide cutters will stand still greater speeds.

3. Types of finish desired. In general, high speeds with fine feeds give the best finish.

4. Rigidity of the machine. No work should be done at speeds and feeds that cause vibration in the machine.

5. Kind of tool being used. Forming tools, taps, and other tools that are expensive and difficult to sharpen should be operated at speeds and feeds that insure long life.

6. Type of coolant used.

Table 15, prepared by the Warner & Swasey Company, gives the following recommended cutting speeds for various materials.

TABLE 15. Cutting Speeds for Various Materials

Material	High-Speed Steel		Carbide	
	Rough	Finish	Rough	Finish
Cast iron	50– 60	80–110	120– 200	350– 400
Semisteel*	40– 50	65– 90	140– 160	250– 300
Malleable iron*	80–110	110–130	250– 300	300– 400
Steel casting* (0.35C)	45– 60	70– 90	150– 180	200– 250
Brass (85–5–5)	200–300	200–300	600–1000	600–1000
Bronze (80–10–10) *	110–150	150–180	600	1000
Aluminum†	400	700	800	1000
SAE 1020*	80–100	100–120	300– 400	300– 400
SAE 1050*	60– 80	100	200	200
Stainless steel*	100–120	100–120	240– 300	240– 300

* Water-soluble oil lubricant.
† Kerosene lubricant.

Special Machining Processes

The shaping of parts made from carbides and other metals difficult to machine has for many years been limited to diamond wheel grinding. Because of the expense of diamond wheels and the time required for grinding, much effort and research have been directed toward the development of more economical methods. There are, at present, no less than four methods, either being used or in the development stage, all of which remove metal by some form of electrical discharge rather than by the usual grinding wheel abrasion. All these processes, *ultrasonic, electrical-discharge machining, electro-arc,* and *electrolytic,* can remove metal from either hard or soft metals, but the rate of metal removal in soft metals is much slower than by conventional machining methods.

Chem-milling, another metal removing process recently developed, is an extension of the etching process. This new technique for controlled metal removal is being used successfully for difficult machining jobs in the airplane industry.

Ultrasonic machining. Ultrasonic machining is a form of planned metal removal produced by abrasive grains which are carried in a liquid between the tool and work and which bombard the work surface at high velocity. This action gradually chips away minute particles of material in a pattern controlled by the tool shape and contour. A transducer causes an attached tool to oscillate linearly at a frequency of 20,000 to 30,000 times per second through an amplitude of 0.001 to 0.005 inch. The tool motion is produced by being part of a sound wave energy transmission line which causes the tool material to change its normal length by contraction and expansion. The tool holder is threaded to the transducer and oscillates linearly at ultrasonic frequencies, thus driving the grit particles into the workpiece. The cutting particles, boron carbide and similar materials, are of a 280-mesh size or finer, depending upon the accuracy and the finish desired.

The tools are made of brass or soft steel and must match the surface to be machined. Tolerances of 0.002 inch can be maintained with 280 grit, or by using finer grit a tolerance of 0.005 inch can be held. Operations that can be performed include drilling, tapping, coining, and the making of openings in all types of dies. Ultrasonic machining is used principally for machining hard and brittle materials such as carbides, tool steels, ceramics, glass, gem stones, and synthetic crystals. Advantages of this process include the absence of thermal stresses, low tooling costs, and ability to use semiskilled workers for precision work.

Electrical discharge machining.   Electrical discharge machining is a process which removes metal from any hard or soft material that conducts electricity.   The machining action is caused by the formation of an electrical spark between an electrode, shaped to the required contour, and the workpiece.   Since the cutting tool has no contact with the workpiece, it can be made of a soft, easily worked material such as brass.   The tool works in conjunction with a fluid such as mineral oil or kerosene, which comes to the work under pressure.   The function of this coolant is to serve as a dielectric, to wash away particles of eroded metal from the workpiece or tool, and to maintain a uniform resistance to flow of current.

Electrical discharge machining, also known as spark machining or electronic erosion, was developed primarily for machining carbides,

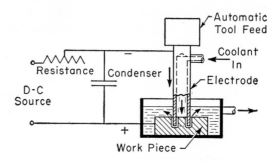

Fig. 10. Simple diagram for electro-spark machining.

hard nonferrous alloys, and other hard-to-machine materials.   Although the principle involved has been known for some time, it is only recently that procedure for utilizing an electrical discharge for the controlled removal of metal particles from a workpiece has been economically developed.   Machining operations such as drilling, tapping, tool grinding, and die sinking can be accomplished, but the machining time in the softer materials is greater than with the conventional methods.

In Figure 10 is shown a diagram of a simple arrangement for electrical discharge machining which was one of the first to be used in laboratory experiments.   A condenser, parallel with the electrode and workpiece, receives a charge of direct current through a resistor. As the condenser is energized, its potential rises rapidly to a value sufficient to overcome the dielectric fluid between the electrode and work.   The gap distance is electronically controlled on modern units so as to maintain a fairly constant potential which is applied, bringing about an electrical breakdown of the dielectric fluid. This distance is only a few thousandths of an inch, so hand control is difficult to maintain. Regardless of the electrode tool area, sparking occurs at the point where the gap is the smallest. The current density at this point is very high and of sufficient force to erode small particles from the workpiece. These particles are then carried away by the dielectric fluid. It is believed that particles of metal are removed entirely by the mechanical force from the spark and not by the presence of heat. Economical removal of metal requires many thousands of discharges per second. This process is especially adapted for use in die-sinking and precision drilling. When provided with a wheel-type rotating electrode, the process is used for automatic single-point tool sharpening and form grinding. Metal removal rates of 0.010 cubic inch per minute are reported when machining steel, and 0.007 cubic inch per minute when machining carbides. Finishes of 8 to 10 microinches are possible with this process.

Electro-arc machining. The electro-arc process is one of metal disintegration caused by the arcing effect of a vibrating electrode. The electrode in this process is negative; and the workpiece, positive. As the vibrating electrode contacts the work, current flows across the small contact areas causing instantaneous heating and melting of the metal contacted. The electrode is withdrawn sufficiently to extinguish the arc, and the metal is instantly cooled by a conducting electrolytic fluid. Metal is removed by the thermal shock received, as well as by vaporization during the arcing. Some metal is consumed on the electrode but most disintegration takes place at the anode or workpiece.

Practical applications of this process include the removal of broken taps from castings, making alterations in hardened dies, and salvaging many parts that otherwise would be lost. Finishes are not as smooth as those obtained by some of the other processes.

Electrolytic process. This process appears to be very good for hand grinding single-point carbide tools. The grinding is performed by a rotating metal disk cathode which is supplied with an electrolyte in much the same manner as a coolant is used on an ordinary grinding wheel. The carbide tool, which is the anode, is slightly separated from the wheel by an electrolytic solution which chemically attacks the tungsten carbide. With the proper electrolyte, the grinding is accomplished electrolytically without the need of much abrasive action. In some cases electrolytic solutions are used in connection with diamond wheels to speed up the cutting action.

In the several electrical processes described, there are a number of interesting characteristics that apply to all of them.

1. All can cut hard materials as well as soft.
2. The cutting tool seldom touches the work so that it need not be of a hard material.
3. There is no appreciable heating in any of the processes.
4. There are no cutting forces involved.

Chem-Milling

Chem-milling is a controlled etching process in which metal is removed to produce complex patterns, light-weight parts, tapered thickness sheets, and integrally stiffened structures. It is the adaptation of an old process to one which can be successfully used to remove metal as in a machining process. The development of this process started in the airplane industry, where many complicated machining problems exist in the removal of excess metal to reduce weight. Although most chem-milling has been done with aluminum alloys, any metal for which an etching solution is available can be processed in this manner.

The process, which is relatively simple, consists first of thoroughly cleaning the sheet or part to be etched. It is then prepared for the etching process by masking those areas not to be affected with a chemically resistant coating. If the entire area is to be reduced, this is unnecessary. The part is then submerged in a hot alkaline solution where metal in the unprotected area is eroded. The amount of metal removed depends mainly on the time the part is in the hot solution. Finally the part is rinsed, and the masking material is removed.

Masking. The success of chem-milling is, to a large extent, due to suitable masking tapes and organic coatings which are capable of resisting the action of the hot alkaline solutions. Adhesive tapes, applied to surfaces, are excellent for chem-milling panels to several thicknesses. Tapes are removed progressively after the etching begins if several panel thicknesses are required. Templates with the design cut out are economical for flat surfaces. The template, which must be well gasketed, is held to the plate by either bolts or clamps. Electroplating of copper upon the area to be masked may also be used, but it is somewhat expensive. Masking by spraying or brushing chemically resistant coatings is another method. Photosensitive coating masking is often used for complex designs (see Figure 11).

Where a uniform weight reduction is necessary on a forging or extrusion, no masking is required. Likewise, sheet metal formed parts, that require a heavy sheet thickness for the operations involved, may be uniformly reduced in weight without masking. Another instance, where no masking is required, is in the tapering of sheets (skins) for airplane use. Here the sheet to be tapered is gradually immersed or withdrawn from the etching solution.

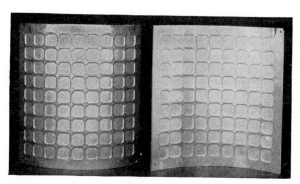

Fig. II. Matched etch-contoured waffle panels ready to be joined to give high-stiffness sandwich construction. (Courtesy North American Aviation, Inc.)

Effect on metal. The operation of chem-milling is uniform on all exposed areas; neither are internal stresses developed, nor is there any change in the metal structure. Tests have indicated that the physical properties of the metal are not impaired by this process if proper control and etchants are used. However, bend and fatigue strength can be reduced somewhat by improper etching, the result of which are rough surfaces and consequent notch effects. Normally a surface roughness of 50 to 60 rms is obtained which is comparable to surfaces on many die castings and ground parts.

Advantages and limitations. Chem-milling is a new process and still in the experimental stage. Further refinements will, no doubt, overcome some present difficulties and increase its usefulness. In comparison with machine milling, the following advantages are claimed for this new process:

1. Material can be removed uniformly from all surfaces exposed to the etching solution.
2. Material can be removed after parts are formed to shape.
3. Sheets and structural members can be uniformly tapered.
4. Highly skilled operators are not required.
5. Close tolerance can be maintained, and surface finish is good.
6. Operating costs are generally less than in machine milling. Likewise, equipment cost is less.

Limitations of the process are difficult to evaluate at this stage of development, but the following might be mentioned:

1. Aluminum is the only metal being chem-milled on a commercial scale.
2. Surface roughness is 50 microinches rms or higher.
3. The depth of cut is limited when masking is used; gases collect under mask and cause uneven etching.
4. Masking techniques for certain conditions are expensive.
5. Gas generated in the process must be disposed of.

REVIEW QUESTIONS

1. What determines the thickness of a chip?
2. What factors influence the frictional force acting on the face of a single-point tool?
3. What effect does cutting speed have on tool forces?
4. Sketch a tool bit and indicate the lip angle, side rake, side clearance, tool face, and side-cutting-edge angle.
5. Why is a side-cutting-edge angle recommended for heavy roughing cuts?
6. What is meant by machinability, and how is it expressed?
7. What factors affect the machinability of a metal?
8. How is tool life measured?
9. What are the causes for cutting tool failure?
10. What are the principal alloying elements in high-speed steel?
11. What are the desirable properties for a tool material?
12. Why are chip breakers used on some tools, and how are they constructed?
13. What desirable properties should a coolant possess?
14. Define the term "cutting-speed." How is it determined on a lathe?
15. Describe the process of ultrasonic machining.
16. How are tools ground by the electrolytic process?
17. Briefly describe the method of operation used in electrical discharge machining.

REFERENCES

Alden, C. R., "Electrospark Machining," *Mechanical Engineering*, September 1953.
Ernst, Hans, "Fundamental Aspects of Metal Cutting and Cutting Fluid Action," *New York Academy of Science,* Vol. 53, June 1951, pp. 936–961.
Hall, R. C., "Machining Hard and Brittle Materials," *Metal Progress*, Vol. 70, No. 2, August 1956.
Machining Theory and Practice, The American Society for Metals, 1950.
Metals Handbook, The American Society for Metals, 1948.
Sanz, M. C., "Machining Aluminum by Etching," *Materials & Methods,* October 1954.

Shaw, M. C., *"Metal Cutting Principles,"* 3d edition, Massachusetts Institute of Technology, 1954.

Stocker, W. M., Jr., and R. Ducat, "How to Understand Spark Erosion," *American Machinist,* April 23, 1956.

Tool Engineers' Handbook, American Society of Tool Engineers, McGraw-Hill Book Company, 1949.

Utrasonic Machining (Bulletin), The Sheffield Corporation, 1955.

CHAPTER 16

LATHES

The *lathe* is a machine that removes material by rotating the work against a cutter. Parts to be machined can be held between centers, attached to a face plate, supported in a jaw chuck, or held in a draw-in chuck or collet. Though this machine is particularly adapted to cylindrical work, it may also be used for many other purposes. Plain surfaces can be obtained by supporting the work on a face plate or in a chuck. Work held in this manner can likewise be centered, drilled, bored, or reamed. In addition, the lathe can be used for cutting threads and turning tapers; with the proper attachment, it can be adapted to simple milling or grinding operations. It is probably the oldest of all the machine tools as well as the most important machine in modern production.

Types of Lathes

It is difficult to make a suitable classification of lathes as there are so many variables in the size, design, method of drive, arrangement of gears, and purpose. In general, the following classification covers most of the lathes used today.

Classification of Lathes

1. Speed lathe
   - (a) Wood working
   - (b) Centering
   - (c) Metal spinning
   - (d) Polishing, etc.
2. Engine lathe
   - (a) Step-cone pulley drive from line shaft
   - (b) Step-cone pulley drive from individual motor
   - (c) Gear-head drive
   - (d) Variable-speed drive
3. Bench lathe
4. Toolroom lathe
5. Special-purpose lathes
   - (a) Crankshaft
   - (b) Car wheel
   - (c) Gap
   - (d) Multicut
   - (e) Duplicating, etc.

Speed lathe. The speed lathe, which is the simplest of all lathes, consists of a bed, a headstock, a tailstock, and an adjustable slide for supporting the tool. Usually it is driven by a variable-speed motor built into the headstock, although the drive may be a belt to a step-cone pulley. Because hand tools are used and the cuts are small, the lathe is driven at high speed, the work being held between centers or attached to a face plate on the headstock.

The speed lathe is used principally in the turning of wood for small cabinet work or for patterns, and for the centering of metal cylinders prior to further work on the engine lathe. In the latter operation, the center drill is held in a small chuck fastened to the headstock, and the work is guided to the center drill either by a fixed center rest or a movable center in the tailstock. Metal spinning is done on lathes of this type by rapidly revolving a stamped or deep-drawn piece of thin ductile metal and pressing it against a form by means of blunt hand tools. The work is revolved at high speeds, and hand tools are used.

Engine lathe. The engine lathe derives its name from the early lathes, which obtained their power from engines. It differs from a speed lathe in that it has additional features for controlling the spindle speed and for supporting and controlling the feed of the fixed cutting tool. There are several variations in the design of the headstock through which the power is supplied to the machine. Lathes that receive their power from an overhead line shaft are belt-driven and equipped with a step-cone pulley, usually a four-step pulley. This gives a range of four spindle speeds driven directly from the line shaft. In addition, these lathes are equipped with back gears which, when connected with the cone pulley, provide four additional speeds. The engine lathe requires an overhead counter-shaft carrying a cone pulley which matches the one on the lathe, plus two additional pulleys equipped with clutches to cause forward and reverse rotation of the work.

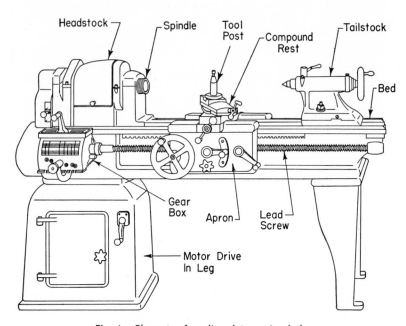

Fig. I. Elements of medium-duty engine lathe.

Another type of engine lathe, as shown in Figure 1, receives its power from an individual motor, mounted either on the side or be-neath the lathe. The general design of the headstock is the same, but the power is supplied through a short belt from the motor or from a small cone-pulley countershaft driven by the motor.

A *geared-head lathe* (see Figure 2) varies the spindle speeds by means of a gear transmission. Various speeds are obtained by setting certain speed levers in the head. Such lathes are usually driven by a constant-speed motor mounted on the lathe, but in a few cases variable-speed motors are used. A geared-head lathe has the advan-tage of a positive drive and has a greater number of spindle speeds available than are usually found on a step-cone-driven lathe. Re-cently some lathes have been developed with a variable-speed mechanism built into the headstock, thus permitting close regulation of the spindle rotation.

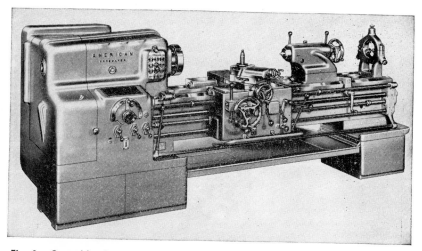

Fig. 2. Geared-head engine lathe. (Courtesy The American Tool Works Company.)

Bench lathe. The name bench lathe is given to a small lathe that is mounted on a work bench. In design it has the same features as ordinary speed or engine lathes and differs from these lathes only in size and mounting. It is adapted to small work, having a maximum swing capacity of 10 inches at the face plate. Many lathes of this type are used for precision work on small parts.

Toolroom lathe. This most modern engine lathe is equipped with all the accessories necessary for accurate tool work, being an individually driven geared-head lathe with a considerable range in spindle speeds. It is equipped with center steady rest, quick change gears, lead screw, feed rod, taper attachment, thread dial, chuck, indicator, draw-in collet attachment, pump for coolant, and frequently a relieving attachment to control the motion of the tool. In some cases a "live" or antifriction center is used in the tailstock which eliminates any scoring of the center, preserving its accuracy. All toolroom lathes are carefully tested for accuracy and, as the name implies, are especially adapted for making small tools, test gages, dies, and other precision parts.

Lathe Construction and Operation

Lathe size. The size of a lathe is expressed in terms of the diameter of the work it will swing; thus a 16-inch lathe is one having sufficient clearance over the bed rails to take work 16 inches in diameter. However, a second dimension is necessary to define further the size capacity of the machine in terms of work piece length. Some manufacturers express this in terms of the maximum work length in inches between the lathe centers, whereas others express it in terms of bed length in feet.

Fig. 3. Back-geared headstock with gear guards removed. (Courtesy South Bend Lathe Works.)

Lathe construction. In studying the construction of a lathe, reference to Figure 1 will be of assistance, since all the principal parts are labeled. All lathes receive their power through the *headstock,* which may be equipped either with a step-cone-pulley drive or a geared-head drive. Figure 3 shows a typical back-geared headstock equipped for a belt drive through a step-cone pulley. Four spindle speeds are available when the pulley is directly connected to the lathe spindle. If slower speeds are desired, the back gears are thrown in mesh with the two gears on either end of the cone pulley and the large gear to the right of the cone pulley is disengaged. Power then is transmitted through the train of four gears to the main spindle, providing four additional speeds.

Figure 2 shows the construction of a geared-head lathe where spindle-speed variations are obtained by regulating the levers on the side of the transmission.

The lathe *tailstock* can be adjusted along the bed of the lathe to accommodate different lengths of stock being turned. It is provided with a hardened center, which may be moved in and out by the wheel adjustment, and with setover screws at its base to be used for adjusting the alignment of the centers and for taper turning.

The *lead screw* is a long, carefully threaded shaft, located slightly below and parallel to the bedways extending all the way from the headstock to the tailstock. It is geared to the headstock in such a way that it may be reversed and is fitted to the carriage assembly so that it may either engage or be released from the carriage during cutting operations.

When it is necessary to change the speed of the lead screw it is done at the *quick-change gear box,* located at the headstock end of the lead screw. It is necessary only to move the extending levers, the amount of tool feed obtained by the change being indicated on the gear box.

The carriage assembly includes the *compound rest, tool post, saddle,* and *apron.* Since it supports and guides the cutting tool, it must be constructed with great accuracy and rigidity. Two hand feeds are provided to guide the tool on a crosswise motion. The upper hand wheel or crank controls the motion of the compound rest; and, since this rest is provided with a swiveling adjustment protractor, it can be placed in various angle positions for short taper turning. A third hand wheel is used to move the carriage along the bed, usually to pull it back to starting position after the lead screw has carried it along the cut. The portion of the carriage that extends in front of the lathe is called an apron. On the face of the apron are mounted the various control wheels and levers. Figure 4 shows an interior view of an apron and the method of drive.

Lathes that are designed for toolroom use are frequently provided with a *relieving attachment.* The function of this attachment is to relieve or back off the flutes of rotary cutters, taps, reamers, end mills, and dies. Figure 5 shows a setup for putting relief on the spiral teeth of a cutter. The relieving attachment drive unit, consisting of the main drive and change gears, is located at the front of the headstock. The drive is taken from the spindle through gearing to the splined shaft which is connected with a cam in the relieving rest, moving the tool back and forth. This motion is synchronized with the spindle rotation giving the tool proper relief. Both internal and external relief may be obtained by the use of this attachment, and it can also be employed in connection with a taper turning attachment.

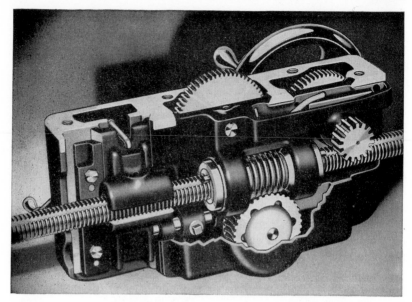

Fig. 4. Interior view of double-wall apron. (Courtesy South Bend Lathe Works.)

Fig. 5. Universal relieving attachment set up for relieving cutters. (Courtesy The American Lathe Tool Works.)

Supporting work between centers. The most common way to support work on a lathe is to mount it between centers, as shown in Figure 6. This method has the advantage of being able to resist heavy cuts and is convenient for long parts. Since the work is mounted between two tapered centers, it will not turn uniformly with the spindle unless it is attached in some further fashion. Such attachment is made through a pear-shaped forging known as a *dog*,

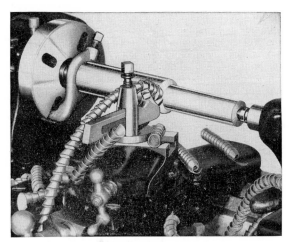

Fig. 6. Turning a steel shaft mounted between centers. (Courtesy South Bend Lathe Works.)

which consists of a main body with an opening to accommodate the stock being turned, a setscrew at the lower end to fasten the work securely, and an elongated portion at the top (known as the tail) which is bent at a right angle—parallel with the stock—so that it may engage a slot in the face plate. After the setscrew is tightened, the tail of the dog is fitted into the face plate, and the work is ready to be turned, as shown in Figure 6. The center in the headstock turns with the work; consequently, no lubrication of that center is necessary. The tailstock center, or dead center, acts as a conical bearing and for this reason must be kept clean and well lubricated. It should not be too tight against the work, nor should it be so loose that there is end play. A check should be made at frequent intervals; for, if it is too tight, the oil film will be broken down, and either the work or the center will be ruined.

In preparing cylindrical work, care must be exercised in locating the center holes before they are drilled. Probably the most convenient method is with a combination square and scriber. The center head of the combination square should be held firmly against the shaft, as shown in Figure 7, and two intersecting lines scribed close to the blade. The intersection of the lines represents the center of the shaft, and this point should be center-punched to facilitate proper starting of the center drill. The sizes of center holes for various-sized shafts are given in the table at the lower part of the illustration.

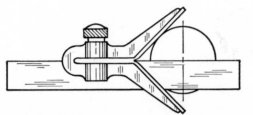

Use of Center Head to Locate Centers

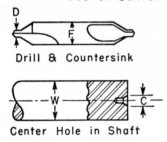

Drill & Countersink

Center Hole in Shaft

Size of Center Holes

Dia. of Work W	Dia. of Hole C	Dia. of Drill D	Dia. of Body F
$\frac{3}{16}''$ TO $\frac{5}{16}''$	$\frac{1}{8}''$	$\frac{3}{64}''$	$\frac{3}{16}''$
$\frac{3}{8}''$ TO $1''$	$\frac{3}{16}''$	$\frac{7}{64}''$	$\frac{1}{4}''$
$1\frac{1}{4}''$ TO $2''$	$\frac{1}{4}''$	$\frac{1}{8}''$	$\frac{5}{16}''$
$2\frac{1}{4}''$ TO $4''$	$\frac{5}{16}''$	$\frac{3}{16}''$	$\frac{7}{16}''$

Fig. 7. Size of center holes and method of locating.

In turning long slender shafts, or boring and threading the ends of spindles, a _center rest_ is used to give additional support to the work. The usual type of center steady rest, shown on the end of the lathe bed in Figure 2, is attached to the bed of the lathe and supports the work by means of the three jaws shown. Another rest, somewhat similar, is known as a _follower rest_. It is attached to the saddle of the carriage and supports work of small diameter that is likely to spring away from the cutting tool. This rest moves with the tool, whereas the center rest is stationary.

Cylindrical work that has been bored and reamed to size may be held between centers by one of several types of mandrels shown in Figure 8. Solid mandrels have hardened, ground surfaces and are available in all standard sizes. The surface is ground with a taper of about 0.0006 inch per inch in length, the small end being 0.0005 inch undersized to facilitate starting the work. The work must be pressed on the mandrel in an arbor press since considerable pressure is needed in this operation. The other type mandrels shown are adapted for holding work that may not have holes accurate to size or in cases where several parts are to be machined in one setup.

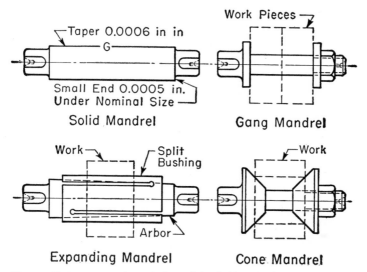

Solid Mandrel   Gang Mandrel

Expanding Mandrel   Cone Mandrel

Fig. 8.   Various types of mandrels used for holding stock between centers.

Supporting work in chuck or on face plate.   In addition to being held between centers, the work can also be held by being

Fig. 9.   Boring an eccentric hole on the face plate of a lathe. (Courtesy South Bend Lathe Works.)

bolted to the *face plate,* by a jaw *chuck,* or by a draw-in *collet.* Figure 9 illustrates work supported by being bolted to a face plate.

Such mounting is suitable for flat plates and parts of irregular shape. The figure illustrates the use of a boring bar for internal turning.

Lathe chucks are made in several designs, and may be classified as:

1. *Universal chuck.* The jaws all maintain a concentric relationship when the chuck wrench is turned.

2. *Independent chuck.* Each jaw has an independent adjustment. (See Figure 10.)

3. *Combination chuck.* Each jaw has an independent adjustment and, in addition, has a separate wrench connection which controls all jaws simultaneously.

4. *Drill chuck.* A small universal screw chuck used principally on drill presses but frequently used on lathes for drilling and centering.

5. *Draw-in collet chuck.* Holds standard-shape bar stock in a centered position. A separate collet is necessary for each work size.

Fig. 10. Four-jaw independent chuck. (Courtesy Warner & Swasey Manufacturing Company.)

Lathe chucks are used for holding short pieces of stock of irregular shape that cannot be held between centers. For example, in making a small gear blank from solid stock, the piece would first be mounted in the chuck with one side faced true. To produce a hole through the blank, the dead center should be removed from the tailstock and a drill chuck mounted in its place. Successive operations of centering, drilling, boring, and reaming can then be performed. The blank is then removed from the chuck and mounted on a mandrel for further machining.

Draw-in collet chucks are the most accurate of all chucks and are especially adapted for holding bar stock. In mounting a collet chuck attachment to a lathe, the live center is removed and a tapered sleeve bushing is put in its place. The proper-sized collet is placed in this sleeve and screwed to the draw bar extending through the spindle, as shown in Figure 11. Work can then be placed in the collet and held by turning the hand wheel on the end of the draw bar. This forces the collet back against the tapered surface of the sleeve and causes the collet jaws to grip the work. Collets are made for round, square, and other shapes, as shown in Figure 12. This means of holding stock is used in precision work for such parts as

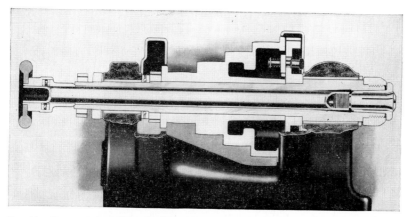

Fig. 11. Cross section of headstock showing the construction of draw-in collet attachment. (Courtesy South Bend Lathe Works.)

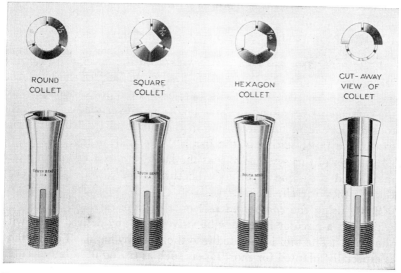

Fig. 12. Side and end view of various types of spring collets. (Courtesy South Bend Lathe Works.)

small tools, spindles, bushings, and screws. The work held by the collet must be the same size as the collet, or its accuracy will be impaired.

Taper turning. Many parts and tools made in lathes have tapered surfaces, varying from the short steep tapers found on bevel gears and lathe center ends to the long gradual tapers found on lathe mandrels. The shanks of twist drills, end mills, reamers, arbors, and other tools are examples of taper work. Such tools, supported by taper shanks, are held in true position and are easily removed.

There are several taper standards found in commercial practice. The following classification lists those commonly used:

1. *Morse taper.* Largely used for drill shanks, collets, and lathe centers. The taper is approximately ⅝ inch per foot.

2. *Brown and Sharpe taper.* Used principally in milling machine spindles: ½ inch per foot.

3. *Jarno and Reed tapers.* Used by some manufacturers of lathe and small drilling equipment. Both systems have a taper of 0.6 inch per foot, but the diameters are different.

4. *Sellers taper.* Used principally in equipment manufactured by William Sellers and Company. The taper is ¾ inch per foot.

5. *Taper pins.* Used as fasteners. The taper is ¼ inch per foot.

Each of these standards is made in a variety of diameters and designated by a number.

External tapers may be cut on a lathe in several ways:

1. By using a taper-turning attachment on the lathe, as illustrated in Figure 13. This attachment is bolted on the back of the lathe and has a guide bar which may be set at the desired angle or taper. As the carriage moves along the lathe bed, a slide over the bar causes the tool to move in or out, according to the setting of the bar. In other words, the taper setting of the bar is duplicated on the work. The advantages of this system are that the lathe centers are kept in alignment, and the same taper may be turned on various pieces, even though they vary in length.

2. By using the compound rest on the lathe carriage. This rest, which has a circular base, may be swiveled to any desired angle with the work. The tool is then fed into the work by hand. This method is especially adapted for short tapers such as truing up a lathe center.

3. By setting over the tailstock center. If the tailstock is moved horizontally out of alignment ¼ inch and a cylinder 12 inches long is placed between centers, the taper will be ½ inch per foot. However, a cylinder 6 inches long will have a taper of 1 inch per foot. Hence, the amount of taper obtained on a given piece depends on the length of the stock, as well as on the amount the center is set over.

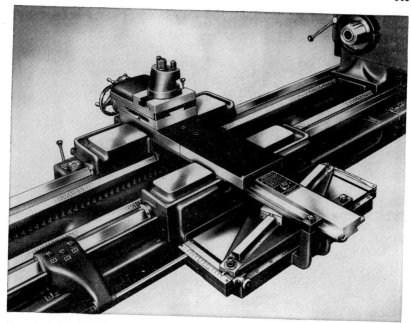

Fig. 13. Lathe taper turning attachment. (Courtesy The American Tool Works Company.)

4. By *manually* operating both hand feeds. This method is not recommended, as it is impossible to cut an accurate taper.

Internal tapers can be machined on a lathe only by using the compound rest or the taper-turning attachment. Small holes for taper pins are first drilled and then reamed to size with a taper reamer.

Lathe Tools

Single-pointed metal-cutting lathe tools consist of small pieces of rectangular tool steel rigidly supported in suitable holders. The tool holder is held on the tool post of the lathe, and the work revolves against the point of the tool.

In order to cut metal efficiently and accurately, the cutting tool must be properly ground to provide a keen cutting edge with correct angles for the kind of metal to be cut. The shapes and angles of the tool vary considerably, depending on the type of cutting operation, kind of material being cut, tool material, and finish desired.

Tools used in lathe work are small rectangular pieces of high-speed tool steel which are held in a tool holder. Because of the high cost of tool materials, it is much more economical to use these small

FEED x RPM = INCHES PER MIN.

inserts in special holders than to use solid forged tools. In Figure 14 is shown a straight shank tool holder and some of the typical shapes of cutter bits used in lathe work. The tool bit is securely clamped as near the cutting edge as possible and held by the set screw with extreme rigidity. The tool post on the lathe carriage supports the tool holder in proper position for cutting.

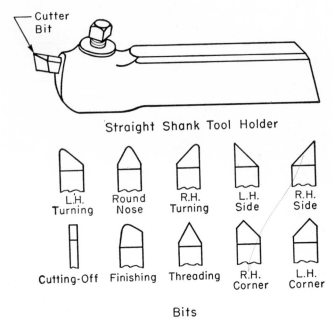

Fig. 14. Straight shank tool holder and suggested shapes for tool bits.

Much lathe work is now done with carbide or cast, nonferrous tools, which are usually of the insert type and fit securely into an appropriate holder. Holding them rigidly is very important because of the brittleness of the hard inserts.

Grinding and setting tools. Provided with adequate grinding equipment, experienced personnel can obtain proper cutting angles on tools. Most uniform results are realized with special tool grinders which can be set to grind accurately any angle desired. If off-hand grinding is necessary, gages and templates should be used by the operator.

Tool bits should be removed from the holder before an attempt is made to grind them. The procedure for grinding the various faces is not of great importance, but it is suggested that the side-rake and side-clearance surfaces be prepared first. After these two angles are ground, the tool end may be given any shape desired. Shapes of typical lathe tool bits are shown in the lower part of Figure 14.

Aluminum oxide wheels are best for rough and finish grinding of high-speed steel tools, whereas silicon carbide and diamond wheels are necessary for cemented carbide tools. A final honing of the cutting edge is recommended to increase tool life.

In most cases it is assumed that the tip of the tool is in line with the center of the work, as shown in the various figures; however, some authorities recommend that the cutting edge of the tool point should be about 5 degrees above center, or $\frac{3}{64}$ inch per inch in diameter of the work. The position of the cutter bit must be taken into account when the various angles are being ground, since the height has considerable influence on the front clearance. For example, if the point is $\frac{1}{10}$ inch above the center lines in turning a 1-inch diameter, the front clearance practically disappears and the back rake is increased materially. All lathes are provided with spherical seats or rockers to assist in setting the tool properly with the work.

REVIEW QUESTIONS

1. What types of surfaces can be machined on an engine lathe?
2. What is a speed lathe, and for what type of work is it used?
3. How is the size of a lathe determined?
4. Name three methods of turning accurate tapers on a lathe.
5. What is an engine lathe? A geared-head lathe?
6. What is the purpose of each of the following lathe parts: face plate, center rest, compound rest, lead screw, and back gears?
7. Describe the operation of a duplicating lathe.
8. What is wrong with a lathe that turns a slightly tapered surface instead of a cylinder? Assume the small diameter to be on the tailstock end.
9. How does a toolroom lathe differ from an ordinary engine lathe?
10. What is a relieving attachment, and for what purpose is it used?
11. Name four types of chucks used in lathe work.
12. How are internal tapers turned on an engine lathe?
13. How does a Morse taper differ from a Brown and Sharpe taper?
14. What is a mandrel? Describe the different kinds used.
15. How are lathe tools supported and set up for operation?

REFERENCES

Boston, O. W., *Metal Processing*, 2d edition, John Wiley and Sons, 1951.
Colvin, Fred H., *Running an Engine Lathe*, McGraw-Hill Book Company, 1941.

Doyle, L. E., *Metal Machining*, Prentice-Hall, 1953.

Hine, C. R., *Machine Tools for Engineers*, McGraw-Hill Book Company, 1950.

How to Run an Engine Lathe, South Bend Lathe Company, 1943.

Jones, F. D., *Machine Shop Training Course*, Industrial Press, 1940.

Judkins, Malcolm F., "Metal Cutting," *Mechanical Engineering*, May 1937.

Machining—Theory and Practice, American Society for Metals, 1950.

Manual of Lathe Operation, 16th edition, Atlas Press Company, 1954.

Parker, H. W., C. H. Lawshe, and O. D. Lascoe, *Machine Shop Operations and Setups*, American Technical Society, 1954.

Tool Engineers Handbook, The American Society of Tool Engineers, McGraw-Hill Book Company, 1949.

CHAPTER 17

TURRET
AND
AUTOMATIC LATHES

Turret and automatic lathes possess special designs and features which particularly adapt them to production work. The "skill of the worker" has been built into these machines, making it possible for operators with little skill to reproduce identical parts. In contrast to this, the engine lathe requires a highly skilled operator and takes more time to reproduce many parts which are dimensionally the same. The principal characteristic of this group of lathes is that the tools for consecutive operations can be continuously set up in readiness for use in the proper sequence. Although considerable skill is required to set and adjust the tools properly, once they are correct, little skill is required to operate them. Furthermore, many parts can be produced before adjustments are necessary. Eliminating the setup time between operations reduces the production time tremendously. The high development of turret and automatic lathes has made interchangeable manufacture what it is today.

Classification

The following classification of turret and automatic lathes, made according to single outstanding design characteristics, will serve as an outline for our discussion.

1. Turret lathe
   (a) Horizontal
       (1) Ram-type
       (2) Saddle-type
   (b) Vertical
       (1) Single-station
       (2) Multistation
   (c) Automatic

2. Automatic lathe
   (a) Horizontal
   (b) Vertical

3. Duplicating lathe

4. Automatic screw machine
   (a) Single-spindle
   (b) Multispindle

This classification may be further subdivided according to special features, such as method of drive, method of chucking, capacity, and number and arrangement of tool slides.

Fig. I. Ram-type turret lathe. (Courtesy Jones & Lamson Machine Company.)

Horizontal turret lathe. This type of lathe is made in two general designs known as the *ram* and *saddle*. In appearance they are much alike, and both may be used for either bar or chucking work. The ram-type turret lathe shown in Figure 1 is so named because of the manner in which the turret is mounted. The turret is placed on a slide or ram which moves back and forth on a saddle clamped to the lathe bed. This arrangement permits quick and easy movement of the turret and is recommended for bar and light work. The saddle, although capable of adjustment, does not move during the operation of the turret. Ram-type machines do not require the built-in rigidity of chucking machines, because in most cases the bar tools can be made to support the work.

A saddle-type turret lathe, shown in Figure 2, has the turret mounted directly on a saddle which moves back and forth with the turret in its operation. Chucking tools overhang and do not support the work, thus causing greater strain on both work and tool support; hence chucking tools must have the greatest possible rigidity. The stroke is also much longer which is an advantage in long turning or boring cuts.

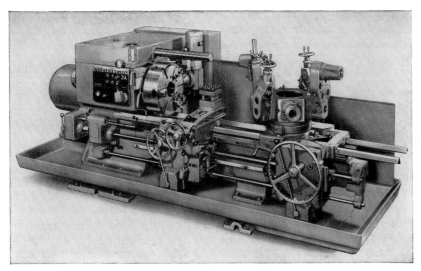

Fig. 2. Saddle-type turret lathe. (Courtesy Warner & Swasey Manufacturing Company.)

Construction. Turret lathes have many features similar to those of modern engine lathes. The headstock in most cases is geared with provision for 6 to 12 spindle speeds. The various spindle speeds, as well as forward and reverse movement, are controlled by levers extending from the head. The drive motor is usually located in the motor leg below the headstock and connected to the geared-head pulley by means of a belt. Some few machines, designed for light work, are driven by a multiple-speed motor mounted directly on the spindle inside the headstock housing. High speeds, up to 3600 rpm, are possible on these machines.

The *cross-slide* unit, on which the tools are mounted for facing, forming, and cutting off, is somewhat different in construction from the tool-post and carriage arrangement used on lathes. It is made up of four principal parts: the *cross slide,* the *square turret,* the *carriage,* and the *apron.* These parts are readily discernible in the various turret-lathe illustrations. Some of the cross slides are supported entirely on the front and lower front ways, permitting more swing clearance for the work. This arrangement is frequently utilized on saddle-type machines, which are to be used for large-diameter chucking jobs. The other arrangement for mounting has the cross slide riding on both upper bedways and is further supported by a lower way. This is used on machines engaged in bar work and in other processes where a large swing clearance is not necessary. An advantage of this type is the added tool post in the rear, frequently used in cutting-off operations.

On top of the cross slide is mounted a *square turret* capable of holding four tools in readiness for use. If several different tools are required, they are set up in sequence and can be quickly indexed and locked in correct working position. In order that cuts may be duplicated, the slide is provided with either a positive stop or a feed trip. Likewise, the longitudinal position of the entire assembly may be accurately controlled by positive stops on the left side of the apron. Cuts may be taken with square-turret tools simultaneously with tools mounted on the hexagon turret.

The outstanding feature of a turret lathe is the use of a *hexagon turret* in place of the usual lathe tailstock. This turret, mounted on either the sliding ram or the saddle, carries the tools for the various operations. The tools are mounted in proper sequence on the various faces of the turret so that, as it indexes around between operations, the proper tools are brought into position. For each set of tools there is provided a stop screw which controls the distance the tool will feed. When this distance is reached, an automatic trip lever stops further movement of the tool by disengaging the drive clutch.

Differences between turret and engine lathes. The main difference between these two machines is that the turret lathe is adapted to quantity-production work, whereas the engine lathe is primarily used for miscellaneous jobbing, toolroom, or single-operation work. The essential features of a turret lathe which make it a quantity production machine are these:

1. Tools may be permanently set up in the turret in the proper sequence of their use.

2. Each tool is provided with a stop or feed trip so that each cut of a tool is the same as its previous cut.

3. Combining cuts can be made—that is, tools on the cross slide can be used at the same time that tools on the turret are cutting.

4. Extreme rigidity in the holding of work and tools is built into the machine.

When a turret lathe is once set up for a certain job, many parts may be machined identically, without further adjustment of the tools. All types of work that can be done on an engine lathe can likewise be done on a turret lathe and, in many cases, can be done quicker: bar and chuck work, thread cutting, taper turning, drilling, reaming, and many other similar operations. Although we now have many other production machines, the turret lathe has been largely responsible for the development of interchangeable manufacture as we know it today.

Methods of Holding Stock

Because the turret lathe is a production machine, special attention is given to methods of holding the work so that it can be done quickly and accurately. Since the operation is usually simple, extreme rigidity can be built into such equipment so that heavy cuts can be made. The usual devices for holding work are *collets, arbors, chucks,* and *special holding fixtures.*

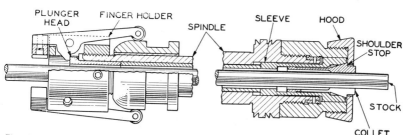

Fig. 3. Stationary-type spring collet. (Courtesy Warner & Swasey Manufacturing Company.)

Collets. Collets, commonly used for bar-stock material, are made with jaws of standard sizes to accommodate round, square, and hexagonal stock. For large stock, collets of the parallel closing type are sometimes used, but in most cases collets of the spring type are recommended. These collets are solid at one end and split on the other end, which is tapered. The tapered end contacts with a similarly tapered hood or bushing, and, when forced into the hood, the jaws of the collet tighten around the stock. Spring collets are made in three designs: the *push-out type,* the *draw-in type,* and the *stationary type.* In each, the operation is similar to that just described. A cross section of a stationary collet is shown in Figure 3. With this type there is no movement of the stock when it is tightened in the collet, since the latter is held in place against the hood. As the tapered surface of the plunger sleeve is pushed against a similar surface on the collet, the jaws are forced against the work. For work that must be accurately located endwise, this type of collet assembly is best. Pushout-type collets are recommended for bar work, since the slight movement of the stock pushes it against the bar stop. This collet is of the same construction as shown in Figure 5 except that there is no hood to stop the forward movement of the bar stock. Draw-back-type collets are not widely employed for bar stock, but are useful when the collets are of extra-capacity size and are utilized for holding short pieces, as shown in Figure 4. The slight back motion in closing forces the work against the locating stops.

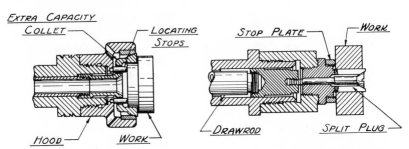

Fig. 4.   Draw-back   extra-capacity   Fig. 5.   Expanding plug-type arbor.
collet.   (Both   photos   courtesy   Warner &
                                         Swasey Manufacturing Company.)

Arbor. Expanding or threaded arbors are used to hold short pieces of stock that have in them a previously machined, accurate hole. The action in holding the work is controlled by a mechanism very similar to that used with collets. An expanding, plug-type arbor is shown in Figure 5. The work is placed on the arbor against the stop plate; and, as the draw rod is pulled, the tapered pin expands the partially split plug and grips the work. The threaded arbor operates in a similar fashion except that the work is screwed on the arbor by hand and is then forced back against a stop tube or flange.

Both collets and arbors may be power-operated by pneumatic, hydraulic, or electrical devices located at the end of the spindle. Such an arrangement is frequently used on high-production work to provide quicker and easier operation.

Chucks. Chucks are used for holding large and irregularly shaped parts and, in general, are the same kind employed in engine-lathe work. These chucks are either bolted or screwed to the spindle and have a very rigid mounting.

In addition to standard chucks, there are several other special types adapted for holding work of irregular shape. One of these, known as a two-jaw box chuck, is designed to hold work with parallel flat sides. Both jaws, on opposite sides of the chuck, move in and out together.

Power chucks, operated by air, hydraulic means, or electricity, relieve the operator of the effort involved in tightening and loosening the work. An additional advantage of the power chuck is that it is quick acting.

Because it is difficult to mount all types of work on standard equipment many special chuck jaws or holding fixtures must be devised. Standard face plates are frequently used for mounting such fixtures. The holding device is held to the face plate either by bolting or by means of the T slots on the face of the plate. Work-holding devices can be used equally well with both automatic and turret lathes.

Tools and tooling principles. As has been stated, once a turret lathe is properly tooled, an experienced machinist is not required to operate it. However, skill is required in the proper selection and mounting of the tools. In small-lot production it is important that work be done in as short a time as possible so as not to consume too much of the total production time which consists of setup time, work-handling time, machine-handling time, and cutting time.

Setup time can be reduced by having all necessary tools in condition and readily available. For short-run jobs a permanent setup of the usual tools on the turret is an excellent means of reducing time. The tools selected are standard and when permanently mounted, they may be quickly adjusted for various jobs. A similar setup can be prepared for chucking jobs.

The *work-handling time,* that time consumed in mounting or removing the work, is largely dependent on the type of work-holding devices used. For bar work this time is reduced to a minimum by having quick means for advancing the stock built into the machine.

The time it takes to bring the respective tools into cutting position is the *machine-handling time.* This can be reduced by having the tools in proper position and sequence for convenient use, and also by taking multiple or combined cuts whenever possible.

The actual *cutting time* for a given operation is largely controlled by the use of proper cutting tools, feeds, and speeds. However, additional time may often be saved by combining cuts as shown in Figure 6. *Combined cuts* refers to the simultaneous use of both slide and turret tools. In bar work combined cuts are especially desirable, as additional support is given to the work, thereby eliminating spring and chatter. In chucking work, internal operations such as drilling or boring, may frequently be combined with turning or facing cuts

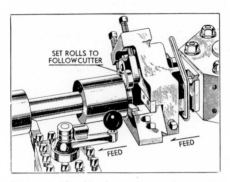

SET ROLLS TO
FOLLOWCUTTER

FEED

FEED

Fig. 6. "Combined Cuts" on bar work. (Courtesy Warner & Swasey Manufacturing Company.)

from the square turret. Time also may be saved by taking *multiple cuts*—that is, having two or more tools mounted on one tool station. Figure 7 shows both boring and turning tools set up on one station of the turret.

To illustrate the method of tooling and sequence of operations for a given job, a basic hexagon-turret setup for making necessary internal cuts on a threaded adapter is shown in Figure 8. Figure 9 shows the details of the internal cuts required to machine the adapter. With reference to the sequence shown in Figure 9, the various operations are:

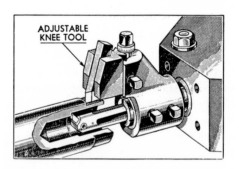

ADJUSTABLE
KNEE TOOL

Fig. 7. "Multiple Cuts" from hexagon turret. (Courtesy Warner & Swasey Manufacturing Company.)

1. The bar stock is advanced against the combination stock stop and start drill and clamped in the collet. The start drill is then advanced in the combination tool, and the end of the work is centered.

2. The hole through the solid stock is drilled the required length.

3. The thread diameter is bored to correct size for the threads specified. A stub boring bar in a slide tool is used.

4. The drilled hole is reamed to size with the reamer supported in a floating holder.

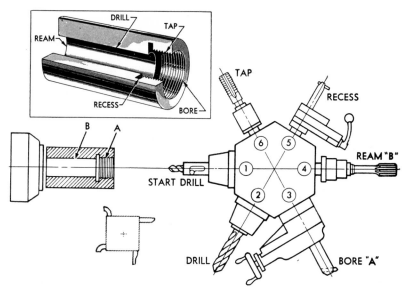

Fig. 8. Basic hexagon-turret setup illustrating the correct sequence of operations to handle required internal cuts on threaded adapter shown in insert. (Courtesy Warner & Swasey Manufacturing Company.)

5. A groove for thread clearance is recessed. For this operation a quick-acting slide tool is used with a recessing cutter mounted in a boring bar.

6. The thread is cut with a tap held in a clutch tap and die holder. For odd-sized threads a single-point tool may be used. This operation is followed by a cutting-off operation not shown in the figure.

Another example of tooling is illustrated in Figure 10. In this case the tool setup is for a shoulder stud shaft made of $2\frac{1}{2}$-inch bar stock. The tooling shown is for a quantity of parts and is slightly more complicated than a setup for producing only a few. With one exception, all operations are external cuts. As shown in the figure, the tools used for the respective operations are as follows:

Operations and Tools used

Operation	Hexagon Turret	Square Turret
1	Feed stock to stop	
2	Turn (3), (4), and (5) diameter Face and chamfer (2)	Turn (6) and (7) to diameter
3	Center drill (1)	
4	Support (1) with center	Neck cuts (8), (9), and (10) with back tools
5	Thread (3)	
6		Cut-off and chamfer

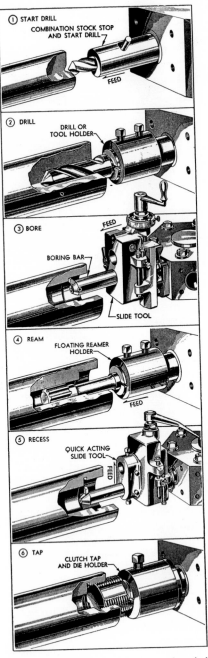

Fig. 9. Setup for machining internal operations on threaded adapter. (Courtesy Warner & Swasey Manufacturing Company.)

Based on an output of 120 pieces the time per piece is estimated to be:

Setup time per piece	1 minute
Work-handling time per piece	½ minute
Machine-handling time per piece	½ minute
Cutting time per piece	5½ minutes
Total production time	7½ minutes per piece

A few of the tools used in turret-lathe work are illustrated in Figure 9. These tools are so designed that they may be quickly mounted in the turret and adjusted for use. In addition to the

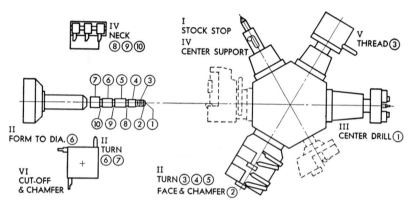

Fig. 10. Tool setup for shoulder stud shaft. (Courtesy Warner & Swasey Manufacturing Company.)

usual operations of drilling, boring, reaming, and internal threading shown in the figure, various other threading, centering, and turning tools are available. Internal threading is frequently done with collapsible taps to facilitate quick removal of the tool. For the same reason automatic die head cutters which open at the end of the thread are used for external threads.

For outside turning a *box tool,* shown in Figure 11, has been developed. As bar stock is supported only at the collet, additional support must be provided in order for heavy cuts to be taken. This is done by means of two rollers which contact the outside diameter of the stock and take up the thrust of the cutting tool. Adjustment of the rolls for varying diameter work is controlled by two setscrews at the top of the holder. When the rolls are set slightly behind the cutting tool, they tend to smooth out or burnish the surface. However, if the turned diameter must be concentric with the adjacent surface, the rolls are set ahead and adjusted to its diameter. For light cuts, a similar box tool which supports the work by means of a V-back rest can be used. Cutters are held in position by two set-screws, and the lever at the back of the assembly is for the purpose of withdrawing the cutter from the work on the return stroke to prevent marking.

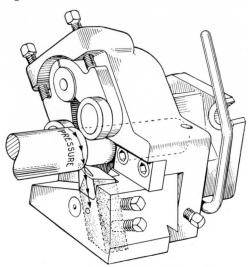

Fig. 11.   Box tool for bar stock.   (Courtesy Warner & Swasey Manufacturing Company.)

Controlled spindle turret lathe.   In order to eliminate the excessive machine handling time on many geared head lathes, controlled electrocycle lathes have been developed for both ferrous and nonferrous machining.   This lathe, shown in Figure 12, is arranged so that all spindle speeds and headstock operations can be preset and automatically controlled through a complete cycle of operations. The cycle is actuated and controlled by the hexagon turret as it is moved to successive stations by the operator.   At the beginning of the cycle, the headstock spindle is started as the turret moves forward, and, from then on, all spindle operations such as speed changes, reversing, stopping, and positioning of spindle are automatic in accordance with the prearranged cycle.   By controlling the cycle, the machine handling time of a job is reduced and the operator is relieved of a considerable amount of work.   Experienced operators are not essential.

Automatic horizontal turret lathe.   The automatic turret lathe in Figure 13 resembles in appearance the standard saddle-type

Fig. 12. Electrocycle turret lathe for machining steel and cast iron products. (Courtesy Warner & Swasey Manufacturing Company.)

Fig. 13. Automatic turret lathe. (Courtesy Potter & Johnston Company.)

machine, but it is completely automatic in operation to the extent that one operator can handle two or more machines. The hexagonal turret is hydraulically operated and is provided with rapid traverse and automatic changeover to the proper feed at any point. There are two cross slides which can be operated singly or together. The movement of these slides is controlled by cams actuated by the forward movement of the turret. Machines of this type are used on long-run chucking jobs, where the expense of setting up and tooling can be spread over many parts. The advantages of automatic operation are elimination of the human element from the time cycle, possibility for the operator to attend several machines, and faster rate of production.

Vertical turret lathe. A vertical turret lathe is a machine resembling a vertical boring mill, but having the characteristic turret arrangement for holding the tools. It consists of a rotating chuck or table in horizontal position, with the turret mounted above on a cross slide. In addition, there is at least one side head provided with a square turret for holding tools. All tools mounted on the turret or side head have their respective stops set so that the length of cuts can be the same in successive machining cycles. It is, in effect, the same as a turret lathe standing on the headstock end, and it has all the features necessary for the production of duplicate parts. This machine was developed to facilitate the mounting, holding, and machining of heavy parts. Only chucking work is done on this kind of machine.

In Figure 14 is shown a 46-inch vertical turret lathe. This machine is controlled with three cutter heads, the swiveling main turret head, the ram head, shown at the left, and the side head. The turret and side heads function in the same manner as the hexagonal and square turrets on a horizontal lathe. In order to provide for angle cuts, both the ram and turret heads may be swiveled 30 degrees right or left of center. The side head has rapid traverse and feed, independent of the turret and without interference provides for simultaneous machining, adjacent to operations performed by the turret. The ram provides another tool station on the machine which can be operated separately or in conjunction with the other two.

A modification of this machine is known as the Man-Au-Trol vertical lathe. Its outstanding feature is that each head can be automatically controlled in all functions, including rate and direction of feed, change in spindle feed, indexing of turret, starting, and stopping. Once a cycle of operations is preset and all tools are properly adjusted, the operator need only load, unload, and start the machine. The production rate of these machines is greatly increased over those manually operated, because they operate almost continuously and make all changes from one operation to another

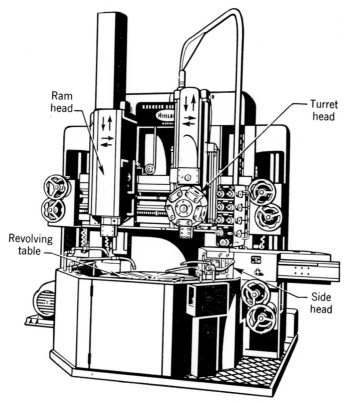

Fig. 14. Vertical turret lathe. (Courtesy The Bullard Company.)

without hesitation or fatigue. By reducing the handling time and making the cycle automatic, an operator can attend more than one machine.

Automatic, vertical multistation lathe. Machines of this type, as illustrated in Figure 15, are designed for high production and are usually provided for either five or seven work stations and a loading position. In some machines two spindles are provided at each station, doubling the capacity for small-diameter work. The work to be machined is mounted in chucks, the larger machines having chucking capacities up to 18 inches in diameter. Both plain and universal heads may be used, the latter providing for tool feed in any direction. All varieties of machining operations can be performed, including milling, drilling, threading, tapping, reaming, and boring. The advantage of this type of machine is that all operations can be done simultaneously. In actual operation all tools are fed to the work, held in chucks or fixtures, at the respective loading stations. When all operations are complete, the tools or work move vertically out of

Fig. 15. Multistation vertical chucking lathe. (Courtesy The Bullard Company.)

the way, the work table indexes one station, and the operations are repeated. The time between indexing operations is controlled by the time of the longest single operation.

Similar multispindle machines are available which operate on a somewhat different cutting principle. The work is rotated and fed past a stationary single-point tool. The cutting tool is controlled by a profile cam which imparts the form to the work. Only turning operations, such as the machining of shells, can be performed on this machine.

Automatic Lathes

Lathes that have their tools automatically fed to the work and withdrawn after the cycle is complete are known as *automatic* lathes.

Since most lathes of this type require that the operator place the part to be machined in the lathe and remove it after the work is complete, they are perhaps incorrectly called automatic lathes. Lathes that are fully automatic are provided with a magazine feed so that a number of parts can be machined, one after the other, with little attention from the operator. Machines in this group differ principally in the manner of feeding the tools to the work. Most machines, especially those holding the work between centers, have front and

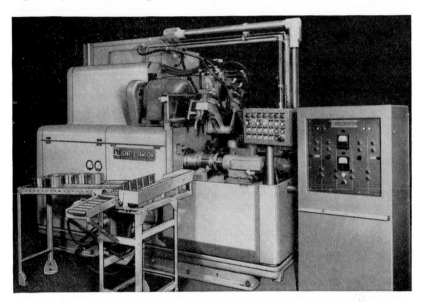

Fig. 16. Eight-inch Fay automatic lathe setup for turning diameters of electric motor stators and chamfering the ends. (Courtesy Jones & Lamson Machine Company.)

rear tool slides. Others, adapted for chucking jobs, have an end tool slide located in the same position as the turret on the turret lathe. These machines may also have the two side-tool slides. Still another construction employs a flat table in front of the chucking spindle, on which can be mounted tool slides at any angle or in any position. Each tool slide has individual feed and receives its power from individual drive shafts at the end of the machine. Several types of automatic lathes are described in the following paragraphs.

An automatic lathe featuring the automatic handling and sorting of workpieces, gaging of the finished diameters, and automatic tool adjustment to compensate for tool wear is shown in Figure 16. The overhead carrier for handling workpieces has two arms, the rear one for picking up incoming pieces and placing them in the fixture, and the front one for removing the finished part and depositing it on a classifying conveyor in front of the machine. Oversized and undersized parts are placed on their respective conveyors, which are parallel with the machine.

Fig. 17. Simplimatic automatic lathe. (Courtesy Gisholt Machine Company.)

The turning tool, located on the front slide, is a 1¼-inch carbide disk which can be fed into the work at 0.0002-inch steps and rotated in steps so as to use its entire periphery. The chamfering tools and gaging head are mounted on the rear slide. The machine control compensates for tool wear after several pieces approach the tolerance limit. If two pieces in succession fall outside this limit, the machine stops and an indication of the cause is shown on the operator's panel.

An automatic lathe, known as a *platen-type* Simplimatic, is shown in Figure 17. Designed primarily for chucking jobs, it is provided with front and rear tool slides, mounted on the platen or table end of the machine. All tools feed simultaneously, performing turning, facing, boring, and chamfering operations at one time. Power for feeding the tools comes to the tool slides from one end through universal couplings and drive shafts. At the end of the cycle the slides retract, and the platen moves back to facilitate unloading. The entire operation of the machine is automatic, and the operator has only to load and unload the machine. Platen-type machines have considerable flexibility in the mounting of the various tool slides and can be adapted to a variety of jobs.

A single-spindle, automatic chucking machine, of somewhat different design, is shown in Figure 18. This machine uses two cross slides and an overhead pentagonal turret for holding the tools. All are operated by cams which are permanently set and do not have to be

Fig. 18. Single-spindle automatic chucking machine. (Courtesy Warner & Swasey Manufacturing Company.)

changed at any time. Automatic control of the spindle speeds, feeds, indexing, and length of cutting stroke are provided by adjustable trips in a selector drum. Accessibility of all tools and controls reduces setup time to a minimum.

Automatic lathes have been developed primarily for quantity production and have done much to reduce machining costs of many parts. All the machines described are rugged in construction and are capable of using modern, high-speed cutting tools. Versatility is sacrificed in some machines, but this is not an important consideration in long-run jobs. The selection of the proper machine for a job which must be carefully considered is influenced by such factors as work size and shape, type of machining to be done, ease of setting up tools, and number of parts to be machined.

Duplicating Lathes

Although the engine lathe is a versatile machine, it is not widely used on quantity production jobs because the setting and accuracy of each cut is largely dependent on the skill of the operator. Lathes provided with duplicating features eliminate hand setting of the tools and frequent checking of measurements by having the tool controlled by a tracer point which follows a template mounted on

Fig. 19. Close-up of duplicating lathe with 45-degree tool rest tracer slide. (Courtesy The Lodge & Shipley Company.)

the rear of the lathe. Such lathes are rapidly replacing automatic lathes. It has been found that many jobs formerly done on automatic lathes can be produced much more cheaply on a tracer-controlled lathe, using only a single-point tool. Tool expenses are materially reduced, and the problem of tool setup is greatly simplified.

Figure 19 shows a duplicating lathe arranged for using a round template between centers at the rear of the machine. The tracing stylus at the rear of the cross slide is hydraulically operated and controls the tool movement by contact with the template. A conventional turning tool is used, and the cut taken is a continuous, uninterrupted one which duplicates the exact shape of the template. The template may be either flat or cylindrical, the latter design being more economical, because it permits standard workpieces to be used as templates. The tool rest, at a 45-degree angle to the work axis, is a special feature of this machine. This permits cutting square shoulders, as well as tapers and radii, by compensating for the continuous longitudinal movement of the carriage. The 45-degree

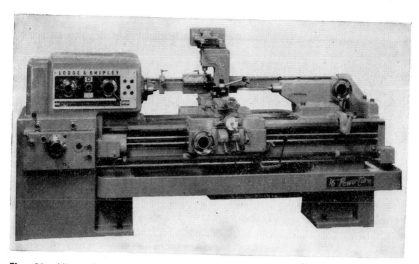

Fig. 20. Ninety-degree tracer slide duplicating lathe. (Courtesy The Lodge & Shipley Company.)

tool rest tracer is the conventional arrangement for longitudinal and cross duplicating and is furnished by most lathe manufacturers.

A 90-degree tracer slide duplicating lathe is shown in Figure 20. This machine utilizes either flat or round templates and has the advantage of having a standard tool rest which operates at 90 degrees. This permits changing the machine quickly from tracer control to regular lathe work. A limitation of this arrangement is that facing operations cannot be done with the tracer attachment. However, it will square shoulder faces, turn tapers in both directions, cut chamfers, and turn both straight diameters and curved contours. A flat triangular stylus is used to control the starting and stopping of the longitudinal feed as well as the direction of cross slide travel. Any change in contour on the template which causes deflection of the stylus stops the carriage travel. The cross slide then feeds out until the stylus clears the shoulder, at which point the carriage automatically resumes travel.

Advantages claimed for tracer-controlled lathes include lower tooling and setup costs, accurate reproduction of parts with a minimum amount of checking required, elimination of need for form tools, and no delays during the operation, since cutting is continuous. Although the machines described are hydraulically and mechanically controlled, pneumatic and electric controlling attachments can be used. Frequently two systems are used in combination. Work specially adapted for quantity production includes drive shafts, axles, valve stems, piston rods, arbors, and bevel gear blanks. Flanged parts such as pump impellers, gas-turbine compressor wheels, and cylinder heads may be duplicated on 45-degree tracer units using the cross-feed and a flat template.

Automatic Screw Machines

The automatic screw machine was invented by Christopher N. Spencer of the Billings and Spencer Company about 75 years ago. The principal feature of the invention was to provide a controlling movement for the turret so that tools could be fed into the work at desired speeds, withdrawn, and indexed to the next position. This was all accomplished by means of a cylindrical or drum cam located beneath the turret. Another feature, also cam-controlled, was a mechanism for clamping the work in the collet, releasing it at the end of the cycle, and then feeding the bar stock up against the stop. These features are still used in about the same way as originally worked out.

An automatic screw machine is essentially a turret lathe designed to use only bar stock. It is so named, because the first machines of this type were used mainly for manufacturing bolts and screws. Since it can produce parts one after the other with little attention from the operator, it is naturally called automatic. Most automatic screw machines not only feed in an entire bar of stock but also are provided with a magazine so that several bars can be fed through the machine automatically.

Automatic screw machines may be classified according to the type of turret used or the number of spindles the machine has. Multispindle machines, however, are not usually spoken of as screw machines, but rather as multispindle automatics. The type of work that the two machines do is the same, although there is considerable difference in the design and production capacity.

Single-spindle automatic. In Figure 21 is illustrated an automatic screw machine designed for bar work of small diameter. This machine has a cross slide, capable of carrying tools both front and rear, and a turret mounted in a vertical position on a slide with longitudinal movement. The two disk cams controlling the cross slide are directly underneath and are driven by the front drive shaft. Also mounted on this same drive shaft are three disk-shaped

Fig. 21. Automatic screw machine. (Courtesy Brown & Sharpe Manufacturing Company.)

carriers, upon which are mounted dogs to engage various trip levers to control the operation of the machine. The one to the extreme right controls the indexing of the turret; the center one controls the collet and feeding of the stock; and the one to the left, the rotation and speed of the spindle. The various tools used in the machine are mounted around the turret in a vertical plane in line with the spindle. This is more clearly illustrated in Figure 22, which shows the turret steup for making a small aluminum coupling. All usual machining operations, such as turning, drilling, boring, and threading, can be done on these machines. The type of bar stock used, whether round, square, hexagonal, or of some special shape, is determined by the cross section preferred in the finished product. Collets for any commercial shape are available.

The machine shown in the figure is usually equipped with an automatic rod magazine to keep it supplied with material for a period of time. When a rod of material is completely used, the machine stops, and another rod is fed into the collet up to the stop. The machine then automatically resumes operation. In addition to attending several machines, the operator checks the work and tools and sees that the magazines are supplied with materials.

Fig. 22. Automatic screw machine tooling for making aluminum coupling. (Courtesy Brown & Sharpe Manufacturing Company.)

Swiss-type screw machine. In Figure 23 is shown the end view of a Swiss-type screw machine developed for precision turning of small parts. The single-point tools used on this machine are placed radially around the carbide-lined guide bushing through which the stock is advanced during machining operations. Most diameter turning is done by the two horizontal tool slides, while the other three are used principally for such operations as knurling, chamfering, cutting off, and recessing. The stock is held by a rotating collet in the headstock back of the tools, and all longitudinal feeds are accomplished by a cam which moves the headstock forward as a unit. This forward motion alvances the stock through the guide bushing and to the single-point tools which are controlled and positioned by cams. By coordinating their movement with the forward movement of the stock, any desired shape can be turned. Diameters on slender parts can be held to tolerances ranging from 0.0002 to 0.0005 inch.

American-made machines of this type vary in sizes from $\frac{3}{32}$- to $\frac{1}{2}$- inch maximum capacity. Their use is fairly well limited to slender workpieces that would be difficult to do on ordinary automatic screw machines. These machines excel in small precision work and can frequently complete jobs that by other means would require several machine settings. Pinion shafts, gear blanks, pivots, and balance staffs are typical of the small parts made for watches and instruments.

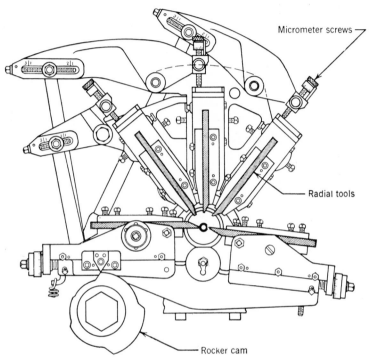

Fig. 23. End view of Swiss-type screw machine showing rocker cam and tool-control mechanism. (Courtesy George Gorton Machine Company.)

Multispindle automatic. Multispindle automatic machines are the fastest type of production machines for bar work. They are fully automatic in their operations and are made in a variety of models, with two, four, five, six, or eight spindles. In these machines all spindles operate simultaneously, and one piece is completed each time the tools are withdrawn and the spindles indexed.

The general construction of a multispindle automatic is shown in Figure 24. The spindles carrying the bar stock are all held and rotated in the spindle carrier. Opposite each spindle are mounted the necessary tools for the respective operations. Most of the tools are supported on the end tool slide, which is centrally located with reference to all spindles. This tool slide does not index or revolve

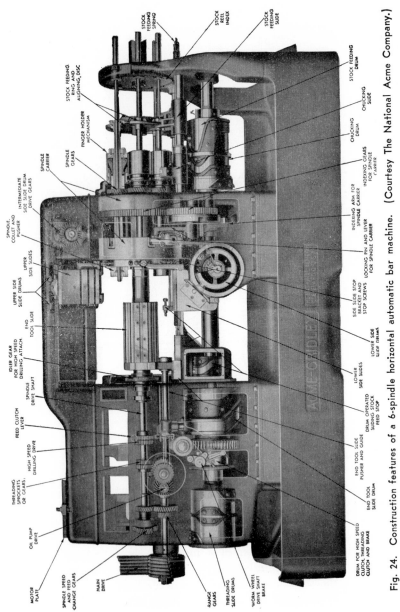

Fig. 24. Construction features of a 6-spindle horizontal automatic bar machine. (Courtesy The National Acme Company.)

with the spindle carrier but slides forward and back on the stem shaft to carry the end working tools to and from contact with the revolving bars of stock. Both above and below the spindle carrier and end tool slide are two cross slides on which side-cutting tools can be mounted. In six- and eight-spindle models there are two additional intermediate or side slides. All slides are independently operated and are used in combination with end-slide tools for such operations as form turning, knurling, thread rolling, slotting, and cutting off.

Fig. 25. Spindle assembly and tool slides for 6-spindle automatic screw machine. (Courtesy Greenlee Bros. & Co.)

Bars of stock are loaded into each spindle when it has been indexed to the first position. If automatic stock feeding is used, it is done in the lower spindle position at the rear of the machine. In operation, the spindle carrier is indexed by steps to bring the bar of stock in each of the work spindles successively in line with the various tools held on the tool slides. All tools in the successive positions are at work on different bars at the same time. The time to complete one part is equal to the time of the longest operation plus the time necessary for withdrawing the tools and indexing to the next position. This time can frequently be reduced to a minimum by dividing the long cuts between two or more operations.

The drive for the multispindle automatic is somewhat complicated, as all tool operations and machine movements are automatically controlled. The motor, mounted on the end of the machine opposite the spindles, operates the entire machine. The main drum shaft is located below the spindles and extends the full length of the machine. This shaft, with its several drum cams and gear connections, controls all tool movements, indexing, stock feeding, and timing of operations.

In Figure 25 is shown the spindle assembly of a six-spindle automatic screw machine in which the respective cross slides provided for each spindle are distributed radially about the spindle carrier. These slides hold the tools for turning, knurling, and cutting off, and each is operated by a separate cam. The balance of the tools for such operations as drilling and threading are mounted on the main center slide which is moved to the point where the feed starts through an intermittent gear. Bar stock may be fed in at two stations to permit the completion of two pieces in one cycle, or, if desired, the machine can be equipped with magazine feed.

Multispindle automatics are not limited to bar stock but may be provided with hydraulic or air-operated chucks for holding individual pieces. In some cases the chucks are loaded by the operator; in others magazine feeders are arranged to load the machine at one of the lower stations. Machines of this type are known as multispindle automatic chucking machines and are similar to the bar machines except for the stock-holding equipment.

The four-spindle automatic chucking machine, shown in Figure 26, is machining cast-iron gears according to the operation schedule listed in the insert. By using combined and multiple cuts, as is done at the second and third stations, the number of operations required is reduced to a minimum.

A great many attachments to permit almost any type of machine operation are available for these machines. Both solid and self-opening dies and taps may be applied in position to suit the work. Taper turning, combined taper turning and taper boring, or recessing attachments are applied to the end tool slide. A spindle-stopping mechanism can be arranged for such operations as milling, slotting, and cross drilling. Many machines are provided with a small chip conveyor which picks up the chips beneath the tooling area and dumps them into a container at the end of the machine. To assist in production records, a chronolog can be used to count the production and record the idle time of the machine.

A great variety of parts can be produced by a multispindle automatic, the only limiting factor being the capacity of the machine. Long-run jobs are necessary to offset the high initial investment,

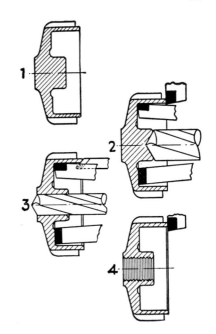

A. Operation for machining cast-iron gear.

1—Loading station.
2—Rough face end. Rough bore large hole. Rough face bottom. Spot.
3—Drill small hole. Finish bore large hole. Finish face bottom. Chamfer inside large hole.
4—Finish face end. Tap.

B. Machining cast-iron cylinder gear on a 4-spindle automatic. (Courtesy The National Acme Company.)

Fig. 26.

high maintenance, and expensive tooling costs. Both single-spindle automatics and hand-turret lathes have wide application and in short- and medium-run work prove to be economical in operation. Each machine is good in its field, but care must be taken in making the initial selection.

REVIEW QUESTIONS

1. Prepare a classification of turret and automatic lathes.

2. How does a turret lathe differ from an engine lathe?

3. Distinguish between the ram and saddle types of turret lathes.

4. What advantages are to be gained in the use of a controlled spindle turret lathe?

5. List the various devices for holding stock on a turret lathe.

6. What type of spring collet is recommended for bar work?

7. What are some of the distinguishing characteristics of automatic lathes that make them different from engine lathes?

8. What four factors make up the total production in turret lathe operation?

9. What is meant by the terms "combined cuts" and "multiple cuts"?

10. How is bar stock supported so that it will not deflect when being cut?

11. Show by sketch the tool setup for making ½-by-2½-inch hexagon-head machine bolts.

12. Prepare an operation sheet for the bolt described in Problem 11.

13. What is the purpose of each of the following: box tool, automatic die head, square turret, spring collet, and bar stop?

14. What type of work is done on a vertical turret lathe?

15. Explain the operation of a vertical automatic multistation lathe.

16. What type of work is done on a platen-type automatic lathe?

17. Describe the construction and operation of a Swiss-type automatic screw machine.

18. Describe the operation of an automatic multispindle screw machine.

19. What advantages do duplicating lathes have over automatic lathes?

REFERENCES

Bolz, R. W., *Production Processes*, Vol. 1, Penton Publishing Company, 1949.

Boston, O. W., *Metal Processing*, 2d edition, John Wiley and Sons, 1951.

How to Machine Parts on a Turret Lathe, Warner and Swasey Company, 1944.

Tool Engineers Handbook, American Society of Tool Engineers, McGraw-Hill Book Company, 1949.

CHAPTER 18

THREADS
AND
THREAD CUTTING

A *screw thread* is a ridge of uniform section, in the form of a helix, on the surface of a cylinder. The terminology relating to screw threads is clearly illustrated in Figure 1. Screw *sizes* are expressed by the outside or major diameter and the number of threads per inch. Thus a ½-inch 13-thread stud indicates a screw ½ inch in diameter and having 13 threads per inch. *Pitch* is expressed by a fraction with 1 as the numerator and the number of threads per inch as the denominator. Thus, a screw having 16 single threads per inch has a pitch of ⅟₁₆. It should be kept in mind that only on single-threaded screws does the pitch equal the lead. By definition the *lead* is the amount a screw advances axially in one revolution. Hence, on a double-threaded screw the lead is twice the pitch, on a triple-threaded screw the lead is three times the pitch, and so on.

Screw threads are used principally on *fasteners* such as machine bolts, stove bolts, and wood screws. Threads of this nature are simple in design and easy to produce. The usual form is a V, although there are several slight variations of this form.

Another use for screw threads is to *transmit power*. The mechanical advantage obtained in the ordinary screw jack illustrates this application. Closely associated with this is the use of threads for *transmitting motion,* such as the lead screw on a lathe.

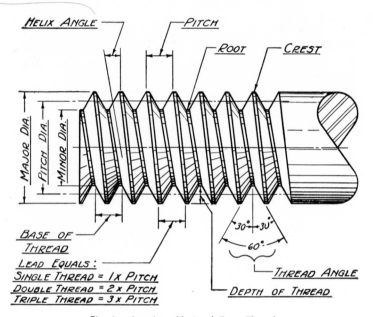

Fig. I.   American National Form Thread.

Finally, screw threads are employed for such *measuring devices* as micrometers. Screw threads sometimes fulfill several of these uses. For example, the screws controlling the work table of a milling machine may be used either for accurate measuring or for controlling the table movement. The form in which the screw is made is naturally influenced by the function it has to fulfill.

Types of Screw Threads

Screw threads have been standardized according to their cross-sectional form. Figure 2 shows the common forms in use and the relationships that exist between the pitch and the principal dimensions. All bolts and similar fasteners have *V-shaped threads,* as shown in *A* of the figure. There are two standards in the United States that utilize this form of thread, namely, the *National Coarse Screw Thread* and the *National Fine Screw Thread.* The National Fine series differs from the National Coarse series only in having more threads per inch for a given size. Such threads have been adopted by the automotive and aeronautical industries, since there is less tendency for them to work loose because of vibrations. This type of thread is characterized by a small flat on top and at the root of the thread, which adds to its strength. V-type threads without these flats,

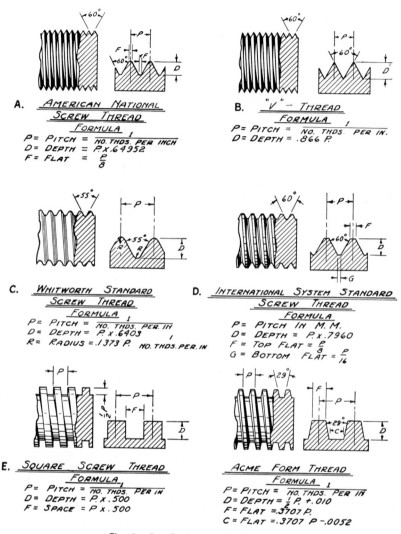

A. *AMERICAN NATIONAL SCREW THREAD*

FORMULA

$P = PITCH = \frac{1}{NO. THDS. PER INCH}$
$D = DEPTH = P \times .64952$
$F = FLAT = \frac{P}{8}$

B. *"V" - THREAD*

FORMULA

$P = PITCH = \frac{1}{NO. THDS. PER IN.}$
$D = DEPTH = .866 P.$

C. *WHITWORTH STANDARD SCREW THREAD*

FORMULA

$P = PITCH = \frac{1}{NO. THDS. PER. IN}$
$D = DEPTH = P \times .6403$
$R = RADIUS = .1373 P. \quad NO. THDS. PER. IN$

D. *INTERNATIONAL SYSTEM STANDARD SCREW THREAD*

FORMULA

$P = PITCH$ IN M.M.
$D = DEPTH = P \times .7960$
$F = TOP FLAT = \frac{P}{8}$
$G = BOTTOM FLAT = \frac{P}{16}$

E. *SQUARE SCREW THREAD*

FORMULA

$P = PITCH = \frac{1}{NO. THDS. PER IN}$
$D = DEPTH = P \times .500$
$F = SPACE = P \times .500$

ACME FORM THREAD

FORMULA

$P = PITCH = \frac{1}{NO. THDS. PER IN}$
$D = DEPTH = \frac{1}{2} P + .010$
$F = FLAT = .3707 P.$
$C = FLAT = .3707 P - .0052$

Fig. 2. Standard screw-thread forms.

shown at *B,* have a greater tendency to fail at the sharp root corners when subjected to loading conditions. The *International Standard Metric Thread* shown in *D* is essentially the same as the National Standard except for a smaller flat at the root and a different number of threads per unit distance. From a standpoint of design, the *Whitworth Standard* used in England is perhaps better than any of those already mentioned, as the filleted top and root add strength to the thread by eliminating sharp corners where fatigue cracks may start. This thread, shown at *C* in the figure, is gradually being replaced by the Unified Standard shown in Figure 3. The Acme thread shown at *F* is principally used for the transmission of power and motion. It has an advantage over other similar screws in that wear may be compensated for by adjusting the half nuts in contact with the screw. This would be impossible with the square threads shown at *E*. Another advantage of the Acme over the square thread is that it may be cut with suitable taps and dies. *Square threads* are more suitable for transmitting power where there is a large thrust on one side of the thread. These threads, however, cannot be cut with taps and dies and must be machined on a lathe. Another type, similar to the square thread, is known as a *buttress thread*. It has one side that slopes 45 degrees; the other is perpendicular. The principal application of this thread is to transmit power, although it has the disadvantage that the thrust can be in only one direction. *Worm threads* are similar to the Acme Standard except that they have a greater depth. This form of thread is used exclusively for worm-gear drives.

The new, *unified screw-thread* standard, shown in Figure 3, was adopted recently by Britain, Canada, and the United States. It is similar to the present American Standard and in most applications will be interchangeable with it. The greatest change in tooling will occur in Britain since they have changed from the 55-degree angle of the Whitworth system to the 60-degree American Standard angle. The basic width of the nut is 1/4 pitch, whereas that of the screw is 1/8 pitch. This increased flat on the nut facilitates tapping and at the same time has proved to be just as serviceable. The shape of the thread crest and root is not mandatory and may be either flat or rounded. Actually it approximates the shape obtained from a worn tool and is similar to many threads produced under the American Standard.

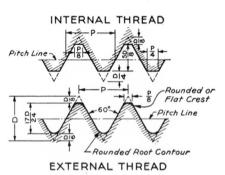

INTERNAL THREAD

EXTERNAL THREAD

Fig. 3. Unified screw-thread standard.

Pipe threads have been standardized according to the American National Standard shown in Figure 4. To insure tight joints, the thread has a taper of ¾ inch per foot. The threads have the conventional V shape, except for the last four or five, which have flat

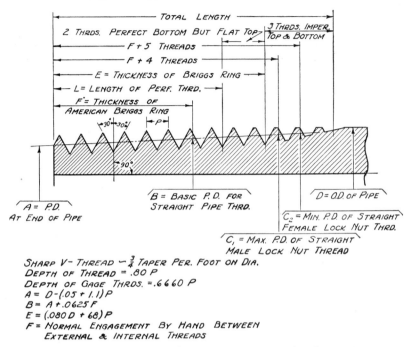

Fig. 4. American (Briggs) Standard Pipe Thread.

tops. These last threads all have imperfect bottoms, as shown in the figure. The usual method of cutting these threads is with suitable taps and dies, although they may also be cut on a lathe by using the taper attachment.

Methods of Making Threads

External threads may be produced by the following manufacturing processes:

1. Cutting to shape on an engine lathe.
2. Using die and stock (manual).
3. Automatic die head (turret lathe).
4. Milling machine.
5. Threading machine (plain or automatic).
6. Rolling between dies (flat or circular).

7. Die casting.
8. Grinding.

Internal threads may be produced by:

1. Cutting to shape on an engine lathe.
2. Using tap and holder.
3. Automatic collapsible tap.
4. Milling machine.

Cutting threads on a lathe. The lathe is the most versatile of all machine tools for cutting threads, since on this machine it is possible to cut all forms of threads; however, the lathe is usually selected when only a few threads are to be cut or when special forms are desired. The form of the thread is obtained by grinding the tool to the proper shape. To insure getting the proper shape, a suitable gage or templet should be used. Figure 5 shows a cutter bit ground for cutting 60-degree V threads and the gage which is used for checking the angle of the tool. This gage is known as a *center gage,* since it is also used for gaging lathe centers. Special form cutters, as shown in Figure 7, can also be used for cutting these threads. These cutters are previously shaped to the correct form and are sharpened by grinding only on the top face.

In setting up the tool for V threads, there are two methods of feeding the tool. First, the tool may be fed straight into the work and the threads formed by taking a series of light cuts, as shown at *A* in Figure 5. With this method there is cutting action on both sides of the tool bit. The disadvantage of this method is that it is impossible to provide any side rake on the cutting tool, although some back rake may be obtained. On materials such as cast iron or brass, where little or no side rake is recommended, this method is satisfactory. However, in cutting steel threads it is advisable to use a side rake on the tool. This necessitates feeding the tool in at an angle, as shown at *B* and *D.* To do this, the compound rest is turned to an angle of 29 degrees, and, by using the cross-feed on the compound rest, the tool is fed into the work so that all cutting is done on the left-hand side of the tool. The tool bit, being ground to an angle of 60 degrees, allows 1 degree of the right-hand side of the tool to smooth off that side of the thread.

It is necessary that the tool be given a positive feed along the work at the proper rate to cut the desired number of threads per inch. This is accomplished by a train of gears located on the end of the lathe, which drive the lead screw at the required speed with relation

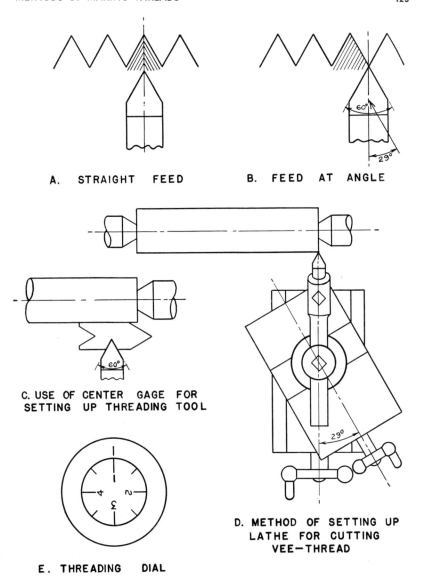

A. STRAIGHT FEED

B. FEED AT ANGLE

C. USE OF CENTER GAGE FOR SETTING UP THREADING TOOL

D. METHOD OF SETTING UP LATHE FOR CUTTING VEE—THREAD

E. THREADING DIAL

Fig. 5. Method of setting tool for thread cutting on lathe.

to the headstock spindle. This gearing may be changed to cut any desired pitch of screw. The lead screw, in turn, engages the half nuts on the apron of the lathe, providing positive drive for the tool.

The older-type, standard change-gear lathes require that the gears be changed manually. Referring to Figure 6, one may see the usual arrangement of gears on such lathes. The *spindle gear* drives through the small *reversing gears* to the *stud gear*. As shown in the figure, both the reversing or tumble gears are in mesh. When the hand lever is raised one of the gears is thrown out of mesh, and, if one gear is eliminated from the train, the rotation of the lead screw is reversed. The speed ratio from spindle gear to stud gear is 1 to 1, or, in other words, there is no increase or decrease in the rotational speed of the stud gear. Keyed to the stud gear is another gear called

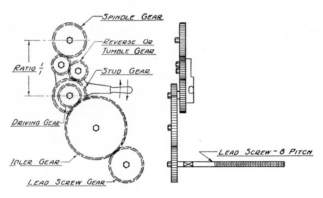

SIMPLE GEARING AT END OF LATHE

Fig. 6. Simple gearing at end of lathe.

the *driving gear*. It connects with the *lead-screw gear* by means of an *idler*. In simple gearing the only two gears to be changed are the driving and lead-screw gears. The correct selection of these gears depends on the number of threads to be cut and the pitch of the lead screw.

Assume, as an example, that it is desired to cut a thread with 13 threads per inch on a lathe having a lead screw with 8 threads per inch. If the ratio from driving gear to lead-screw gear is 1 to 1, the tool will advance $\frac{1}{8}$ inch for each revolution of lead screw and will cut 8 threads per inch. In order to cut 13 threads per inch, the lead-screw speed must be slowed down somewhat in relation to the spindle speed. The ratio that must exist in this case is 8 to 13. Hence, a driving gear and a lead-screw gear having this ratio will cut the desired thread. The rule for determining the proper gear ratio is:

$$\frac{\text{Number of threads on lead screw}}{\text{Number of threads to be cut}}$$

In this case the ratio is 8 to 13.

By multiplying both the numerator and denominator by a number, the ratio may be expressed as numbers of teeth in each gear. Hence,

$$\frac{8 \times 3}{13 \times 3} = \frac{24T \quad \text{(driving gear)}}{39T \quad \text{(lead-screw gear)}}$$

If no gears are available with these numbers of teeth, some other multiplier must be used, or, if the ratio is too large, compound gearing is necessary.

Fig. 7. Thread cutting on a lathe. (Courtesy South Bend Lathe Works.)

All the newer-type lathes are provided with quick-change gearboxes, as shown in Figure 1 and 2 of Chapter 16. No computation is necessary, because the chart on the cover of the gearbox states the correct position of levers needed to obtain the number of threads per inch.

After the lathe is set up, the cross-feed screw is set at some mark on the micrometer dial, and a light cut is taken to check the pitch of the thread. At the end of each successive cut, the tool is removed from the thread by turning back the cross-feed screw. This is necessary, since any back play in the lead screw would prevent the tool from returning in its previous cut. The tool is returned to original position, the cross-feed screw is set at the same reference mark, the tool is fed the desired amount for the next cut, and another cut is taken. These operations are repeated until the thread is cut to a proper depth. To check the work a ring thread gage or a standard nut is used. Figure 7 illustrates the tool setup for thread cutting on a lathe.

Fig. 8. Threading dial on lathe. (Courtesy South Bend Lathe Works.)

Most lathes are equipped with a *thread dial indicator* as shown in Figures 5 and 8. Close by the dial is a lever (shown in Figure 8) which is used to engage and disengage the lead screw with a matching set of half nuts in the carriage. At the end of each cut, the half nuts are disengaged and then re-engaged at the correct time so that the tool always follows in the same cut. The indicator is connected to the lead screw by means of a small worm gear, and the face of the dial, which revolves, is numbered to indicate positions at which the half nuts may be engaged. The position at which the half nuts should be closed depends on the size of thread, as follows:

1. For even-numbered threads: any line on the dial.
2. For odd-numbered threads: any *numbered* line.
3. For threads involving half threads: any odd-numbered line.
4. For threads involving quarter threads: return to original starting point each time.

Taps and dies. Taps are used principally for the manual production of internal threads, although with proper mounting they may also be used in machine threading. Figure 9 is a graphic illustration of a *tap* with the various parts of the tool labeled. The tool itself is a hardened piece of carbon or alloy steel resembling a bolt, with flutes cut along the side to provide the cutting edges. For hand tapping these are furnished in sets of three for each size, as shown in Figure 10. In starting the thread, the *taper tap* should be used, since it insures straighter starting and more gradual cutting action on the threads. If it is a through hole, no other tap is needed. For closed or blind holes where it is desired to have threads to the very bottom, the *taper, plug,* and *bottoming taps* should all be used in the order named. Many other taps are available and are usually named according to the kind of thread they are to cut.

In all cases, where a hole is to be tapped, the hole that is drilled before the tapping operation must be of such size as to provide the necessary metal for the threads. Such a hole is said to be a *"tap-size"* hole. If a ⅜-inch, 16-thread hole is to be cut, the tap-size drill is ⁵⁄₁₆ inch in diameter. This is equivalent to the root diameter of a ⅜-inch 16 standard screw and allows sufficient metal in the hole for the threads.

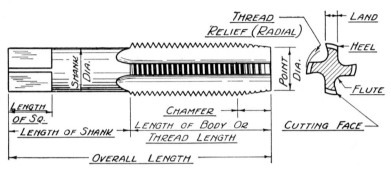

Fig. 9. Tap nomenclature.

In order to cut external threads, *dies* similar to those shown in Figure 11 are used. The most common type is the adjustable die because it can be made to cut slightly undersized or oversized. When used for hand cutting, the die is held in a die stock which provides the necessary leverage to turn the die in making a cut.

For successful operation of either taps or dies, some consideration must be given to the nature of the material to be threaded. The shape and angle of the cutting face influence the performance, since no tool can be made to work successfully for all materials. Another important factor is

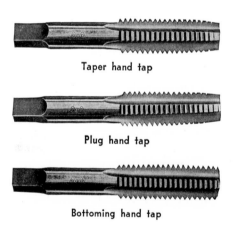

Taper hand tap

Plug hand tap

Bottoming hand tap

Fig. 10. Hand taps. (Courtesy Greenfield Tap and Die.)

proper lubrication of the tool during the cutting operation. This insures longer life of the cutting edges and results in smoother threads. Since no one lubricant can be recommended for all cases, it is advisable to consult specialists or handbooks in making a selection.

Both the taps and dies described may also be used in the machine cutting of threads. Because of the nature of the cutting operation, they must be held in a special holder, so designed that the tap or die can be withdrawn from the work without injury to the threads. This is frequently accomplished by reversing the rotation of the tool or work after the cut has been made. Numerous tapping attachments are available for internal thread cutting on a drill press. These attachments are usually provided with two spindles which operate in opposite directions. The tap is rotated into the work at the proper cutting speed until the threads are made. As soon as the tap is raised

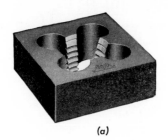 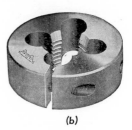

(a)   (b)

Fig. II. (a) Square die, (b) round die. (Courtesy Greenfield Tap and Die.)

upward, the other spindle is engaged by means of a ball or friction clutch, and the rotation of the tap is reversed, thus removing it from the work. The withdrawing speed is usually much faster than the cutting speed. The same procedure is used in cutting external threads with nonopening dies.

In small production work on a turret lathe, the tap is held by a special holder, which prevents the tap from turning as the threads are cut. Near the end of the cut the turret holding the tool is stopped, and the tap holder continues to advance until it pulls away from a stop pin a sufficient amount to allow the tap to rotate with the work. The rotation of the work is then reversed, and, when the tap holder is withdrawn, it is again engaged with the stop and held until the work is rotated from the tap. External threads may also be cut with a die utilizing this same procedure, although in most cases such threads are cut with self-opening dies.

Thread chasing. In production work self-opening dies and collapsible taps are used to eliminate back tracking of the tool and to save time. The tools have individual cutter dies, known as chasers, mounted in an appropriate holder, which are capable of adjustment or replacement. With chasers more accurate work can be done, the cutters can be kept in proper adjustment, and there is no danger of damaging the cut thread as the tool is withdrawn. In some cases the tool is held stationary and the work revolves; in others the reverse procedure may be used. All precision screws require a lead screw feed to obtain accuracy.

Two types of *automatic die heads* are used. In one type the cutters or chasers are mounted *tangentially,* as shown in Figure 12; in the other they are in a *radial* position. Radial cutters can be

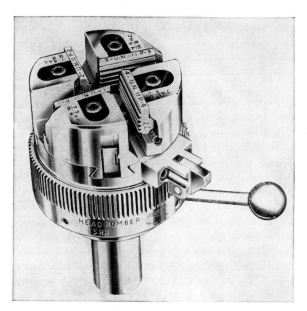

Fig. 12. Stationary tangent die head. (Courtesy Landis Machine Company.)

changed quickly and as a consequence are used for threading materials that are hard to cut. The die head shown is commonly used on turret lathes and is of the stationary type. The work rotates and the chasers open automatically at the end of the cut so that they may be withdrawn from the work without damage.

For large diameter internal work, collapsible taps are used, having either radial or circular chasers. Circular chasers wear longer but can be used only in large-diameter holes. Both stationary and rotating types are available, and the selection depends upon the machine used. In Figure 13 is shown a collapsing tap designed for tapping straight threads. The smallest thread size that can be made is $1\frac{1}{4}$ inches. This design may be used on either stationary or rotary applications.

Threading machine. In Figure 14 is shown a double-spindle threading machine used for threading spindles, bolts, pipe, and parts up to 1½ inch in diameter. Parts are held by double-acting vises which are opened and closed by the hand wheels shown. For accuracy in pitch of threads, the use of a lead screw for feeding the carriage is recommended, especially for threads of large diameter.

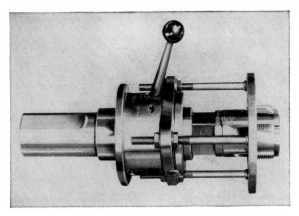

Fig. 13. Collapsing tap for threads over 1¼ inches. (Courtesy Landis Machine Company.)

Very often no mechanical positive feed is used for small diameter threads, as the lead on the threading die feeds the work at the proper rate. Tangential dies are shown which open automatically when the required length of thread is cut.

Machines of this type may also be used for tapping nuts by using a tap chuck in the die head and gripping the nut in the vise. A long shank tap is used for this work and, as the nuts are tapped, they feed back onto the shank of the tap.

Tapping machines. Although much tapping is done on drill presses equipped with some form of tapping attachment, most production tapping is done on specially constructed machines. Such machines are automatic in operation, and the blanks to be threaded are usually fed from an oscillating hopper to the working position. When the operation is finished, the spindles are reversed at double the tapping speed, and the nuts are discharged to individual containers.

A common type of tapping machine, usually a multispindle arrangement, is provided with taps having extra long shanks. The tap is advanced through the nut by the lead screw and, upon completion of the threading, continues downward until the nut is released. The spindle then returns to its upper position with the tapped nut on its shank. When the shank has been filled with nuts, the tap is removed

Fig. 14. Double-spindle threading machine. (Courtesy The Hill-Acme Company.)

and the nuts are emptied into a container. Important factors in the success of high-speed tapping are the use of a proper cutting oil, rigidity of the machine, proper cutting speed for the material involved, and the percentage of thread remaining in the tapped hole.

Thread milling. Accurate threads of large size, both external and internal, can be cut with standard or hob-type cutters. For long, external threads a threading machine is used which is similar in appearance to a lathe. Work is mounted either in a chuck or between centers, and the milling attachment is at the rear of the machine. In cutting a long screw a single cutter is mounted in the plane of the thread angle and fed parallel to the axis of the threaded part.

A planetary-type thread-milling machine[1] intended for mass production of short internal or external threads is shown in Figure 15. The figure shows the cutter-head setup for external threads using annular milling cutters which cover the full length of the cut.

In operation, a work-holding fixture is mounted on the machine table which holds the work rigidly. The milling head carrying the

[1] See Chapter 21 for additional information on planetary milling.

hob is revolved eccentrically about the work and is simultaneously rotated on its own axis, advancing by means of a lead screw for a sufficient distance to produce the desired thread. The cutter spindle, after completing the milling operation, automatically returns to center position. A reversing switch is then contacted, and the sleeves

are brought back to the original starting position. The depth of the thread is controlled by adjustment in the eccentricity of the spindle sleeve. After proper adjustment the entire cycle of operation is automatic.

Thread rolling. A large proportion of the standard bolts and screws manufactured have their threads cold-formed by being rolled between suitable dies. In this process the metal on the cylindrical blank is cold-forged, under considerable pressure, by the rolling action of the blank between either rotating

Fig. 15. Enlarged view of cutter head for outside threads. (Courtesy Murchey Machine & Tool Company.)

cylindrical dies or reciprocating flat dies. The surface of the dies have the reverse form of the thread that is rolled. Rolling under pressure results in a plastic flow of the metal in such a way that the

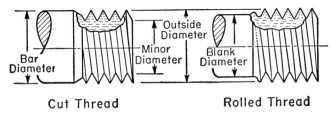

Cut Thread   Rolled Thread

Fig. 16. Illustrating stock material saving of rolled threads over cut threads.

dies penetrate to form the root of the thread, and the displaced metal is raised to form the crest. Slightly less material is required for threaded parts made in this fashion over cut threads as illustrated in Figure 16. This saving ranges from 16% to 25%. In the case of a ½-in. 13 thread screw size, the saving is 19%. The diameter of the

stock used is approximately equal to the pitch diameter of the screw.
In this process no chips are formed, and the accuracy and uniformity of the threads are excellent if the blanks are held to the correct
size.

There are two methods employed in the rolling of threads. In
one case the bolt is rolled between two flat dies, each being provided
with parallel grooves cut the size and shape of the thread. One die is

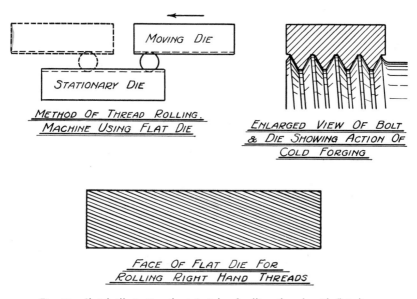

Fig. 17. Sketch illustrating the principle of rolling threads with flat dies.

held stationary while the other reciprocates and rolls the blank between the dies. This operation is shown diagrammatically in Figure 17. The process may be illustrated by rolling a screw between
two soft boards under pressure. On examination of the boards, we
note that each has impressed into its surface a series of angular,
parallel lines. By reversing this illustration and starting with similar
grooves in hardened steel, threads will be rolled into a piece of soft
steel rod placed between them.

The other process, shown in Figure 18, employs either two or three
grooved rollers. In the two-die method the blank is placed on the
work rest between the two parallel, cylindrical rotating dies, and the
right-hand die is fed into the blank until the correct size is reached,
returning then to its starting position. The three-die machine
utilizes cylindrical rotating dies mounted on parallel shafts driven

synchronously at the desired speed. They advance radially into the blank by cam action, dwell for a slight period, and then withdraw.

Although most threaded fasteners are rolled on special machines, threaded roll dies may be adapted to standard automatic screw machines. All types of rolling machines may be manually operated

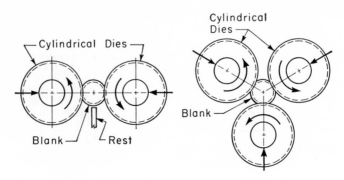

Fig. 18.   Thread rolling using either two or three cylindrical dies.

or arranged with an automatic feeding device. In most cases the entire thread is formed at once by the in-feed method although end-feeding is used on long screws.

The advantages of the thread rolling process include:

1. Improved tensile, shear and fatigue strength are obtained.
2. There is a smooth surface finish (4 to 32 microinches).
3. Close accuracy is maintained (dependent upon accuracy of die).
4. Less material is required.
5. Production rate is high.
6. A wide variety of thread forms is possible.

Limitations of the thread rolling process include:

1. Blank tolerance must be close since no metal is removed.
2. It is not economical for short-run jobs.
3. Only external threads can be rolled.
4. Material having a hardness exceeding Rockwell C37 should not be rolled.

Thread grinding.   Grinding is used as either a finishing or a forming operation on many screw threads where accuracy and smooth finish are required.   This process is particularly applicable for threads that have been heat-treated to eliminate possible errors resulting from the treatment.

In general, there are two types of wheels used in thread grinding, as illustrated in Figure 19. The method shown at *A* employs a single wheel, shaped to correct form, which traverses the length of the screw. The wheel is rotated against the work, usually at speeds ranging from 7500 to 10,000 surface feet per minute, and at the same time traverses the length of the screw at a speed determined by the pitch of the thread. The surface speed of the work is determined by many fac-

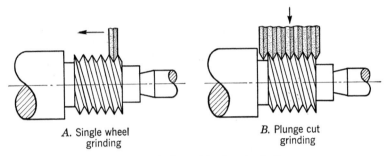

A. Single wheel   B. Plunge cut
grinding   grinding

Fig. 19. Methods used in thread grinding.

tors such as depth of cut and kind of material, but for most cases it ranges from 1½ to 10 surface feet per minute. It is possible to cut a complete thread by one pass of the wheel; however, most threads are formed by two or more passes, the last one removing only a few thousandths in the interest of accuracy and finish. The form of the grinding wheel must be dressed periodically by a diamond truing device to compensate for gradual wear. The movement of the diamonds is controlled either from template formers or through a pantograph mechanism. Although the truing action is automatic, it must be predetermined by the operator.

Short threads may be ground by the plunge-cut method, as shown at *B* in the figure. With this method the wheel is fed in the entire depth of the thread before the work is started. The work then makes one revolution while it traverses a distance equal to one pitch, thus completing the thread. A little overtravel is provided to insure a perfect thread over the entire length. Multiribbed wheels may be used to traverse-grind as is done with single wheels, but this is not recommended owing to the greater wear on the leading ribs. The dressing of plunge-cut wheels is usually done by a *crush-roll process*. The operation consists of slowly rolling the grinding wheel in crushing contact with a hardened roller which has on it threads the same as will appear on the work. This method of dressing is rapid and accurate and provides the wheel with sharp cutting edges so essential for good grinding. The process is limited to the use of vitrified wheels, and there is a gradual decrease in roll accuracy as repeated dressings are made.

Most thread-grinding machines are characterized by having an operating cycle that is entirely automatic from the time the operation starts until the thread is complete. Compensating devices are usually provided to allow for the decreased diameter of the wheel after dressing so that the work size is not altered and no resetting of the wheel is necessary. A similar arrangement is often provided to compensate for backlash so that the wheel may traverse back and forth for rapid cutting. Thread grinding lends itself to the production of threads on either hard or soft material. The process also produces a high degree of accuracy and finish which is so important for precision and highly stressed screw threads.

REVIEW QUESTIONS

1. Name and sketch five standard screw threads. Indicate angle on each thread.

2. To what various uses may screw threads be put?

3. Distinguish between lead and pitch on a screw thread.

4. What advantages does an Acme thread have over a square thread?

5. List the various methods by which external threads can be made.

6. Briefly describe the new unified screw-thread standard.

7. How do the American National Pipe threads differ from the National Coarse threads?

8. What methods can be used for cutting internal threads?

9. How are threads cut on a turret lathe?

10. Sketch the gears on the end of an engine lathe, and, assuming the pitch of the lead screw to be 8, indicate the number of teeth in the driving and lead-screw gears necessary to cut 11 threads per inch.

11. What is a thread dial indicator, and how does it work?

12. What is a tap? Name six kinds.

13. How would you cut an internal square thread?

14. How are threads cut on a turret lathe?

15. What type of threading equipment should be used for cutting internal threads on a drill press?

16. What three methods are employed in rolling threads?

17. What types of screw threads may be produced by rolling?

18. Describe the operation of a planetary-type thread-milling machine.

19. Describe two methods of producing threads by grinding.

20. What are the advantages and limitations of the thread-rolling process?

REFERENCES

American Machinist's Handbook, McGraw-Hill Book Company, 1955.

Flanders, Ralph E., "American Thread Grinding Practice," *Machinery,* September 1939.

Gaillard, John, "New American Standard for Screw Threads Presents Unified Series," *Modern Machine Shop,* May 1949.

Kent's Mechanical Engineers' Handbook, 12th edition, John Wiley and Sons, 1950.

Peterka, A. E., *Bolts, Nuts, and Screws,* Lamson and Sessions Company, 1941.

Screw Thread Cutting Manual, Geometric Tool Company, 1946.

Tool Engineers Handbook, American Society of Tool Engineers, McGraw-Hill Book Company, 1949.

CHAPTER 19

SHAPERS

AND

PLANERS

A *shaper* is a machine having a reciprocating cutting tool, of the lathe type, which takes a straight-line cut. By moving the work across the path of this tool, a plane surface is generated, regardless of the shape of the tool. With this method of producing a flat surface, perfection is not dependent on the accuracy of the tool as it is when a milling cutter is used for the same type of work. By means of special tools, attachments, and devices for holding the work, a shaper can also cut external and internal keyways, spiral grooves, gear racks, dovetails, T slots, and other miscellaneous shapes.

Classification of Shapers

According to general design, shapers can be classified as follows:

1. Horizontal—push cut
   (*a*) Plain (production work)
   (*b*) Universal (toolroom work)

2. Horizontal—draw cut

3. Vertical
   (*a*) Slotter
   (*b*) Keyseater

4. Special purpose, as for cutting gears

Power can be applied to the machine by an individual motor either through gears or belt, or by step-cone pulley from the lineshaft. The reciprocating drive of the tool can be arranged in several ways. Some of the older shapers were driven by gears or by feed screw, but most shapers are now being driven by an oscillating arm and crank mechanism, as illustrated in Figure 3.

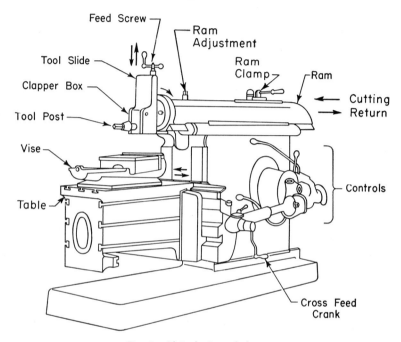

Fig. I. Plain horizontal shaper.

Horizontal-Type Shapers

Construction. Figure 1 is a diagrammatic sketch of a plain horizontal shaper commonly used for production and general-purpose work. This shaper, consisting of a base and frame which supports a horizontal ram, is quite simple in construction. The *ram,* which carries the tool, is given a reciprocating motion equal to the length of the stroke desired. The *quick-return mechanism* driving the ram is designed so that the return stroke of the shaper is faster than the cutting stroke to reduce the idle time of the machine to a minimum. The tool head at the end of the ram can be swiveled through an angle and is provided with means for feeding the tool into the work. On it is fastened the *clapper-box tool holder,* pivoted at the upper end to permit the tool to rise on the return stroke so as not to dig into the work.

The work table is supported on a crossrail in front of the shaper. By means of a lead screw in connection with the crossrail, the work can be moved crosswise or vertically by either hand or power drive. A *universal* shaper has these same features and, in addition, is provided with swiveling and tilting arrangements to permit accurate machining at any angle. The swiveling adjustment takes place about an axis that is parallel to the motion of the ram. The tilting feature is in the table top which provides a means to set the table at an angle to the swiveling axis. Both adjustments are equipped with protractors to assist the operator in setting the table at any angle.

The work on a shaper is held by bolting it to the work table or by fastening it in either a vise or some special fixture. The table is provided with T slots which permit bolts to be inserted to facilitate the holding of work or fixtures. Reference to the illustrations shows clearly how this is accomplished.

Quick-return mechanism. Several types of quick-return mechanisms have been developed for shapers, but the most common type is the *pillar* or *oscillating-arm* type shown diagrammatically in Figure 2. It consists of a rotating crank driven at a uniform speed which is connected to an oscillating arm by a sliding block. Referring to the figure, we note that the cutting stroke takes up 220 degrees of the crank revolution while the return is made through only 140 degrees movement of the crank. Hence the ratio,

$$\frac{\text{Cutting stroke}}{\text{Return stroke}} = \frac{220}{140} = \frac{1.57}{1}$$

The quick return is due to the crank end, with the sliding block, being close to the arm fulcrum during the lower half of rotation. The stroke length is varied by changing the length of the crank.

The drive mechanism and quick return for an oscillating-arm shaper is illustrated in Figure 3. The sliding block works in the center of the rather massive oscillating arm. The crank is contained in the large gear and may be varied by a screw mechanism. The crank gear is driven by the transmission gears, as shown in the figure. To change the position of the stroke, the clamp holding the connecting link to the screw is loosened, and the hand wheel at the end of the screw is turned. As the screw is fastened to the ram, it can be moved backward or forward by turning this wheel.

Cutting speed. Cutting speed on horizontal shapers is the average speed of the tool during the cutting stroke and depends primarily on the number of ram strokes per minute and the length of the stroke. If the stroke length is changed and the number of

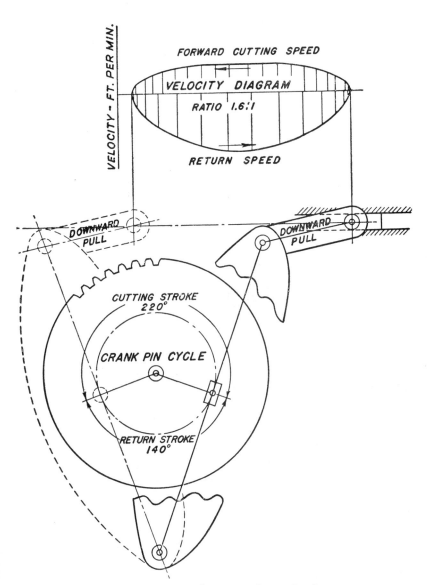

Fig. 2.   Pillar-type quick-return mechanism for shaper.

strokes per minute remains constant, the average cutting speed is changed. The ratio of cutting speed to return speed enters into the calculation as it is necessary to determine what proportion of time the cutting tool is working. Thus, with the ratio

$$\frac{\text{cutting stroke}}{\text{return stroke}} = \frac{3}{2},$$

Fig. 3. Quick-return drive mechanism used on a Hendey horizontal push-cut shaper. (Courtesy The Hendey Machine Company.)

the cutter is working three-fifths of the time and the return takes two-fifths of the time. Cutting speed may be determined by the following formula:

$$\text{C.S.} = \frac{NL}{12C} = \text{feet per minute}$$

where $N =$ strokes per minute,
$L =$ stroke length in inches,
$C =$ cutting time ratio $\left(\dfrac{\text{cutting time}}{\text{total time}}\right)$

This calculation is unnecessary when a hydraulic shaper is used because the speed is uniform and shown on an indicator.

Draw-cut shaper. This shaper is so named because the tool is pulled across the work by the ram instead of being pushed. In Figure 4 is shown a machine of this type equipped with a small jib crane and hoist. Horizontal draw-cut shapers are especially recommended for heavy cuts, being widely used for cutting large die blocks and machining large parts in railroad shops. During the cut, the work is drawn against the adjustable back bearing or face of the column, thereby reducing the strains on the crossrails and saddle

Fig. 4. Draw-cut shaper. (Courtesy Morton Manufacturing Company.)

bearings. There is little tendency for vibration, as a tensile stress is exerted in the ram during the cut. This permits the use of large forming tools without resulting tool chatter marks on the work.

Hydraulic shaper. The hydraulic shaper is similar in appearance to those driven by some form of mechanism, as may be noted in Figure 5. One of the principal advantages claimed for this type of shaper is that the cutting speed and pressure in the ram drive are constant from beginning to end of the cut. Both the cutting-stroke length and its position relative to the work may be changed quickly without stopping the machine, by the use of two small handles at the side of the ram. Another feature is that the ram movement can be reversed instantly anywhere in either direction of travel. The

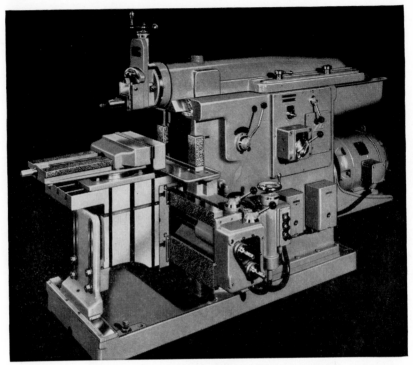

Fig. 5. Hydraulic shaper. (Courtesy Rockford Machine Tool Company.)

hydraulic feed takes place while the tool is clear of the work and the entire operation of the machine is quiet. The maximum ratio of cutting stroke to return stroke is about 2 : 1.

Tool shapes. Shaper tools are similar to lathe tools and are frequently held in the same type of holders. The same tool angles prevail, except that an end angle clearance of 4 degrees is sufficient. For steel the side rake angle should be around 15 degrees, and for cast iron, around 5 degrees.

Vertical shapers. Vertical shapers or *slotters* (see Figure 6) are used principally for internal cutting and planing at angles, and for operations that require vertical cuts because of the position in which the work must be held. Operations of this nature are frequently found on die work, metal molds, and metal patterns. The shaper ram operates vertically and has the usual quick-return feature like the horizontal-type machines. Work to be machined is supported on a round table having a rotary feed in addition to the usual table movements. The circular table feed permits the machining of curved surfaces, a process which is particularly desirable for many irregular parts that cannot be turned on a lathe. Plane surfaces are cut by using either of the table cross-feeds.

A special type of vertical shaper known as a *keyseater* is especially designed for cutting keyways in gears, pulleys, flywheels, and similar

Fig. 6. Vertical shaper. (Courtesy Pratt & Whitney.)

parts. The work is clamped to a horizontal table, and the tool is reciprocated in a vertical position through its center. The work is fed to the cutter by table adjustments.

The Planer

A *planer* is a machine tool designed to remove metal by moving the work in a straight line against a single-edged cutting tool. The type of work is very similar to that done on a shaper except that a planer is adapted to much larger work. The cuts are all plain surfaces, but they may be horizontal, vertical, or at an angle. In addition to machining large work, the planer is frequently used in production work to machine multiple small parts held in line on the platen.

Differences between planer and shaper. Although both the planer and shaper are adapted to the machining of flat surfaces, there is not much overlapping in their fields of usefulness; they differ widely in construction and in method of operation. When the two machines are compared in construction, operation, and use, the following differences may be seen:

1. The planer is specially adapted to large work; the shaper can do only small work.

2. On the planer the work is moved against a stationary tool; on the shaper the tool moves across the work which is stationary.

3. On the planer the tool is fed into the work; on the shaper the work is usually fed across the tool.

4. The drive on the planer table is either by gears or by hydraulic means. The shaper ram can also be driven in this manner, but in most cases a quick-return link mechanism is used.

5. Most planers differ from shapers in that they approach constant-velocity cuts.

Planer and shaper size. The usual method of designating the size of planers and shapers is as follows:

Shaper—Maximum length of work that can be machined (inches).
Vertical shaper or slotter—Maximum length of stroke × diameter of work table (dimensions in inches).
Planer—Width of table (inches) × distance from table to rail (inches) × length of table (feet).

Classification of Planers

Planers may be classified in a number of ways, but according to general construction there are five types:

1. Double-housing planer (Figure 7).
2. Open-side planer (Figure 8).
3. Universal planer (cuts on both strokes).
4. Pit-type planer (Figure 9).
5. Edge or plate planer (Figure 10).

Planer drive. Each of the above types may vary, according to the method of drive. In such a classification there are gear drive (both spur gear and spiral), hydraulic drive, screw drive, belt drive, variable-speed motor drive, and crank drive. The first two mentioned are generally used. The screw drive is employed principally on plate planers, whereas the crank drive is found only on some small planers. Variable-speed-reversing motors, controlled by stops at each end of the stroke, are used on some planers.

Hydraulic drives are highly satisfactory for planers. Uniform cutting speed is attained throughout the entire cutting stroke. The acceleration and deceleration of the table take place in such a short distance of travel that they need not be considered as a time element. A second advantage is that the inertia forces to be overcome are less in a hydraulic planer than in the conventional gear-driven planer. The gear-driven planer, with its fast-revolving parts, including the rotor of the drive motor, has several times more inertia force to overcome than the simple piston rod and piston of the hydraulic drive. Overcoming inertia consumes energy, and, with rapid short strokes, the difference in power consumption is noticeable. Further advantages of hydraulic drives are uniform cutting pressure, quick table reversal, rapid means of varying the stroke, and less noise in operation.

Double-housing planer. This type of planer consists of a long heavy base on which the table or platen is reciprocated. At the side of the base near the center is located the upright housing. This supports the crossrail upon which the tools are fed across the work. The diagrammatic front view of a Gray double-housing planer, shown in Figure 7, illustrates how the tools are supported and the manner in which they can be adjusted for angle cuts. These tools may be fed manually or by power in either a vertical or a crosswise direction. The motor drive is usually at one side of the planer near the center, and the drive mechanism is located under the platen.

The accuracy of a planer is determined largely by its rigidity and the manner in which the ways in the bed are machined. Most medium-sized planers have one flat and one double-V way which allow for unequal bed and platen expansions. Large planers having three ways will have a double-V way at the center and flat ways at each side. The controls for operation are all at the upright housing. Adjustable dogs at the side of the bed control the stroke length of the platen.

Open-side planer. A variation in housing construction, shown in Figure 8, having the housing on one side only, is known as an *open-side* planer and is adapted to handle wide work. The planer shown in the figure is hydraulically driven.

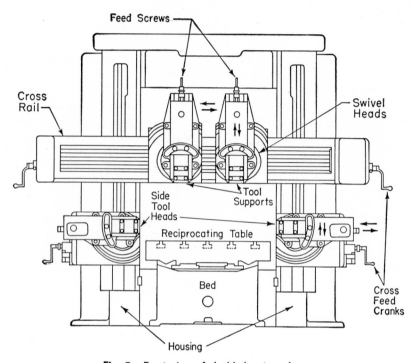

Fig. 7. Front view of double-housing planer.

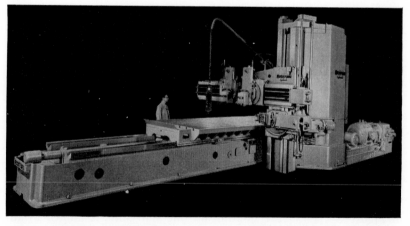

Fig. 8. Hydraulic open-side planer. (Courtesy Rockford Machine Tool Company.)

Both double-housing and open-side planers can be equipped with duplicating attachments for machining irregular surfaces. A master form is mounted on one side of the table so that, as the tracer moves over the surface, the cutting tool is moved accordingly. Such devices are usually hydraulically operated and are similar in operation to the duplicating units used on other machine tools.

Fig. 9. Pit-type planer. (Courtesy Mesta Machine Company.)

Universal planer. The main feature of a *universal planer* is that it will cut on both forward and reverse strokes. In one case a two-edged tool is pivoted in the fixed holder which normally holds it in a center position by a flat spring. As the tool engages the work, it pivots slightly and is held against the block during the cut. At the end of the stroke the other cutting edge is brought into position in the same way. This cutting edge is somewhat longer than the other so that it will yield the proper depth cut on the return stroke. Another tooling provides two separately pivoted tools for two-way planing. A common use for this type of tooling is the cutting of slots in machine tables.

Pit-type planer. A pit-type planer is massive in construction and differs from an ordinary planer in that the bed is stationary and the tool is moved over the work. Figure 9 shows such a planer designed for work up to 14 feet in width and 35 feet in length. Two ram-type heads are mounted on the crossrail, and each is furnished with double clapper block tool holders for two-way planing. The two reversing housings which support the crossrail slide on ways and are screw-driven from an enclosed worm drive at one end of the bed. All feeds are automatic and reversible and are designed to operate either at both ends of the planing stroke or at one end only.

Fig. 10. Plate or edge planer. (Courtesy Consolidated Machine Tool Company.)

Plate or edge planer. For the fabrication of heavy steel plates for pressure vessels and armor plate, a special type of planer, known as a *plate* or *edge planer,* has been devised. Such a planer, having a plate width capacity up to 40 feet, is shown in Figure 10. The plate is stationary and is clamped to a large bed on one side of the housing. To further insure having the work securely held, a series of clamps come down from the cross housing and hold the plate edge in place. The cutting tool is attached to a carriage which is supported on the heavy ways of the planer. A large screw drive is used for moving the carriage, carrying the operator and tools, along the work. The size of the plates that can be edge-machined is limited by the width and height of the machine opening, but there is no limit to the length the plate may extend behind the machine.

Tools and Work-Holding Devices

The tools used in shaper and planer work are of the same general type as those used on a lathe, but are heavier in construction. Some forged tools are used, but generally tool holders with removable bits are more satisfactory since heavy tools are required on the large machines. The holder should be designed to secure the bit near the center line of the holder or the pivot point, rather than at an angle as is customary with lathe tool holders. With the tip of the tool back, there is less tendency for it to dig into the metal and cause chatter.

Cutting tool shapes for common planer operations, shown in Figure 11, are usually tipped with high-speed steel, cast alloy, or carbide inserts. High-speed steel or cast alloys are commonly used in heavy roughing cuts and carbides for secondary roughing and finishing. Caution must be exercised in using carbide tools on machines not equipped with an automatic lifting device for the tool on the return stroke. If the tool is permitted to rub the work, the cutting edge is likely to be chipped.

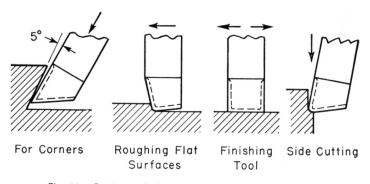

For Corners   Roughing Flat   Finishing   Side Cutting
               Surfaces   Tool

Fig. 11. Cutting tool shapes for common planer operation.

Cutting angles for tools depend on the type of tool used and the material being cut. They are similar to angles used on other single-point tools, but the end clearance need not exceed 4 degrees. Cutting speeds are affected by the rigidity of the machine, how the work is held, tool material, and the number of tools in operation.

Work tables on planers and shapers are constructed with T slots on their surfaces to provide means for holding and clamping down parts that are to be machined. On large machines it is very important that work be securely held because of the heavy cuts that are taken. A heavy-duty vise held by bolts engaging T slots in the work table is suitable for small objects and is the usual method of holding work on a shaper. On planers most work is held by clamping directly to the platen, and a wide variety of clamps, stop pins, and holding devices have been developed for this purpose, as shown in Figure 12. Note

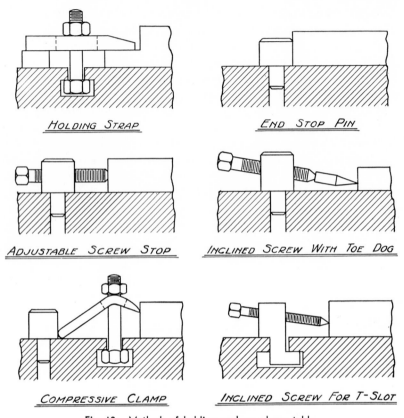

Fig. 12.   Methods of holding work on planer table.

that several of these arrangements are adapted to holding down plates so that the entire surface may be machined.

REVIEW QUESTIONS

1. What type of work can be done on a shaper?

2. Show by sketch how the quick-return motion is accomplished on a shaper.

3. If a shaper makes 36 complete strokes a minute and the length of stroke is 9 inches, what is the cutting speed in feet per minute?   The ratio of return stroke to cutting stroke is 2 to 3.

4. For what type of work is a draw-cut shaper used?

5. What advantages are claimed for hydraulic drives on shapers and planers?

6. What kind of work is done on a vertical shaper?

7. How does a planer differ from a shaper?

8. List the various types of metal planers.

9. What is the main feature of an open-side planer, and why is it so constructed?

10. How is the quick-return motion on a planer accomplished?

11. Describe the operation of a pit-type planer.

12. What is a plate planer, and how does it operate?

13. What kind of cutting tools are used on shapers and planers?

14. How is the cutting tool supported on a planer?

15. How is the work held on a planer bed?

16. Describe the operation of a universal planer.

REFERENCES

American Machinist's Handbook, McGraw-Hill Book Company, 1955.

Bolz, R. W., *Production Process,* Vol. 1, Penton Publishing Company, 1949.

Murphy, J. J., "The Shaper as a Manufacturing Tool," *Machinery,* June 1949.

Tool Engineers Handbook, American Society of Tool Engineers, McGraw-Hill Book Company, 1949.

CHAPTER 20

DRILLING
AND
BORING MACHINES

One of the simplest machine tools used in production and toolroom work is the ordinary *drill press*. It consists of a spindle which imparts rotary motion to the drilling tool, a mechanism for feeding the tool into the work, a table on which the work rests, and a frame. It is essentially a single-purpose machine, although a number of similar machine operations can be performed with the addition of appropriate tools.

The operation of *drilling* consists of producing a hole in an object by forcing a rotating drill against it. The same results are accomplished in some machines by holding the drill stationary and rotating the work, such as drilling on a lathe with the work held and rotated by a chuck.

Other methods of producing a hole are by punching, flame cutting, and coring. The punching process, which is very rapid and specially adapted to thin materials, produces accurate holes, but the punches and dies are expensive. Flame cutting by the use of oxyacetylene or oxygen lances will cut holes through any thickness of commercial material though the holes are accurate neither in size nor in shape.

456

Coring is used principally on large holes in castings to save metal and reduce machining costs.

✔ *Boring* is the enlarging of a hole that has already been drilled or cored. Principally, it is an operation of truing a hole that has been drilled previously with a single-point lathe-type tool. To perform this operation on a drill press a special holder for the boring tool is necessary.

Counterboring is enlarging one end of a drilled hole. The enlarged hole, which is concentric with the original one, is flat on the bottom. The tool for this operation is similar to an end mill and is provided with a pilot pin which fits into the drilled hole to center the cutting edges. Counterboring is used principally to set bolt heads and nuts below the surface. To finish off a small surface around a drilled hole is known as *spot facing*. This is a customary practice on rough surfaces to provide smooth seats for bolt heads. If the top of a drilled hole is beveled to accommodate the conical seat of a flat-head screw, the operation is called *counter-sinking*.

– *Reaming* is the operation of enlarging a machined hole to proper size with a smooth finish. A reamer is an accurate tool and is not designed to remove much metal; hence, the allowance for reaming should not exceed 0.015 inch. Although this operation and those previously mentioned can be done on a drill press, other machine tools are equally well adapted to perform them.

Classification of Drilling Machines

Drilling machines are classified according to their general construction:

1. Portable drill

2. Sensitive drilling machine
   (a) Bench mounting
   (b) Floor mounting

3. Upright drilling machine
   (a) Light duty
   (b) Heavy duty

4. Radial drilling machine
   (a) Plain
   (b) Semiuniversal
   (c) Universal

5. Gang drilling machine

6. Multispindle drilling machine
   (a) Single unit
   (b) Way-type

7. Automatic-production drilling machine
   (a) Indexing table
   (b) Tranfer type

8. Deep-hole drilling machine
   (a) Vertical
   (b) Horizontal

These drilling machines vary considerably in size, method of feeding the drills, and application of power.

Drilling machine size. Portable drilling units are specified according to the maximum diameter drill which they will hold. The size of a sensitive or upright drilling machine is designated in inches by the diameter of the largest work piece that can be drilled. Thus a 24-inch machine is one that has at least 12 inches clearance between the center line of the drill and the machine frame. Most drilling machines are in the range of 16 to 48 inches.

The size of radial drilling machines is based upon the length of the arm in feet. Usual sizes are 4, 6, and 8 feet. In some cases the diameter of the column in inches is also used in expressing size.

Portable and sensitive drills. Portable drills are small compact drilling machines used principally for drilling operations which can not be conveniently done on a regular drill press. The simplest of these is the hand-operated drill. Most portable drills, however, are equipped with small electric motors. These drills operate at fairly high speeds and accommodate drills up to ½ inch in diameter. Similar drills, using compressed air as a means of power, are used where sparks from the motor may constitute a fire hazard.

The *sensitive* drilling machine is a small high-speed machine of simple construction similar to the ordinary upright drill press. It consists of an upright standard, a horizontal table, and a vertical spindle for holding and rotating the drill. Machines of this type are hand-fed, usually by means of a rack and pinion drive, on the sleeve holding the rotating spindle. These drills may be driven directly by a motor, by a belt, or by means of a friction disk. The friction-disk drive has considerable speed regulation, although it is not suitable for slow speeds and heavy cuts. Sensitive drill presses are suitable only for light work and are seldom capable of rotating drills over ⅝ inch in diameter.

Upright drills. *Upright* drills are similar to sensitive drills, except that they have power-feeding mechanisms for the rotating drills and are designed for heavier work. Figure 1 shows a 21-inch machine with a box-type upright. A box-column machine is more rigid than a round-column machine and consequently is adapted to heavier work. This machine is provided with nine spindle speeds offered in several speed ranges from 75 to 3500 rpm. Feed rates of 0.004, 0.008, 0.014, and 0.020 inch per revolution are controlled by a single feed lever. The feed clutch is automatically controlled so that the spindle will be disengaged when it reaches its upper or lower limit of travel. It also can be set to disengage at any predetermined depth if the feed trip dial on the left of the sliding head is set. This machine can be used for tapping as well as for drilling.

Radial drilling machine. The *radial* drilling machine is designed for large work where it is not feasible for the work to be moved around if several holes are to be drilled. Such a machine is shown in Figure 2. It consists of a vertical column supporting an arm which carries the drilling head. The arm may be swung around to any position over the work bed, and the drilling head has a radial adjustment along this arm. These adjustments permit the operator to locate the drill quickly over any point on the work. *Plain* machines of this type will drill only in the vertical plane. On *semi-universal* machines the head may be swiveled on the arm to drill holes at various angles in a vertical plane. *Universal* machines have an additional swiveling adjustment in either the head or the arm and can drill holes at any angle.

Gang drilling machine. When several drilling spindles are mounted on a single table, it is known as a *gang drill*. There are two types, those with spindle units permanently spaced along the table and those with an adjusting feature permitting the spindles to be spaced at various distances. The first and most common type is adapted to production work

Fig. I. Twenty-one-inch upright drill. (Courtesy Cincinnati Bickford Tool Company.)

where several operations must be performed. The work is usually held in a jig which can be easily slid on the table from one spindle to the next. If several operations must be performed, such as drilling two different-sized holes and reaming them, four spindles are set up. With automatic feed control, two or more of these operations may be going on simultaneously, attended by only one operator. The arrangement is similar to operating several independent drill presses, but is much more convenient because of its compactness. A four-spindle machine is shown in Figure 3. This machine has sepa-

Fig. 2.   Radial drilling machine.   (Courtesy The American Tool Works Company.)

rate motors for each spindle and is equipped with power feed and lead-screw tapping arrangement.

When the job demands that several holes be drilled in line on a long piece, it is necessary to have spindle units that can be adjusted to give the desired hole spacing. Machines of this type are used for any straight-line, multiple-hole drilling applications, as in pipes, channels, castings, angles, and plates.

Multispindle drilling machine. Multispindle drilling machines have been developed for the purpose of drilling several holes simultaneously. These machines are essentially production machines and, when once set up, will drill many parts with such accuracy that all parts are interchangeable. In some applications drilling jigs are unnecessary, but in most cases a plate provided with hardened bushings is essential to guide the drills accurately into the work. Multispindle drilling machines differ principally in the way the drills are held and in the way the feed is accomplished.

Fig. 3. Four-spindle gang drilling machine. (Courtesy Barnes Drill Company.)

Most multispindle machines are of the vertical type. The head assembly has a number of fixed upper spindles driven from pinions surrounding a central gear. A corresponding number of spindles are located below this gear and are connected to the upper ones by a tubular drive shaft and two universal joints. These lower spindles, carrying the drills, may be adjusted over a wide area. The entire head assembly carrying all of the spindles travels on vertical double-V ways. The drilling cycle consists of rapid advance of drills to the work, proper feed, and rapid return of drills to starting position.

Multiple drilling machines frequently use a table feed in place of the one just described, thus eliminating the movement of the heavy geared-head mechanism which rotates the drills. This may be done in several ways: by rack and pinion drive, by lead screw, or by a rotating plate cam. The last method is well adapted to provide varying motions which give rapid approach, uniform feed, and quick return to the starting position.

Fig. 4. Vertical hydraulic drilling machine equipped with indexing table and two horizontal way-type units. (Courtesy Baker Brothers.)

Way-type, semiautomatic drilling machines are used extensively in production work. These are usually two-, three-, or four-way drilling machines designed principally for single-purpose jobs. Engine block castings and similar parts requiring the drilling of many holes are typical examples of the work done on these machines. A large three-way drilling machine, illustrated in Figure 4, is an example of building up a multiple drilling machine by utilizing a standard, heavy-duty vertical machine and two horizontal way-type units. The vertical drill is hydraulically operated and can be used either with a single drill up to 3 inches or with a multispindle head, operating several smaller drills. The two horizontal way-type machines, each equipped with portable hydraulic feed units, are used for production jobs requiring holes on three sides; however, if they are used with an indexing table, other type jobs are possible.

Automatic production drilling machines. Frequently designated as *automated* machines, they complete a series of machining operations at successive stations and transfer the work from one sta-

Fig. 5. Special unit for drilling, chamfering, and tapping operations, consisting of three vertical production drilling machines with indexing table. (Courtesy Barnes Drill Company.)

tion to the next. They are, in effect, a production line of connected machines which are synchronized in their operation so that the work piece, after being loaded at the first station, progresses automatically and without manual handling through the various stations to its completion. In general the automatic machines are of the indexing table or the in-line transfer types.

1. INDEXING TABLE. Parts requiring only a few operations are adapted to indexing table machines which are made with either

turns work to successive stages.

Fig. 6. Fifteen-station automatic-transfer machine for processing automobile cylinder heads. (Courtesy Greenlee Brothers & Company.)

vertical or horizontal units, spaced around the periphery of the indexing table. A special three-unit, vertical machine with a four-station indexing table is shown in Figure 5. This machine is arranged to hold two clutch housing castings in each station, and at successive stations the parts are drilled, chamfered, spot-faced, and tapped. Indexing is automatic from the start of the cycle until its completion. This unit is made up of three standard hydraulic production machines with the specially provided indexing table. Reaming, facing, and, in some cases, milling operations can also be performed on these machines.

2. TRANSFER TYPE. Machines known as *transfer machines* are not limited to drilling, reaming and boring but may perform milling, threading, and other operations. The principal feature of these machines is that they are provided with suitable handling or transfer means between successive stations.

In Figure 6 is shown a 15-station unit for processing automobile cylinder heads. The cycle time of 37.2 seconds is based on the time consumed by the longest series of operations performed at one of the stations and includes the time for transfer and for clamping and unclamping the work, as well as the time for tool movements and operation. Some 96 holes are processed at the various stations, and at one a milling operation is performed. Provision is made at the fourth and eighth station for a 360-degree turnover fixture for dumping chips; parts may also be removed at these stations if necessary. The production rate for the machine is 77 pieces per hour when it is operating at a normal efficiency of 80%.

Automatic-transfer machines range from comparatively small units having only two or three stations to long, straight-line machines with as many as 80 stations. They have been used primarily in the automobile industry where, by high production schedules, it is possible to offset their high initial cost by savings in labor. Products processed by these machines include cylinder blocks, cylinder heads, refrigeration compressor bodies, axle housings, and similar parts.

Deep-hole drilling machine. Several problems not encountered in ordinary drilling operations arise in the drilling of long holes in rifle barrels, long spindles, connecting rods, and certain oil-well drilling equipment. As the hole length increases, it becomes more and more difficult to support the work and the drill properly. The rapid removal of chips from the drilling operation becomes necessary to insure the proper operation and accuracy of the drill. Rotational speeds and feeds must be carefully determined, since there is greater possibility to deflection than when a drill of ordinary size is used.

To overcome these problems, deep-hole drilling machines have been developed. In design these machines may be of either the horizontal or the vertical type; they may be of single-spindle or multi-spindle construction; and they may vary as to whether the work or the drill is caused to revolve. In Figure 7 is illustrated a two-spindle machine of the horizontal type. The work is supported at one end in the headstock and on the other end by the work carriage at the center of the machine. Rotation is given to the work from the headstock spindles. The work carriage supports the drills by means of hardened bushings at a point just adjacent to where they enter the work. The other end of the drill is supported by the drill carriage at the right, and, if necessary, center supports are also used. The feeding of the drill is obtained from the lead screw which forces it slowly into the rotating work. The drill feed must be light to avoid deflecting the drill. Much work is also being done on precision boring machines upon which gun drills are rotated. This is necessary where it is impractical to rotate the part, due to its size or shape. Holes drilled in these machines are very accurate.

Fig. 7. Two-spindle horizontal deep-hole drilling machine. (Courtesy Pratt & Whitney Company.)

Kinds of Drills

Straight fluted drills. There are two kinds of straight fluted drills used for deep hole drilling as shown in Figure 8. The upper one, known as a *trepanning drill,* has no dead center and leaves a

Fig. 8. Types of single-fluted drills for deep-hole drilling. (Courtesy National Twist Drill and Tool Company.)

solid core of metal. As the drill advances, the core acts as a continuous center guide at the point where the cutting is done. This prevents the drill from running to one side, and the hole accuracy is easy to maintain. The design of this drill, with the cross section of a hole, is illustrated in Figure 9. The other type, known as a *center-cut gun drill*, has been the conventional drill for many years. It is still used for much deep hole drilling, such as the drilling of blind holes where a core-type drill cannot be used.

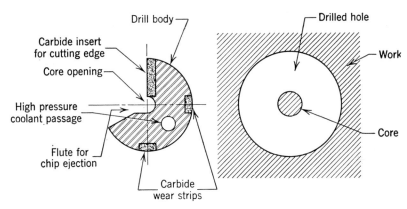

Fig. 9. *Left.* Cross section of carbide-tipped, trepanning deep-hole drill illustrating drill design. *Right.* Cross section of hole being drilled showing solid core of metal at center. (Courtesy National Twist Drill and Tool Company.)

Each type has only a single cutting edge with a straight flute running throughout its length. Oil, under considerable pressure, is brought to the tip of the drill through the hole in the lip. The chips are carried out of the hole along the flute of the drill as rapidly as they are formed. Greater accuracy and finish may be obtained in deep holes by subsequent use of special reamers or broaching tools.

Twist drills. The most common type of drill is the twist drill, having two flutes and a cutting edge. In Figure 10 the nomenclature of this drill, as well as the usual point, clearance, and end angles, are shown. The drill is held and properly centered in the socket of the drilling-machine spindle by means of the *tapered shank*. This has a Morse Taper of approximately $\frac{5}{8}$ inch per foot, which is standard for drills, reamers, and other similar tools. The *tang* at the end of the taper fits into a slot in the socket to prevent slipping of the tapered surface. Straight-shank drills are held and properly centered in a drill chuck. These drills are cheaper than those having a tapered shank, and such construction is common for small drills.

Several kinds of drills, varying as to the number and angle of the flutes, are shown in Figure 11. Two-fluted drills with either interior or exterior oil channels are frequently used on turret-lathe-production drilling. Three-fluted drills are used principally for enlarging holes

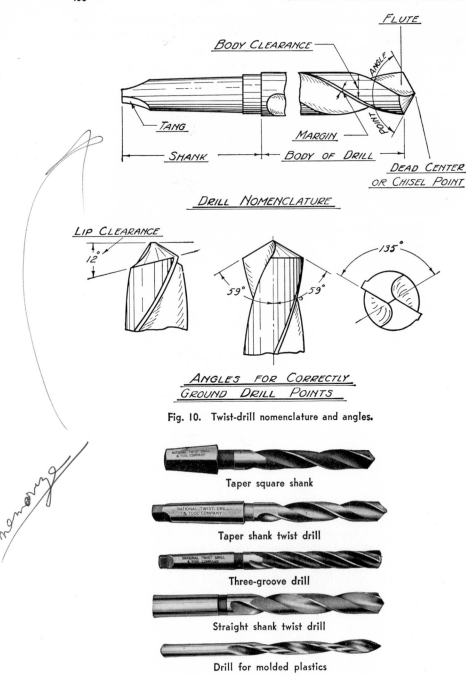

Fig. 10.   Twist-drill nomenclature and angles.

Taper square shank

Taper shank twist drill

Three-groove drill

Straight shank twist drill

Drill for molded plastics

Fig. 11.   Types of drills.   (Courtesy National Twist Drill and Tool Company.)

previously punched, drilled or cored. The same applies to four-fluted drills. Both have the advantage of greater productivity and improved finish over two-fluted drills. Various other drills with different flute angles have been developed, to give improved drilling

Fig. 12. Cutter for making round holes in thin metal. (Courtesy Armstrong-Blum Manufacturing Company.)

Fig. 13. Cutting with a fly cutter. (Courtesy Robert H. Clark Company.)

to special materials and alloys. In addition, some drills are made in combination with other tools, such as the combination drill and tap or the drill and countersink.

Special drills. For drilling large holes in pipe or sheet metal, twist drills are not suitable because the drill tends to dig into the work, or the hole is too large to be cut by a standard-size drill. Round holes are easily cut in thin metal by means of a hole cutter, as shown in Figure 12. _Saw-type cutters_ of this design can be obtained for a wide range of sizes. For very large holes in thin metal a _fly-cutter_ is used. Such a cutter, shown in Figure 13, consists of tool bits held in a horizontal holder, which can be adjusted to accommodate a wide range of diameters. Both cutters cut in the same path, but one is set slightly below the other.

A drill designed by the Black Drill Company, for hardened steel, operates at high speed and develops sufficient friction to anneal the steel and permit cutting without softening the drill point. This drill has a triangular section with three flutes, although for counter-boring work a flat end can be used. The point angle for best results is 130 degrees. Drills of this type are used for carburized stock, spring steel, die sections, knives, and similar hard materials.

Drill Performance

In evaluating drill performance, the material of which the drill is made must not be overlooked. It has been previously stated that high-speed steel tools will stand about twice the cutting speed of carbon-tool steel. For hard and extremely abrasive materials, drills tipped with tungsten carbide give excellent service. Stellite and other nonferrous, hard-surfacing alloys are also being used for similar difficult materials. Many drills are now chrome plated to provide a hard wearing surface.

Point angle. To obtain good service from a drill it must be properly ground. The point angle should be correct for the material that is to be drilled. For steel, aluminum, brass, and most metals, 118 degrees has proved satisfactory, but for plastics, this angle should be reduced to 90 degrees or under. Some of the harder steel alloys however, use angles greater than 118 degrees. In grinding this angle, care must be exercised to get the lips the same length as well as to have the angle the same on each side of the drill center line. The clearance angle (see Figure 10) should be 12 degrees.

Helix angle. Drill performance is also affected by the helix angle of the flutes. Although this angle may vary from 0 to 45 degrees, the usual standard for steel and most materials is 30 degrees. The smaller this angle is made, the greater is the torque necessary to operate a given feed. As the angle is increased appreciably, the life of the cutting edge is reduced. Some materials are drilled more efficiently by drills with special helix angles. For example, an angle of 45 degrees works very satisfactorily for zinc alloys and aluminum, whereas a 20-degree angle is recommended for Bakelite.

Cutting fluids. To obtain best performance and long life for cutting edges, some lubricant or coolant should be used. The purpose of a cutting fluid is to reduce friction between the drill and the work, to facilitate removal of chips, and to cool the work and tool. In production drilling the matter of cooling is most important. To insure long tool life a cooling medium should be selected that will carry away the heat at the same rate that it is generated. A few of the suggested coolants are:

Aluminum—⅔ lard oil, ⅓ kerosene   Glass—Kerosene
Brass—⅔ lard oil, ⅓ kerosene   Magnesium—Dry
Bronze—Soluble oil   Malleable iron—Soluble oil
Copper—Soluble oil   Steel—Soluble oil
Cast iron—Dry   Tool steel—Lard or soluble oil[1]

Cutting speed. The amount of metal removed is a function of both the cutting speed and feed. The *cutting speed,* expressed in feet per minute, is a measure of the peripheral speed of the drill. Frequently, this speed is arbitrarily chosen without regard to efficient operation. For high-speed drills on ordinary steels it should be around 110 fpm. Cutting speeds vary from 20 to 250 fpm, depending on the material hardness. Carbon steel drills should be operated at about one-half the speed recommended for high-speed drills.

Drill feed. In all drilling operations it is more efficient to remove metal in thick chips than in thin ones. The best tool life for a given rate of metal removal is obtained by using the highest possible feed which will still give free chip ejection.[2] If the feed is held constant, tool life increases as the cutting speed is decreased.

Drill feeds are expressed in inches per revolution. In making the proper selection, the cutting speed of the metal being worked on as well as the drill material must be taken into consideration. Feeds for high-speed drills below 1 inch usually range from 0.0025 to 0.012 inch per revolution; however, reference should be made to feed tables in handbooks dealing with the subject for the proper feeds and speeds to use for various situations.

Drilled-hole size. Hole accuracy depends largely upon how the drilling operation is performed as well as upon such factors as point angle and lip lengths. Conventional, two-fluted drills will normally drill slightly oversize in most metals. Tests conducted under the auspices of the Metal Cutting Tool Institute indicate that the amount of hole oversize obtained from drills ranging from ⅛ to 1 inch in diameter may be computed by the following simple relationships:

$$\text{Average oversize} = 0.002 + 0.005D*$$
$$\text{Maximum oversize} = 0.005 + 0.005D$$
$$\text{Minimum oversize} = 0.001 + 0.003D$$

* D = nominal drill diameter in inches.

These relationships apply not only to holes drilled in steel and cast iron, but also to most nonferrous metals.

[1] From *Tool Engineers Handbook,* American Society of Tool Engineers, McGraw-Hill Book Company, 1949.

[2] Carl Oxford, Jr., "Some Recent Research on Twist Drill, and Drilling," *The Tool Engineer,* March 1955.

Methods of Producing Accurate Holes

Multiple operation method.   To obtain a hole of accurate size, some precision sizing operation must usually follow the drilling. A hole should be drilled undersize and then accurately finished to size by boring, reaming, or both.   Because of the bluntness of the drill point, it is difficult to start a drill accurately without a centering

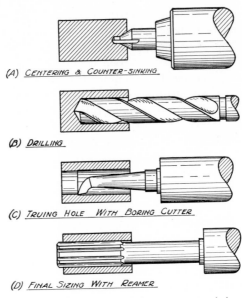

(A) CENTERING & COUNTER-SINKING

(B) DRILLING

(C) TRUING HOLE WITH BORING CUTTER

(D) FINAL SIZING WITH REAMER

Fig. 14.   Procedure for producing accurate holes.

hole.   The operations needed to produce an accurate hole, as illustrated in Figure 14, include locating and centering the hole, the actual drilling, truing the hole with a boring tool, and reaming the hole to accurate size.   This is common practice for producing accurate holes on lathes and milling machines.   If drilling jigs are used, the centering and boring operation may be omitted.

Double-margin drills.   Because of the expense of multiple operations in producing accurate holes, much research has been devoted to this problem.   The *double-margin drill,* shown in Figure 15, is one development which differs from the conventional drill by having an additional secondary margin on the trailing edge of each land. This provides four guide points and results in greatly improved drill stability, tending to keep the drill on a straight path.   In addition to improved straightness, oversize drilling is reduced.

Step drill. Another method of producing a straight hole is by using a _double-margin step drill_ as shown in Figure 16. This drill combines into one operation the drilling of a small pilot or center

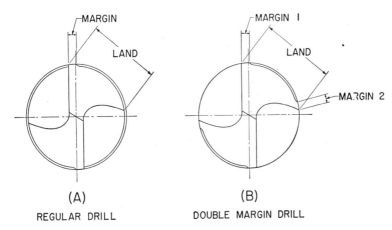

(A)
REGULAR DRILL

(B)
DOUBLE MARGIN DRILL

Fig. 15. End views of conventional (A) and double-margin (B) drills, showing difference in construction. (Courtesy National Twist Drill and Tool Company.)

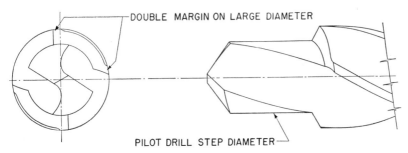

Fig. 16. Construction of double-margin step drill. The pilot diameter is not relieved in order to provide improved piloting action. (Courtesy National Twist Drill and Tool Company.)

hole, the enlarging of the hole, and the finishing of the hole to size. The small pilot drill portion steadies the drill, while the double-margin portion finishes the hole to size. The hole is considerably less oversize than those produced by the conventional twist drills.

Reamers and Miscellaneous Tools

A _reamer_ is a tool used to finish a hole previously drilled or bored. The material removed by this process should be around 0.015 inch and for accurate work should not exceed 0.005 inch. Because of the small stock removed by this process, reamed holes are perfectly round and have a smooth surface. Any tolerance is above the nominal size. In some cases it is desirable to have the hole a fraction of a thousandth oversized in order to produce certain fits.

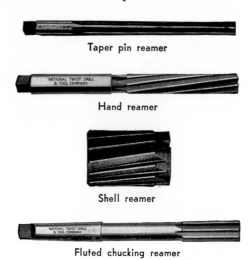

Taper pin reamer

Hand reamer

Shell reamer

Fluted chucking reamer

Fig. 17. Types of reamers. (Courtesy National Twist Drill and Tool Company.)

Reamers are available for different materials and applications. They are:

1. Hand reamer
2. Chucking reamer
3. Shell reamer
4. Taper reamer

5. Expansion reamer
6. Adjustable reamer
7. Special-purpose reamer

Illustrations of several types of reamers are shown in Figure 17. The *hand reamer* is a finishing tool for very accurate holes. Only a few thousandths of an inch of metal should be removed. It is slightly tapered at the end to facilitate starting and has very little clearance on the flutes. This type, as well as most of the others, is made with both straight and spiral flutes. *Chucking reamers* are designed to be power-driven at slow speeds and are made in two general types, rose and fluted reamers. *Rose reamers* do all cutting on the beveled end. There is no relief on the lands of the flutes, and they have a very slight taper toward the shank to prevent binding. *Chucking fluted reamers* cut on the straight flutes, which are backed off or relieved the entire length. Both reamers are made with straight or taper shanks. A reamer, when set up on a machine, should be "floating" so as to center itself properly with the hole. *Shell reamers,* made in both types, consist of a shell end mounted on an arbor. This construction results in an economy where high-priced alloys

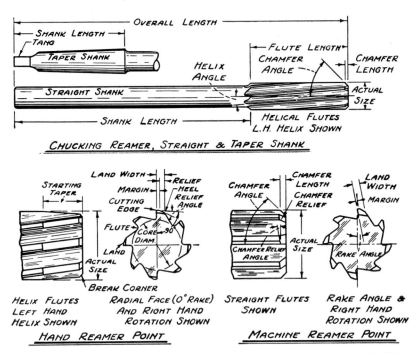

Fig. 18. Sketch illustrating terms applying to reamers, American Standard B5.14–1941. (Courtesy American Standards Association.)

are used, since the arbor can be salvaged when the reamer is worn out. *Expansion reamers* can be adjusted either to compensate for wear or purposely to ream oversized holes. *Adjustable reamers* differ in that they can be manipulated to take care of a considerable range in sizes. *Taper* and other special-purpose reamers are similar to those described, except that they are shaped for some special job. The sketches shown in Figure 18 illustrate terms applying to reamers as proposed by the American Standards Association.

Drilling Jigs

In production work, where many parts are to be drilled and interchangeability is desired, it is essential to provide means for quickly and accurately locating the drill with reference to the work. This is accomplished by building a *jig* which holds the part and guides the

cutting tool to the proper location. Such a device is a good example
of the transfer of skill from a mechanic to an accessory part of a
machine, thus permitting the operation to be accurately accomplished

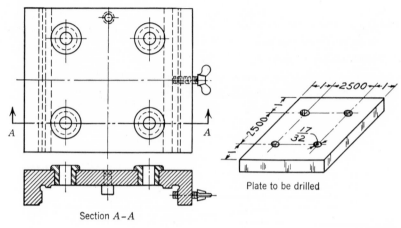

Section *A–A*

Fig. 19. Plate drilling jig.

by an unskilled operator. This is well illustrated in the drilling
of four holes in a plate by using a plate or channel jig similar to the
one shown in Figure 19. The jig is made with hardened steel bush-

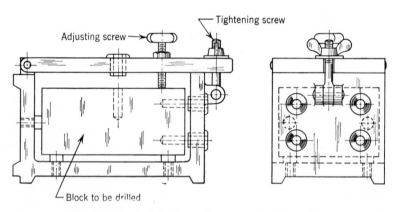

Fig. 20. Box-type jig for drilling two sides of a block.

ings which accurately locate the positions of the four holes. Any
number of plates may be clamped in this jig, and each part will be
identical with the other.

Jigs all perform the same function but differ widely in appearance

according to the shape and design of the part to be worked on.
Classification is based on their general appearance and construction.
In Figure 20 is shown a box-type jig with open sides arranged for
drilling two sides of a block. Figure 21 illustrates a table-type jig
for drilling four holes in a flange.
Other types in general use include
templet, open, indexing, diameter,
and universal.

A jig should be designed to
provide quick and easy loading
and unloading. Likewise, clamping devices must be positive, and
the design should be such that
there is no question about the
proper location in the part of the
jig. Clearance is usually provided
under drill bushings to allow chips
to escape without having to go
through them. This is important
if much metal is to be removed.
In addition, provision should be
made for rapid cleaning of chips
from the jig. Most jigs utilize the
many standard parts that are

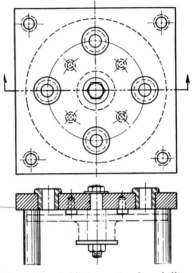

Fig. 21. Table-type jig for drilling
flange holes.

available, such as drill bushings, thumb screws, knobs, rest buttons,
toggle clamps, springs, jig bodies, and numerous other parts. Jigs
are not limited to drilling operations but are also used on tapping,
counterboring, and reaming operations.

Boring Machines

Several machines have been developed that are especially adapted
to boring work. One of them, known as a *jig borer,* is constructed for
precision work on jigs and fixtures. Similar in appearance to a drill
press, it will do both drilling and end-milling work in addition to
boring. The *vertical boring mill* and the *horizontal boring machine*
are adapted to large work. Although the operations that these machines perform can be done on lathes and other machines, their
construction is justified by the ease and economy obtained in holding
and machining the work.

Jig boring machine. In Figure 22 is shown a machine designed
for locating and boring holes in jigs, fixtures, dies, gages, and other
precision parts. Jig boring machines consist of a rigid frame, a fixed

precision spindle for holding the various tools, and a movable table provided with accurate measuring devices upon which the work rests. On the machine shown in the figure, table measurements are made by precision end measures, with which each slide is equipped. Even

Fig. 22.   Precision jig borer.   (Courtesy Pratt & Whitney Company.)

inches are measured with solid end measures graduated in inches and fractions by an inside micrometer.   At the end of the device is a dial indicator which acts as a pressure gage and maintains the zero reading with constant pressure.   This means of measuring permits readings to an accuracy of 0.0001 inch.   Another method of measuring used on some jig boring machines is by means of micrometer lead screws.   This method is accurate for small machines and is

Fig. 23. Vertical boring mill. (Courtesy Giddings & Lewis.)

advantageous in that the work is both moved and measured simultaneously. For long lead screws some sort of compensating device is necessary to take care of known screw inaccuracies.

A jig borer must be well equipped with proper small tools and accessories. The time in boring holes is so short that setting up is often the longest part of the job. Much time can be saved by using spotters or locating tools, reamer drills, and end reamers with the same-size straight shank. These tools, held in a collet, can be quickly changed. Additional tools and accessories should include boring bits, adjustable boring chucks, rotary table, collets for tools, and the necessary bolts and straps to hold the work.

Because of the speed and accuracy with which jig boring machines can perform, they are frequently used on short-run production jobs.

Vertical boring mill.   The vertical boring mill is so named because the work rotates on a horizontal table in a fashion similar to
the old potter's mill.[3]   The cutting tools are stationary, except for
feed movements, and are mounted on the adjustable-height crossrail.
These tools are of the lathe and planer type and are adapted to
horizontal facing work, vertical turning, and boring.   This machine
is sometimes called a rotary planer, and its cutting action on flat
disks is identical with that of a planer.   It may also be compared
to a lathe placed in a vertical position with the rotating chuck or
face plate horizontal.   The cutting action would be the same in
turning the outside diameter of a large cylinder.   These machines,
rated according to their table diameter, vary in size from 3 to 40 feet.
The large machine shown in Figure 23 is a typical example.

The vertical boring mill is able to hold large heavy parts, since
the work can easily be placed on the table with a crane and does not
require much bolting down to hold it in place.   It also takes up very
little floor space compared with other machines that might do the
same work.   Examples of work machined on a vertical boring mill
are large pulleys, grinding disks for glass plants, large flange fittings,
vertical housings for pumps and motors, flywheels, and numerous
other circular-shaped parts.   Very accurate work can be done on
these machines because of their extreme rigidity and simplicity of
design.

Precision boring machines.   Precision boring machines are constructed for either horizontal or vertical operation and are frequently
equipped with several work stations.   Figure 24 shows a 3-station
machine precision-boring automotive rocker arms at the rate of 578 per
hour.   Escapements drop the pieces out of the magazine one at a
time for machining.   A continuous conveyer then takes them to the
next operation after they are unchucked.

Other machines are specially designed for precision boring of
automobile cylinders.   These machines bore all cylinders simultaneously, and accurate alignment is maintained between all holes.

Horizontal boring machine.   The horizontal boring machine,
which differs from the vertical boring mill in that the work is stationary and the tool is revolved, is adapted to the boring of horizontal holes, as can be seen by reference to Figure 25.   The horizontal spindle for holding the tool is supported in an assembly at one
end which can be adjusted vertically within the limits of the machine.   This movement and the rotary motion given the tool are the
only movement the tool usually has.   A work table having longitu-

[3] See also discussion of vertical turret lathe in Chapter 17.

dinal and crosswise movements is supported on ways on the bed of
the machine. In some cases the table is capable of being swiveled
to permit indexing the work and boring holes at desired angles. At
the other end of the machine is an upright to support the outer

Fig. 24. Precision-boring automotive rocker arms on 3-station automatic machine.
(Courtesy The New Britain Machine Company.)

end of a boring bar when boring through holes in large castings.
On some machines, designed for work on extremely large parts, the
parts are bolted to a large face plate permanently mounted on the
floor. The upright carrying the boring spindle is then mounted on
ways to provide means of crosswise adjustment with the work. The
longitudinal feed of the rotating spindle is accomplished by having
two spindles, one inside the other, the inside one having an independent traverse feed.

Boring Tools

Boring is the enlarging of holes previously drilled or cored.
Drilled holes are frequently bored to eliminate any possible eccen-

tricity and to enlarge the hole to a reaming size. Boring tools may also be used to finish holes to correct size as is frequently done on large holes or on odd-sized holes for which no reamer is available.

Tools used in horizontal boring machines are mounted in either a heavy bar or a boring head which in turn is connected to the main spindle of the machine. Most boring operations on this ma-

Fig. 25. Horizontal boring machine. (Courtesy The Bullard Company.)

chine use a single-point cutter as shown in Figure 26 as they are simple to set up and maintain. The bar serves to transmit the power from the machine spindle to the cutter as well as to hold it rigidly during the cutting operation. The workpiece is normally stationary, and the rotating cutter is fed through the hole. It is often necessary to provide additional support for the bar as shown in the figure. The bar must be long enough to reach the end support and also must provide the necessary longitudinal traverse for the machining operation.

For precision boring work on milling machines, jig borers, or drill preses, it is necessary to use a tool having micrometer adjustment. Such tools are held in a cutter head and rotate. Hence, any increase in hole size must be obtained by adjusting the tool radially from its center.

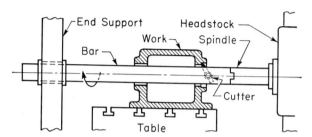

Fig. 26. Straight boring on horizontal boring machine using line bar and end support.

The most popular double-cutter arrangement is the block type, shown in Figure 27, which consists of two opposing cutters resting in grooves on the block. Screws are provided to lock the cutters in position as well as to adjust them. The entire assembly fits into a

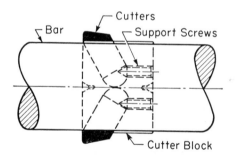

Fig. 27. Block-type boring cutter.

rectangular slot in the bar and is keyed in place. Cutters are ground while assembled in the block and are held in alignment by the center holes provided. The responsibility for tool accuracy and setup belongs to the tool room personnel rather than the operator.

The boring tool commonly used in small machines such as lathes, is a single-pointed tool, supported in a manner that permits its entry into a hole. This tool, shown in Figure 28A, is forged at the end and then ground to shape. It is supported in a separate holder which fits into a lathe tool post. For turret lathes, slightly different holders and forged tools, similar to the one shown at B, are used. A modification of this tool is the boring bar shown at C, which is de-

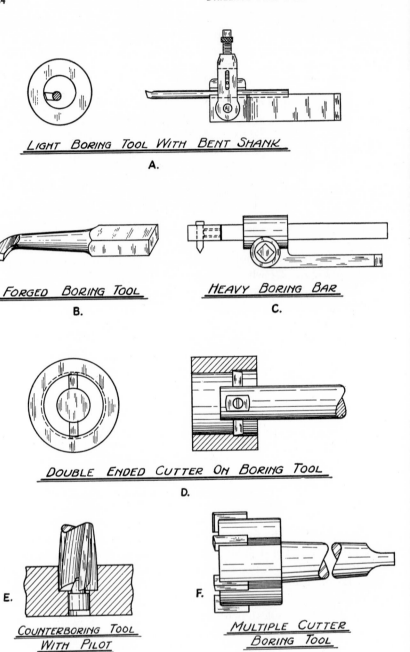

LIGHT BORING TOOL WITH BENT SHANK

A.

FORGED BORING TOOL

B.

HEAVY BORING BAR

C.

DOUBLE ENDED CUTTER ON BORING TOOL

D.

E.

COUNTERBORING TOOL
WITH PILOT

F.

MULTIPLE CUTTER
BORING TOOL

Fig. 28. Types of boring tools.

signed to hold a small, high-speed steel tool bit at the end. The bar supporting the tool is rigid and may be adjusted according to the hole length. Although the clearance, rake, and cutting angles of these tools should be similar to those recommended for lathe work, these angles cannot be used if the holes are small. Greater end clearance is necessary, owing to the curvature of the hole surface, and back rake is almost impossible to attain because of the position of the tool. This may be seen by reference to the illustration showing the tool in working position. The side-rake and side-clearance angles have no restrictions placed on them and may be ground correctly. As the internal diameter is increased, properly shaped tools with correct angles can be used.

In production work boring cutters with multiple-cutting edges are widely used. These cutters, shown at F, resemble shell reamers in appearance but are usually provided with inserted tooth cutters which may be adjusted radially to compensate for wear and variations of diameter. Boring tools of this type have longer life than single-pointed tools and, hence, are more economical for production jobs. The counterboring tool at E, provided with pilots to insure concentric diameters, is designed to recess or enlarge one end of a hole.

REVIEW QUESTIONS

1. What are the common methods of producing a hole in metal?
2. Describe the operation of drilling and the type of tools used.
3. For what type of work is a gang drill used?
4. What are the features of a universal radial drilling machine?
5. What two types of automatic production drilling machines exist, and how do they operate?
6. What type products are machined on transfer machines?
7. What effect does the helix angle have on drill performance?
8. Why should cutting fluids be used in drilling operations?
9. How is the cutting speed of a drill determined?
10. How is drill feed expressed?
11. What is the procedure for producing an accurate hole?
12. What is the function of a reamer?
13. What is a jig?
14. How are holes located and drilled in precision parts?
15. For what type of work is a vertical boring machine used?
16. Describe the tools used on a horizontal boring machine.

REFERENCES

American Machinist's Handbook, McGraw-Hill Book Company, 1955.

Bolz, R. W., *Production Processes*, Penton Publishing Company, Vol. 1, 1949.

Colvin, F. H., and L. L. Haas, *Jigs and Fixtures*, 4th edition, McGraw-Hill Book Company, 1943.

Horizontal Boring, Drilling and Milling Machine Handbook, Giddings and Lewis Machine Tool Company, 1947.

Hinman, C. W., *Practical Design for Milling and Drilling Tools*, McGraw-Hill Book Company, 1938.

Hoagland, F. O., "Drill Points for Deep-Hole Drilling," *Machinery*, October 1940.

Tool Engineers Handbook, American Society of Tool Engineers, McGraw-Hill Book Company, 1949.

CHAPTER 21

MILLING MACHINES

AND

CUTTERS

A milling machine is a machine tool that removes metal as the work is fed against a rotating cutter. Except for rotation, the circular-shaped cutter has no other motion. It is called a *milling cutter* and has a series of cutting edges on its circumference, each of which acts as an individual cutter in the cycle of rotation. The work is held on a table which controls the feed against the cutter. In most machines there are three possible table movements, longitudinal, crosswise, and vertical, but in some the table may also possess a swivel or rotational movement.

The milling machine is the most versatile of all machine tools. Flat or formed surfaces may be machined with excellent finish and great accuracy. Angles, slots, gear teeth, and recess cuts can be made by using various cutters. Drills, reamers, and boring tools can be held in the arbor socket by removing the cutter and arbor. Since all table movements have micrometer adjustments, holes and other cuts can be accurately spaced. Most operations performed on shapers, drill presses, gear-cutting machines, and broaching machines can likewise be done on the milling machine. It produces a better finish and holds to accurate limits with greater ease than a shaper. Heavy cuts can be taken with no appreciable sacrifice in finish or accuracy. Cutters are efficient in their action and can be used a long time before being resharpened. In most cases the work is completed in one pass of the table. These advantages plus the availability of a wide variety of cutters make the milling machine indispensable in the shop and toolroom.

Classification of Milling Machines

Milling machines are made in a great variety of types and sizes. The drive may be either a cone-pulley-belt drive or an individual motor. The feed of the work may be by hand, by mechanical means, or by a hydraulic system. There is also a variety of possible table movements. The usual classification is in accordance with the general design, but even in this classification there is some overlapping. According to design, the distinctive types are:

1. Column and knee type
   (a) Hand miller
   (b) Plain milling machine
   (c) Universal milling machine
   (d) Ram-type universal
   (e) Vertical milling machine

2. Planer milling machine

3. Fixed-bed type
   (a) Simplex milling machine
   (b) Duplex milling machine
   (c) Triplex milling machine

4. Special types
   (a) Rotary table machine
   (b) Drum milling machine
   (c) Planetary milling machine
   (d) Stationary long table machine
   (e) Offset milling machine
   (f) Duplicator or profiling machine
   (g) Pantograph milling machine

Types of Milling Machines

Hand milling machine. The simplest type of milling machine is hand-operated. It may have either the column and knee construction or the table mounted on a fixed bed. Machines operated by hand are used principally in production work for light and simple milling operations, such as cutting grooves, short keyways, and slotting. These machines have a horizontal arbor for holding the cutter and a work table which is usually provided with three movements. The work is fed to the rotating cutter either by the hand movement of a long lever or by a hand screw feed.

Plain milling machine. The plain milling machine is similar to the hand machine except that it is of sturdier construction and is provided with a power-feeding mechanism to control the table movements. Plain milling machines of the column and knee type have three motions, longitudinal, transverse, and vertical. Those of the *fixed-bed type* have only longitudinal table travel but have provision for transverse and vertical adjustments on the spindle which holds the milling cutter arbor.

Figure 1 is a diagrammatic sketch of a column and knee plain milling machine with the principal parts labeled. Although this is a general-purpose machine, it has considerable use in production work. The three table movement hand controls are indicated, but,

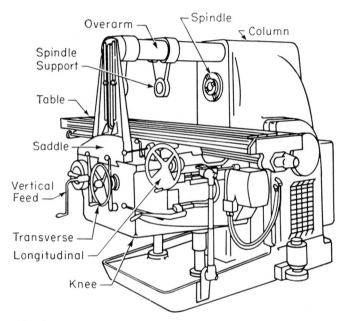

Fig. I. Plain knee-type milling machine. (Courtesy Kearney & Trecker Corporation.)

in addition, each movement is provided with power feed in either direction and rapid traverse. Where the machine is to be used for a production job exclusively, the table can be provided with an automatic cycle. All adjustments on the knee, saddle, and table are controlled by lead screws, provided with micrometer adjustment at the hand wheel.

Cutters are mounted on the horizontal arbor which is rigidly supported by the overarm, spindle, and end braces. The spindle of the machine is hollow, with a taper ($3\frac{1}{2}$ inches per foot) at the end to accurately locate the arbor. Arbors are held in place by a long bolt which screws into the tapered end and is fastened at the back of the machine.

Universal milling machine. The universal machine is essentially a toolroom machine constructed for very accurate work. In appearance it is quite similar to the plain type of milling machine, but differs in that the work table is provided with a fourth movement whch permits the table to swivel horizontally. It is equipped with an index or dividing head. The machine was originally designed with the swiveling feature to permit the cutting of spirals, such as are found on drills, milling cutters, and cams. In addition to being equipped with the dividing-head equipment, universal millers may also be provided with vertical milling attachment, rotary-table attachment, vise, and other similar accessories, all of which add to its utility as a toolroom machine. Aside from doing all types of milling operations, these machines will also do practically any type of operation that can be done on a shaper or a drill press.

A modification of the universal machine is called an *omniversal*. This machine is provided with an additional adjustment so that the table may be tilted and, in that position, fed horizontally.

Ram-type universal machine. Another universal machine, known as a ram-type, is shown in Figure 2. The cutter head is pivoted to the face of the ram and is capable of any angle adjustment between vertical and horizontal. The ram, which carries the cutter head, is provided with an in-and-out movement over the work table. With the combined adjusting features of the cutter head, ram, and work table, it is possible to do conventional horizontal, angular, or vertical milling. This range of adjustment often makes it possible to complete jobs with one setup without having to change to some other machine.

Vertical milling machine. A typical vertical machine, shown in Figure 3, is so called because of the vertical position of the cutter spindle. The table movements are the same as in plain machines. Ordinarily, no movement is given to the cutter other than usual rotational motion. However, the spindle head may be swiveled, which permits setting the spindle in a vertical plane at any angle from vertical to horizontal. This machine is also provided with a short axial spindle travel to facilitate step milling. Some vertical milling machines are provided with rotary attachments or rotating work tables to permit the milling of circular grooves or continuous milling of small production parts. Cutters are all of the end-mill type.

Uses of the machine include drilling, boring, and reaming, accurate spacing of holes because of the micrometer adjustment of the table, facing cuts, and finishing in recesses. Profiling and die-sinking machines are very similar to vertical milling machines in their operation.

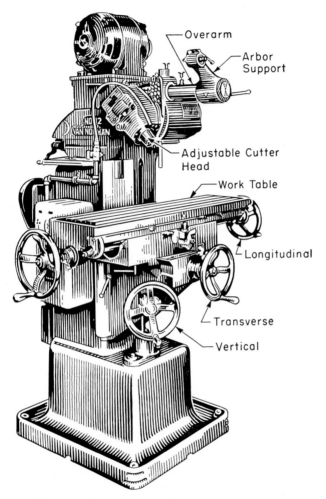

Fig. 2. Ram-type Universal miller. (Courtesy Van Norman Company.)

Planer-type milling machine. This type of milling machine receives its name from its resemblance to a planer. The work is carried on a long table, having only a longitudinal movement, and is fed against the rotating cutter at the proper speed. The variable table-feeding movement and the rotating cutter are the principal features that distinguish this machine from a planer. Transverse and vertical movements are provided on the cutter spindle. These machines are designed for milling large work requiring heavy stock removal and for accurate duplication of contours and profiles. A hydraulically operated unit of this type is shown in Figure 4.

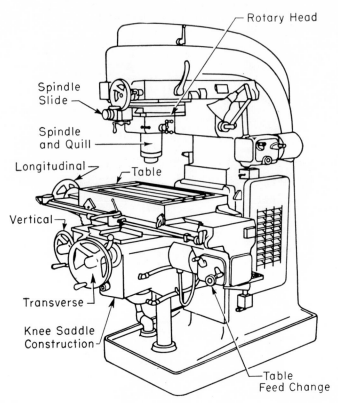

Fig. 3. Rotary head vertical milling machine. (Courtesy Kearney & Trecker Corporation.)

Fixed-bed types of milling machines. Machines of this type are essentially production machines and are of rugged construction. The names *simplex, duplex,* and *triplex* indicate that the machine is provided, respectively, with single, double, and triple spindle heads. Figure 5 illustrates the tooling on a fixed-bed single-head machine for the simultaneous milling of slots in the ends of four valve tappets. In this case two hand clamping fixtures are mounted on each end of a swiveling base. After the operator loads one set of fixtures, he swivels the index base 180 degrees and by pulling a lever actuates the following table cycle: rapid advance to work, feed work to cutter, reverse, rapid return and stop. Since this is a production ma-

Fig. 4. Planer-type milling machine. (Courtesy Giddings & Lewis Machine Tool Company.)

Fig. 5. Simultaneous milling of slots in ends of 4-valve tappets. (Courtesy The Cincinnati Milling Machine Company.)

chine, it is often equipped with a tracer control which guides the tool and permits the cutting of irregular contours. A discussion of this type of tool control is given later on in this chapter.

Special Milling Machines

Rotary table milling machine. Rotary table machines, like the one shown in Figure 6, are adaptations of the vertical milling machine to a rather specialized use. In this case there are two vertical

Fig. 6. Rotary table milling machine. (Courtesy The Ingersoll Mining Machine Company.)

spindles, each equipped with a facing mill. Cylinder heads are roughed at the first station and then finish-milled as they pass the second station. The operation is continuous and there is ample time for the operator to load and unload the machine during the milling. This machine is fast but is obviously limited to the milling of flat surfaces.

Drum-type milling machine. Drum-type millers are special machines designed for production work. They have a large drum fixture similar to the turret on a turret lathe upon which the work is mounted. In operation, the drum fixture rotates slowly, carrying the work against the rotating cutters. Usually there are four cutter spindles. The operation is continuous, since the parts are removed and new ones added after the work has completed its cycle. Most of the work formerly done on drum millers is now done on broaching machines or process lines where the part is transferred from one station to another.

Offset milling machine. The offset miller is another production-type machine. In most of these millers the cutter is mounted on a vertical spindle which extends into a fixture. This fixture is offset, or mounted eccentrically with the cutter, so that, as it revolves, the work is milled as it passes by. The operation is similar to internal grinding with the work being rotated. Only single milling operations, such as slotting or straddle cutting, are performed in this manner.

Planetary milling machine. Planetary milling machines are used for milling both internal and external short threads and surfaces. The work is held stationary, as shown on the machine in Figure 7, and all movements necessary for the cutting are made by the milling cutters. At the start of a job, the rotating cutter is in center or neutral position. It is first fed radially to the proper depth and then given a planetary motion either inside or around the work. The relation between the work and the cutters is illustrated by the line diagram above the machine in the figure. Both internal and external work can be done simultaneously. Typical applications of this machine include the milling of internal and external threads of all kinds of tapered surfaces, bearing surfaces, rear axle end holes, airplane crankcases, shell and bomb ends.

Stationary long table milling machine.[1] This machine was developed to do contour milling on main spars, channel beams, and cap strips for modern airplanes. Because of the length of the parts to be machined the bed of the machine is stationary and is made up in sections varying in length from 30 to 90 feet. All cutters are contained and operated within a carriage which is mounted on and travels the length of the bed. Work mounted on the bed is automatically milled to shape by vertical and horizontal cutters which, in turn, receive their direction from individual templets beside the work.

Duplicating and profiling machines. A large variety of machines which have been developed for die and mold cutting, engraving, and profiling are known as *duplicators, die sinkers, profiling machines, pantograph machines,* etc. Most of them are a special adaptation of a vertical milling machine, although a few operate with the spindle in a horizontal position. The hand-profiling machine is perhaps the

[1] A machine of this type is manufactured by the Onsrud Machine Works.

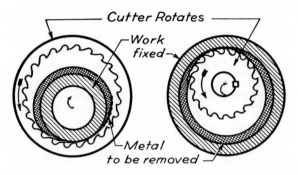

A. EXTERNAL MILLING   B. INTERNAL MILLING

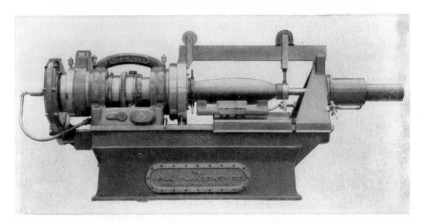

Fig. 7. Planetary milling machine setup for milling threads on bomb end. A and B show cutter action for both external and internal milling. (Courtesy The Hall Planetary Company.)

simplest, having a rotating cutter whose motion is controlled by hand movements of the work table. These movements are guided by moving the table so that the guide pin is in contact with some form or templet as shown in Figure 8. This, in general, is the principle involved in all machines of this type, except that in many of them the movement is automatically controlled from a templet by hydraulic or electrical means.

Pantograph engraving machines. These machines receive their name from the pantograph linkage used to reproduce from a templet at either an enlarged or a reduced scale.

A two-dimensional pantograph, designed for heavy-duty work, is shown in Figure 9. This is a motorized operation with everything automatic within the cycle. The tracer is attached to an endless

Fig. 8. Profiling with former pin. (Courtesy Pratt & Whitney Division—Niles-Bement-Pond Company.)

Fig. 9. Two-dimensional heavy-duty pantograph machine. (Courtesy George Gordon Machine Company.)

chain in the master form and is motor driven at the required speed
for the job. The work cycle is as follows: rapid traverse of cutter
to work, standard downfeed of cutter until it has reached bottom

Fig. 10. Automatic duplicator machine for die work. (Courtesy Ingersoll Milling
Machine Company.)

of cut, controlled feed of cutter by tracer, and finally rapid up-
traverse of cutter to clear casting. By changing the link arrangement of the pantograph, any figure or design can be enlarged or
reduced in size according to required proportions. Machines of this
same general design are also used for engraving silverware and in
light metal die work. A three-dimensional machine is available for

machining parts of any shape or contour. It, too, is equipped with a pantograph mechanism, so an increase or reduction in size can be obtained.

The production of large forming dies for automobile fenders, tops, and panels is an important use of duplicator machines. Such a machine, of large capacity, is illustrated in Figure 10. The machine itself rests on a track and is entirely automatic in operation. Both the templet and the die block are supported on the large angle bracket in front of the machine. A templet of the part to be produced is first prepared and is mounted above as shown in the figure. These templets are made of hard wood, plaster of Paris, or other easily worked materials because the only purpose they serve is to guide the pointer which controls the tool position. The method of cutting and general operation of the machine can be seen by referring to the figure.

Controls for Milling Cutters

The manual control of tools on profilers and pantograph machines, where the operator guides the tool from a templet or model, is satisfactory for certain types of work, but is not economical in production jobs involving the removal of much metal. Automatically controlled tracer methods have been developed which are operated by electrical or hydraulic means. The movement of a roller or tracer on a templet is transferred through a properly arranged circuit to the cutting tool. During this movement forces are released which move the various machine slides in a manner to give the cutter identical movements with that of the tracer. In Figure 11, two slides of the vertical Hydro-tel milling machine, at right angles to one another, are hydraulically controlled by the 360-degree tracer unit, and all four connecting rods are simultaneously milled. Duplicate fixtures are provided to eliminate loading and unloading time.

For complete circumferential milling of an object, vertical milling setups are necessary, the axis of the tracer unit being parallel to the milled surface. When cutters are used on horizontal arbors, only 180-degree movement of the cutter is possible. In this case the tracer unit and the templet which it rides are next to the machine column. As the milling machine table is fed, the cutters rise and fall as dictated by the tracer unit following the templet. Contour milling with the unit having 180-degree movement may also be done with vertical mills, the work and tracer being fed either in a straight line or rotated on duplex rotating tables.

Rise-and-fall movements on milling tables may also be accomplished by the use of heavy cams with roll followers in combination with trip dogs which start and stop various slide movements. This direct control of the motion of one slide while the other is moving at a uniform feed rate imposes heavy loads on the driving mechanism and is not satisfactory for steep climbs. Hydraulically controlled tools require only light contact with form or templet and

Fig. 11. Four-spindle vertical Hydro-tel milling machine hydraulically controlled by the 360-degree tracer unit. (Courtesy The Cincinnati Milling Machine Company.)

have a much greater range of movement. Automatic-tracer-controlled tools provide rapid and accurate machining of irregular surfaces otherwise difficult to machine with economy.

The Velvetrace Kellering Attachment for three-dimensional reproduction, shown in Figure 12, can be adapted to most conventional vertical milling machines. The tracer, electrically controlled, is so designed that it follows the shape of a model, but does not touch it. Basically, the tracer utilizes a high tension spark gap of high voltage, low current, which produces a minute spark of constant length between the tracer point and the electrically conductive model. Any variation in the spark gap produces a proportional change in voltage across the gap, which is instantly amplified and used to control the cutter spindle. Applications for accurate reproduction of three-dimensional forms include metal molds and dies for silverware, art metal, plastics, and glass manufacture.

Fig. 12. Velvetrace Kellering attachment for 3-dimensional reproduction. (Courtesy Pratt & Whitney.)

The Index Head and Its Operation

An *index* or *dividing head* is used to rotate the work through a certain number of degrees or through a fraction of a revolution, or while the table is feeding, as when cutting helical gears. It is a regular piece of equipment on a universal milling machine but may be used on other machines as well. In Figure 13 is shown an index head and its footstock mounted on the work table of a machine. Since much of the work to be machined has to be supported between centers, both units are necessary.

The index head is nothing more than a worm-gear reducer having a ratio of 40 to 1; that is, 40 turns of the crank will rotate the work one complete revolution. The work spindle which is attached to the worm gear has a tapered hole to receive the live center and is also threaded to hold a chuck. A U-shaped piece is ordinarily on the spindle to give positive motion to the work through a dog. Just back of this piece is a direct index plate having 24 equally spaced holes. The entire spindle assembly may be swiveled from horizontal to vertical position. The shaft which operates the worm gear extends to the side of the mechanism and through the index plate and sector. On its end is a crank, having an index pin which fits into the holes on the index plate. Since the plate does not turn, the crank is locked when the index pin is engaged in one of the holes. The index plate is provided with several concentric circles of equally spaced holes to assist in determining the proper number of revolutions of the handle where a fraction of a revolution is involved. The sector arms on the plate are to eliminate the counting of spaces when the handle is being turned between cuts.

The three types of indexing used are *simple, direct,* and *differential.* Most indexing is of the first type and is accomplished by turning the crank a number of turns to rotate the work the desired amount, the index plate being held in a fixed position. With a ratio of 40 to 1, one revolution of the crank will rotate the work $\frac{1}{40}$ of a revolution.

Fig. 13. Index-head assembly for milling a spur gear. (Courtesy Cincinnati Milling Machine Company.)

Hence, in cutting a gear with 40 teeth the crank would be locked to the plate by the index pin and a cut would be made. After the cut, the handle would be turned one revolution and another cut taken, and so on. To cut a gear with 20 teeth would require 2 turns of the handle, or to cut 8 flutes on a reamer, 5 turns. As long as the number of cuts to be taken is a factor of 40, it is a simple matter to calculate the number of handle turns. By following these simple calculations, it is quite obvious that an expression can be set up to compute the number of handle turns for a given condition. The rule to use is

$$\text{Turns of index handle} = \frac{\text{turns of handle to produce 1 turn of work (usually 40)}}{\text{cuts to be made in 1 revolution of work}}$$

When the number of cuts to be made is not evenly divisible into 40, it follows that fractional turns must be made; and for this it is necessary to use the sector device. Assume that 32 teeth are to be cut on a spur gear. If the afore-mentioned rule is used, the number of turns of the index handle would be $^{40}\!/_{32}$ or $1\frac{1}{4}$ turns. First, select a circle on the index plate that is divisible by 4. If a 24-space circle is available, set the sector arms so that there are 6 spaces between them. Hence 1 revolution of the crank plus 6 spaces would give the work the required movement. The same results could be obtained by using a circle with 48 spaces and turning one turn plus 12 spaces. To cut a gear with 72 teeth, the number of turns would be in the ratio of $^{40}\!/_{72}$ or $\frac{5}{9}$. If a 54-space circle were available, the sector arms should be set for 30 spaces. In setting the arms, spaces and not holes should be counted.

Direct indexing is accomplished by using the index plate attached to the work spindle. This plate has 24 divisions and is engaged by a plunger pin on the head. The worm is disengaged from the worm gear, and the plate is turned the required amount by hand. This system of indexing is limited only to those divisions that are factors of 24. It is a quick method of indexing and is used when only a few cuts are required in a revolution.

When indexing is done by degrees with a 40-to-1 index head, each turn of the handle represents $^{360}\!/_{40}$ or 9 degrees. If a 27-space circle were selected, a movement of three spaces of the handle would move the work 1 degree. Four spaces on a 36-hole circle would also represent 1 degree, whereas one space would move the work only $\frac{1}{4}$ degree. By similar calculations the work may be moved any number of degrees or through most common fractions of a degree.

Differential indexing is used when the work has to be turned an amount that cannot be obtained by simple indexing, owing to the lack of a circle on the index plate with the correct number of spaces. For such conditions the index plate is unlocked and connected to a train of gears which receive their motion from the worm-gear spindle. As the handle is turned, the index plate also turns, but at a different rate and perhaps in the opposite direction. Its movement depends on the gears used to drive it. Information for calculating the correct gears to use for a given condition can be found in machine instruction books. After the gears are set up, the operation is similar to simple indexing. Differential indexing makes it possible to rotate the work any fraction of a revolution with the usual index plates furnished with the equipment.

Spiral milling is accomplished by rotating the work as it moves against the rotating cutter. This is done with the use of connecting gears from the lead screw of the work table to the handle spindle of the index head. The lead of the spiral, the distance it advanced in one revolution, is controlled by these gears. With a 40-to-1 reduction in the index head and a 4-pitch lead screw, the lead would be 10 inches if no increase or reduction in the outside gears is assumed. The ratio for computing these gears is

$$\frac{\text{Product of the driving gears}}{\text{Product of the driven gears}} = \frac{10}{\text{desired lead}}$$

Spiral milling is used in cutting spiral gears, flutes on various tools, screws, worm gears, and some types of cams.

Types of Milling Cutters

The milling machine is most versatile because of the large variety of milling cutters available. These cutters are usually classified according to their general shape, although in some cases they are classified by the way they are mounted, the material used in the teeth, or the method used in grinding the teeth.

There are three general designs of cutters:

1. Arbor cutters. These cutters have a hole in the center, for mounting on an arbor.

2. Shank cutters. Cutters of this type have either a straight or tapered shank integral with the body of the cutter. When in use, these cutters are mounted in the spindle nose or in a spindle adapter.

3. Face cutters. These cutters are bolted or held on the end of short arbors and are generally used for milling plane surfaces.

Classification according to materials follows similar classifications of other types of cutting tools. Milling cutters are made of high-carbon steels or various high-speed steels, with sintered-carbide tips, or of certain cast nonferrous alloys. High-carbon steel cutters have a limited use, since they dull quickly if high cutting speeds and feeds are used. Most general-purpose cutters are made of high-speed steels, because such steels maintain a keen cutting edge at temperatures around 1000 to 1100 F. Consequently, they may be used at cutting speeds 2 to $2\frac{1}{2}$ times those recommended for carbon-steel cutters. Cast nonferrous metals, such as Stellite, Crobalt, or Rexalloy, and carbide-tipped cutters, have even greater resistance to heat and are especially adapted to heavy cuts and high cutting speeds. These materials are either used as inserts held in the body of the cutter or are brazed directly on the tips of the teeth.

Cutting speeds of face cutters range from two to five times those recommended for high-speed steel.

Teeth in milling cutters are made in two general styles according to the method used in sharpening them. *Profile cutters* are sharpened by grinding a small land back of the cutting edge of the tooth. This also provides the necessary relief at the back of the cutting edge. *Formed cutters* are made with the relief (back of the cutting edge) of the same contour as the cutting edge. To sharpen these cutters the face of the cutter is ground so as not to destroy the tooth contour.

The types of cutters most generally used, shown in Figure 14, are classified principally according to their general shape or the type of work they will do.

1. Plain milling cutter. A plain cutter is a disk-shaped cutter having teeth only on the circumference. The teeth may be either straight or spiral, but they are usually spiral if the width exceeds ⅝ inch. Wide spiral cutters of this type used for heavy slabbing work may have notches in the teeth to break up the chips and facilitate their removal.

2. Side milling cutter. This cutter is similar to a plain cutter except that it has teeth on the side. In some cases, where two cutters operate together, the cutter is plain on one side and has teeth on the other. Side milling cutters may have straight, spiral, or staggered teeth.

3. Metal slitting saw cutter. This cutter resembles a plain or side cutter except that it is made very thin, usually 3⁄16 inch or less. Plain cutters of this type are relieved by grinding the sides to afford clearance for the cutter.

4. Angle milling cutter. Any cutter, angle-shaped, comes under this classification. They are made into both single- and double-angle cutters. The single-angle cutters have one conical surface, whereas the double-angle cutters have teeth on two conical surfaces. Angle cutters are used for cutting ratchet wheels, for dovetails, flutes on milling cutters, and reamers.

5. Form milling cutters. This name is applied to any cutter on which the teeth are given a special shape. This group includes convex and concave cutters, gear cutters, fluting cutters, corner-rounding cutters, and many others.

6. End-mill cutters. These cutters have an integral shaft for driving and have teeth on both periphery and ends. The flutes may be either straight or helical. Large cutters called shell end mills, have the cutter part separate and are held to a stub arbor, as shown in Figure 15. Owing to the cost of high-speed steel, this construction

Fig. 14.   Types of milling cutters.   (Courtesy Brown & Sharpe Manufacturing Company.)

(a) Spiral end mill cutter.
(b) T-slot milling cutter.
(c) Plain cutter with spiral teeth.
(d) Angle milling cutter.
(e) Woodruff keyseat cutter.
(f) Plain milling cutter.

(g) Inserted tooth cutter.
(h) Metal slitting saw cutter.
(i) Form cutter for gear teeth.
(j) Side milling cutter.
(k) Spiral double-end end mill.
(l) Extra-long spiral end mill.

results in a considerable saving in material cost. End mills are used for surfacing projections, squaring ends, cutting slots, and in recess work such as die making.

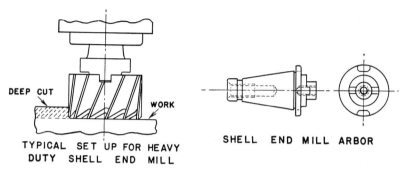

TYPICAL SET UP FOR HEAVY DUTY SHELL END MILL

SHELL END MILL ARBOR

Fig. 15. Shell end mill and arbor.

7. T-slot cutters. Cutters of this type resemble small plain or side milling cutters which have an integral straight or tapered shaft for driving. They are used for milling T slots. A special form is the Woodruff keyseat cutter, which is made in standard sizes for cutting the round seats for Woodruff keys.

8. Inserted tooth cutter. As cutters increase in size, it is economical to insert the teeth made of expensive material into less expensive ordinary steel. Teeth in such cutters may be replaced when worn out or broken.

Milling-Cutter Teeth

A typical milling cutter, with various angles and cutter nomenclature, is shown in Figure 16. For most high-speed cutters positive *radial rake angles* of 10 to 15 degrees are used. These values are satisfactory for most materials and represent a compromise between good shearing or cutting ability and strength. Milling cutters made for softer materials, such as aluminum, can be given much greater rake with improved cutting ability.

Usually only saw-type and narrow, plain milling cutters have straight teeth with zero axial rake. As cutters increase in width, a positive-axial-rake angle is used to increase cutting efficiency.

For high-speed milling with carbide-tipped cutters, negative-rake angles (both radial and axial) are generally used. Improved tool life is obtained by the resultant increase in the *lip angle;* also, the tooth is better able to resist shock loads. Plain milling-type cutters, with teeth on the periphery, usually are given a negative rake of

5 to 10 degress when steel is being cut. Alloys and medium-carbon steels require greater negative rake than soft steels. Exceptions to the use of negative-rake angles for carbide cutters are made when soft nonferrous metals are milled.

The *clearance angle* is the included angle between the land and a tangent to the cutter from the tip of the tooth. It is always positive and should be small so as not to weaken the cutting edge of the tooth. For most commercial cutters over 3 inches in diameter, the

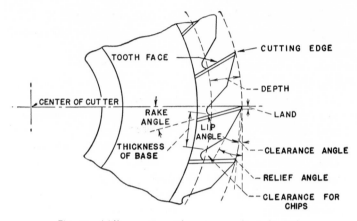

Fig. 16. Milling cutter with various angles indicated.

clearance angle is around 4 to 5 degrees. Smaller-diameter cutters have increased clearance angles to eliminate tendencies for the teeth to rub on the work. Clearance values also depend on the various work materials. Cast iron requires values of 4 to 7 degrees, whereas soft materials such as magnesium, aluminum, and brass are cut efficiently with clearance angles of 10 to 12 degrees. The width of the land should be kept small; usual values are $\frac{1}{32}$ to $\frac{1}{16}$ inch. A *secondary clearance* is ground back of the land to keep the width of the land within proper limits.

Much research on cutter form and size has proved that coarse teeth are more efficient for removing metal than fine teeth. A coarse-tooth cutter takes thicker chips and has freer cutting action and more clearance space for the chips. As a consequence, these cutters provide increased production and decreased power consumption for a given amount of metal removed. Also, fine-tooth cutters have a greater tendency to chatter than those with coarse teeth. However, they are recommended for saw cutters used in the milling of thin materials.

Cutting Speed and Feed

The cutting speed of a milling cutter is determined by the peripheral or surface speed of the cutter. The movement of the work past the cutter is not considered in this calculation. The cutting speed may be expressed by the following equation:

$$CS = \frac{\pi D N}{12} = \text{feet per minute}$$

D is diameter of cutter in inches and N is revolutions per minute.

Since the cutting speed is seldom the unknown, the equation is generally expressed in terms of spindle revolution.

$$N = \frac{12\,CS}{\pi D} = \text{rpm of spindle}$$

If the cutter diameter and cutting speed of the given material are known, this expression gives the proper rotational speed of the spindle. In the selection of the proper cutting speed, the following factors should be considered:

1. *Cutter material.* Cutting speeds are usually given in values for high-speed steel cutters. These values are twice those for carbon-steel cutters and one-half to one-fifth those recommended for carbide-tipped cutters.

2. *Kind of material being cut.* The Brinell hardness of a material is an excellent guide as to its ease of machining. Soft materials like magnesium and aluminum can be milled at much higher speeds than harder materials. Approximate cutting speeds for various materials are given in Table 15, p. 364.

3. *Type of finish required.* The best finishes are obtained with light feeds and high cutting speeds. In general, the cutting speed of finishing cuts should be about 20% higher than roughing cuts.

4. *Cutter life.* Heavy cuts, which accumulate heat rapidly, must be taken more slowly than light cuts. Low cutting speeds should be used for long cutter life.

5. *Use of coolant.* High cutting speeds generate much heat which must be dissipated to protect cutter and work. To accomplish this, the tool and the work should be flooded with a coolant such as soluble, sulfurized, or mineral lard oil. An exception to this is cast iron, which is often milled dry because of the abrasive action of the chips. Kerosene is frequently used as a coolant for aluminum. Since water mixtures present a fire hazard in machining magnesium, only straight cutting oils should be used.

There are two methods of feeding work to the cutter, as shown in Figure 17. Feeding the work against the cutter, as indicated in A, is usually recommended, since each tooth starts its cut in clean metal and does not have to break through possible surface scale. However, tests have proved that, when the work is fed in the same direction as cutter rotation (as shown at B), the cutting is more efficient. Larger chips are removed, and there is less tendency for

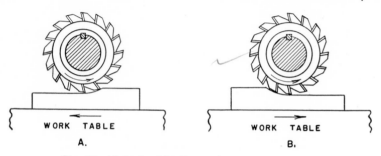

A.   B.

Fig. 17. Methods of feeding work on milling machine.

chatter. This method is frequently used in production work where large cuts are to be taken and the surface of the work is free from scale.

Feed on milling machines is expressed in either of two ways. On some machines it is expressed in thousandths of an inch per revolution of cutter. Such machines have feed changes ranging from 0.006 to as high as 0.300 inch. The other way is to express the feed of table in inches per minute, the usual range being from ½ to 20 inches per minute.

Fixtures

All milling-machine work must be accurately located and rigidly held during the cutting operation. This is ordinarily done by using a *fixture* which holds the work securely but does not guide the tool. Fixtures should be designed with the following points in mind:

1. Work clamps should be quick acting for loading and unloading the part.
2. The work piece must be accurately positioned within the fixture.
3. Provision should be made for the disposal of chips.
4. Fixture should be rigid.

The various fixtures mounted on machines, as shown in Figures 5, 6, and 11, produce interchangeable parts at a reduced operation time.

REVIEW QUESTIONS

1. What machining operations can be done on a milling machine?

2. What additional operations can be performed if the machine is equipped with an index head?

3. How is simple indexing done and for what is it used?

4. Compare a vertical milling machine with a vertical drill press and state what kind of work each will do.

5. How are table or cutter adjustments made on a fixed-bed milling machine?

6. What type of work can be done on rotary-table milling machines?

7. Explain how a planetary milling machine operates.

8. What are the essential differences between a planer and a planer type milling machine?

9. What type of milling machine do you recommend for the following jobs: cut teeth on gear, mill long spars for airplanes, mill impression in metal die, mill surface on aluminum ingot, and cut recess in small casting?

10. Name and describe the different kinds of milling cutters used.

11. A spur gear is to have 35 teeth. How many turns of the index head crank should be made between cuts?

12. How would you mill the hexagon sides on a large hexagon head bolt?

13. How would a T-slot be milled in a casting?

14. How is the cutting speed of a milling cutter determined?

15. How is feed expressed on a milling machine?

16. Sketch a milling cutter tooth and indicate rake, clearance and lip angle.

17. What are some of the important points to be considered in the design of a milling fixture?

REFERENCES

American Machinist's Handbook, McGraw-Hill Book Company, 1955.

A Treatise on Milling and Milling Machines, 3d edition, Cincinnati Milling Machine Company, 1951.

Hinman, C. W., *Practical Design for Drilling and Milling Tools,* McGraw-Hill Book Company, 1938.

Lucht, Fred W., "Face-Milling with Carbide," *Mechanical Engineering,* March 1945.

Machinery's Handbook, 13th edition, Industrial Press, 1948.

Martellotti, M. (*a*) "Milling Cutters and How to Use Them," *American Machinist,* August 17, 1944. (*b*) "Special Rake Angles Used for Carbide Tools," *American Machinist,* February 15, 1945. (*c*) "Clearance and Relief Angles for Milling Cutters," *American Machinist,* March 15, 1945. (*d*) "Selection and Application of Milling Cutters," *American Machinist,* March 16, 1944.

Tool Engineers Handbook, American Society of Tool Engineers, McGraw-Hill Book Company, 1949.

CHAPTER **22**

GEARS AND
GEAR-CUTTING MACHINES

Gears are commonly used to transmit power or rotary motion from one shaft to another. They have the advantage over friction and belt drives in that they are positive in their action, a feature which most machinery requires, since exact speed ratios are essential. However, friction and surface-contact drives have some use in industry where high speeds and light loads are required, and, in a few cases, where loads subjected to impact are transmitted. A gear differs from a friction disk in that it has projections or teeth built up on its circumference so that it may transmit motion through the meshing teeth without slippage.

If the teeth were to be built up on the circumferences of two rolling disks in contact with each other, recesses would have to be provided between the teeth so as to eliminate interference. The original diameter of each disk, known as the *pitch diameter,* would still figure in the gear calculations. It is only an imaginary circle and cannot be seen by inspecting a gear. A portion of a gear is shown in Figure 1 with the pitch circle indicated.

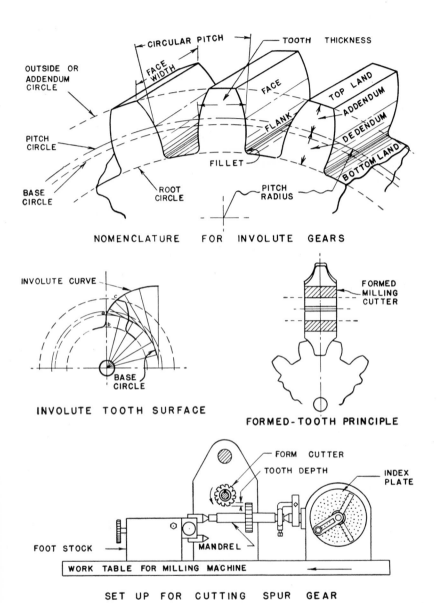

NOMENCLATURE   FOR   INVOLUTE   GEARS

INVOLUTE TOOTH SURFACE

FORMED-TOOTH PRINCIPLE

SET UP FOR CUTTING SPUR GEAR

Fig. I. Nomenclature for involute gears.

Kinds of Gears

The gears most commonly used are those that transmit power between two parallel shafts. Such gears having their tooth elements parallel to the rotating shafts are known as *spur gears*. If the elements of the teeth are twisted or helical, as shown in Figure 2, they

Fig. 2. Helical gears. (Courtesy Foote Brothers Gear and Machine Corporation.)

are known as *helical gears*. These gears may also be made for connecting shafts that are at an angle in the same or different planes. The advantage of helical gears is that they are smooth acting, because there is always more than one tooth in contact. Some power is lost because of end thrust, and provision must be made to compensate for this thrust in the bearings. The *herringbone gear* is equivalent to two helical gears, one having a right-hand and the other a left-hand helix.

Usually when two shafts are in the same plane, but at an angle with one another, a *bevel gear* is used. Such a gear is similar in appearance to the frustum of a cone having all the elements of the teeth intersecting at a point, as shown in Figure 7. Bevel gears are made with either straight or spiral teeth. When the shafts are at right angles and the two bevel gears are the same size, they are known as *miter gears* (see Figure 3). *Hypoid gears,* an interesting modification of bevel gears (see Figure 4), have their shafts at right angles, but they do not intersect as do the shafts for bevel gears. Correct teeth for these gears are difficult to construct, although a generating process has been developed that produces teeth with satisfactory action. *Zerol* gears have curved teeth but have a zero helical angle. They may be produced on machines that cut spiral bevels and hypoids. *Worm gearing* is used where a large speed reduction is desired. The

Fig. 3. Miter bevel gears. (Courtesy Foote Brothers Gear and Machine Corporation.)

small driving gear is called a *worm* and the driven gear a *wheel*. The worm in appearance resembles a large screw and is set in close to the wheel circumference, the teeth of the wheel being curved to conform

Fig. 4. Zerol, spiral, and hypoid bevel gears. (Courtesy Gleason Works.)

to the diameter of the worm. The shafts for such gears are at right angles but not in the same plane. These gears are similar to helical gears in their application, but differ considerably in appearance and method of manufacture. Several worm-gear sets are shown in Figure 5.

In addition to the various kinds of gears just discussed, there are
several special types that deserve mention. *Rack gears,* which are
straight and have no curvature, represent a gear of infinite radius,
and are used in feeding mechanisms and for reciprocating drives.
They may have either straight or helical teeth. If the rack is bent in

Fig. 5. Worm-gear sets. (Courtesy Foote Brothers Gear and Machine Corporation.)

the form of a circle, it becomes a bevel gear having a cone apex angle
of 180 degrees known as a *crown gear.* The teeth all converge
at the center of the disk and mesh properly with a bevel gear of
the same pitch. A gear with internal teeth, known as an *annular
gear,* can be cut to mesh with either a spur or a bevel gear, depending
on whether the shafts are parallel or intersecting.

Gear Nomenclature

The system of gearing used in the United States is known as the
involute system, since the profile of a gear tooth is principally an
involute curve. An *involute* is a curve generated on a circle, the
normals of which are all tangent to this circle. The method of generating an involute is shown in Figure 1. Assume that a string having

a pencil on its end is wrapped around a cylinder. The curve described by the pencil as the string is unwound is an involute, and the cylinder on which it is wound is known as the *base circle*. The portion of the gear tooth, from the base circle at *A* to the outside diameter at *C*, is an involute curve and is the portion of the tooth that contacts other teeth. From *B* to *A* the profile of the tooth is a radial line down to the small fillet at the root diameter. The location of the base circle on which the involute is described is inside the pitch circle and is dependent on the angle of thrust of the gear teeth. The relationship existing between the diameter of the pitch circle and base circle is as follows:

$$D_b = D \cos \theta,$$

where D_b = diameter of base circle, and
$\quad \theta$ = angle of thrust between gear teeth.

The two systems most commonly used have their thrust angles or lines of action at 14½ and 20 degrees, respectively. Other angles may be used, but the larger the angle is made the greater will be the radial force component tending to force the gears apart. If a common tangent is drawn to the pitch circles of two meshing gears, the line of action or angle of thrust is drawn at the proper angle (14½ degrees) to this line. The base circles, on which the involutes are drawn, are tangent to the line of action.

Most gears, transmitting power, use the 20-degree full-depth, involute tooth form. Such gears have the same tooth proportion as the 14½-degree full-depth involute but are stronger at their base because of greater thickness. The 20-degree, fine-pitch involute gears are similar to the regular 20-degree involute and are made in sizes ranging from 20 to 200 diametral pitch. These gears are used primarily for transmitting motion rather than power. The 20-degree stub tooth gear has a smaller tooth depth than the 20-degree full-depth gear and is consequently stronger. Involute gears fulfill all of the laws of gearing and have the advantage over some other curves in that the contact action is not affected by slight variation of gear center distances.

Referring again to Figure 1, we see the nomenclature of a gear tooth illustrated. The principal definitions and tooth parts for standard 14½- and 20-degree involute gears are:

The *addendum* of a tooth is the radial distance from the pitch circle to the outside diameter or addendum circle. Numerically, it is equal to one divided by the diametral pitch.

The *dedendum* is the radial distance from the pitch circle to the root or dedendum circle. It is equal to the addendum plus the tooth clearance.

Tooth thickness is the thickness of the tooth measured on the pitch circle. For cut gears the tooth thickness and tooth space are equal. Cast gears are provided with some *backlash*—the difference between the tooth thickness and tooth space, measured on the pitch circle.

The *face* of a gear tooth is that surface lying between the pitch circle and the addendum circle.

The *flank* of a gear tooth is that surface lying between the pitch circle and the dedendum circle.

Clearance is a small distance provided so that the top of a meshing tooth will not touch the bottom land of the other gear as it passes the lines of centers.

Table 16 gives the proportions of standard 14½-degree and 20-degree involute gears, expressed in terms of diametral pitch and number of teeth.

TABLE 16. AGMA Standard for Involute Gearing

	20° Full Depth	14½° Full Depth	20° Fine Pitch	20° Stub Tooth
Addendum	$\dfrac{1}{P}$	$\dfrac{1}{P}$	$\dfrac{1}{P}$	$\dfrac{1}{P}$
Clearance	$\dfrac{0.250}{P}$	$\dfrac{0.157}{P}$	$\dfrac{0.2}{P} + 0.002$	$\dfrac{0.2}{P}$
Dedendum	$\dfrac{1.250}{P}$	$\dfrac{1.157}{P}$	$\dfrac{1.2}{P} + 0.002$	$\dfrac{1}{P}$
Outside diameter	$\dfrac{N+2}{P}$	$\dfrac{N+2}{P}$	$\dfrac{N+2}{P}$	$\dfrac{N+1.6}{P}$
Pitch diameter	$\dfrac{N}{P}$	$\dfrac{N}{P}$	$\dfrac{N}{P}$	$\dfrac{N}{P}$

Pitch of Gears

The *circular pitch* p is the distance from a point on one tooth to the corresponding point on an adjacent tooth, and it is measured on the pitch circle. Expressed as an equation,

$$p = \frac{\pi D}{N}$$

where D is diameter of pitch circle and N is number of teeth.

The *diametral pitch P* is the ratio of the number of teeth to the pitch diameter. It may be expressed by the following equation:

$$P = \frac{N}{D}$$

Multiplying these two equations, we obtain the following relationship between circular and diametral pitch:

$$p \times P = \frac{\pi D}{N} \times \frac{N}{D} = \pi$$

Hence, knowing the value of either pitch, we may obtain the other by dividing it into π.

All gears and gear cutters are standardized according to diametral pitch, as this pitch can be expressed in even figures or fractions. Circular pitch, being an actual distance, is expressed in inches and fractions of an inch. A 6-pitch gear (6 diametral pitch) indicates one that has 6 teeth per inch of pitch diameter. If the pitch diameter is 3 inches, the number of teeth is 3 × 6 or 18. The outside diameter of the gear is equal to the pitch diameter plus twice the addendum distance, or 3 inches + 2 × ⅙, which is 3.333 inches.

Any involute gear of a given pitch will mesh properly with a gear of any other size of the same pitch. However, in cutting gears of various diameters, a slight difference in the cutter is necessary to allow for the change in curvature of the involute as the diameter increases. The extreme case would be a rack tooth, which would have a straight line as the theoretical tooth profile. For practical reasons, the number of teeth in an involute gear should be not less than 12.

Methods of Making Gears

Most gears are produced by some machining process. Accurate machine work is essential for high-speed, long-wearing, quiet-operating gears. Gears operating at slow speeds and under exposed conditions may be sand-cast, but such gears are not efficient in their power transmission. Die casting of small gears carrying light loads has proved very satisfactory. The materials for such gears are limited to low-temperature-melting metals and alloys; consequently, these gears do not have the wearing qualities of heat-treated steel gears. Stamping, although reasonably accurate, can be used only in making thin gears from sheet metal.

The various commercial methods employed in producing gears may be summarized as follows:

1. Casting
   (a) Sand and plaster casting
   (b) Die casting
2. Stamping
3. Machining
   (a) Formed-tooth process
       (1) Form cutter in milling machine
       (2) Form cutter in broaching machine
       (3) Form cutter in shaper
   (b) Templet process
   (c) Cutter generating process
       (1) Cutter gear in shaper
       (2) Hob cutter
       (3) Rotary cutter
       (4) Reciprocating cutters simulating a rack
4. Powder metallurgy
5. Extruding

Formed-Tooth Process.   A formed milling cutter, as shown in Figure 1, is commonly used for cutting a spur gear.   Such a cutter is used on a milling machine, and the setup is shown in the lower part of the figure.   The cutter is formed according to the shape of the tooth space to be removed.   Theoretically, there should be a different-shaped cutter for each size of gear of a given pitch, as there is a slight change in the curvature of the involute.   However, one cutter can be used for several gears having different numbers of teeth without much sacrifice in their operating action.   Each pitch cutter is made in eight slightly varying shapes to compensate for this change.   They vary from no. 1, which is used to cut gears from 135 teeth to a rack, to no. 8, which cuts gears having 12 or 13 teeth.   The eight standard involute cutters are listed in the following table:

TABLE 17.   Standard Involute Cutters

No. 1. 135 teeth to a rack	No. 5. 21 to 25 teeth
No. 2. 55 to 134 teeth	No. 6. 17 to 20 teeth
No. 3. 35 to 54 teeth	No. 7. 14 to 16 teeth
No. 4. 26 to 34 teeth	No. 8. 12 and 13 teeth

The method of setting up a milling machine to cut gears is discussed in Chapter 21.   The formed milling process may be used with accurate results for cutting spur, helical, and worm gears.   Although sometimes used for bevel gears, the process is not accurate because of the gradual change in the tooth thickness.   When it is used for bevel gears, at least two cuts are necessary for each tooth space.   The usual practice is to take one center cut of proper depth and about equal to the space at the small end of the tooth. Two shaving cuts are then taken on each side of the tooth space to give the tooth its proper shape.

The formed-tooth principle may also be utilized in a broaching machine by making the broaching tool conform to the tooth space. Small internal gears can be completely cut in one operation by having

Fig. 6. Looking up inside the cutter head of a "Shear-Speed" gear shaper. The cutter head has moved to loading position after completing a spur shoulder gear. (Courtesy Michigan Tool Company.)

a round broaching tool made with the same number of cutters as the gear has teeth. Broaching is limited to large production because of the high cost of the cutters.

A recent development in the roughing and semifinishing of spur and spiral gears is the "shear speed" gear shaper. This machine is designed so that all teeth on a gear are cut simultaneously by a ring of form-cutting tools or blades surrounding the gear blank. In Figure 6 is shown a view looking up inside the cutter head of this machine after a spur shoulder gear has been cut. The gear is clamped on an arbor and the cutting head lowered and locked into position. A ram holding the gear blank is reciprocated, and at each up stroke the radial blades are fed into the work an equal amount. At the upper end of the stroke the blades are retracted slightly to provide clearance as the work returns to starting position. As the blades approach the proper tooth depth, the feed is reduced by the controlling cam.

This method of gear cutting is very rapid; in many cases the actual

cutting cycle is less than one minute. Accurate finishing of gears
produced by this method is done on a gear-shaving machine.

Templet Gear-Cutting Process

In the *templet* process for cutting gear teeth, the form of the tooth
is controlled by a templet instead of by a formed tool. The tool itself
is similar to a side-cutting shaper tool and is given a reciprocating

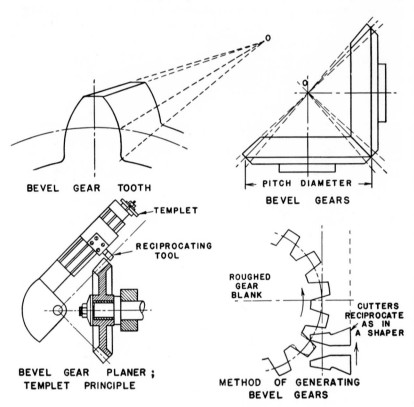

BEVEL   GEAR   TOOTH

PITCH DIAMETER

BEVEL   GEARS

TEMPLET

RECIPROCATING
TOOL

ROUGHED
GEAR
BLANK

CUTTERS
RECIPROCATE
AS IN
A SHAPER

BEVEL GEAR   PLANER ;
TEMPLET   PRINCIPLE

METHOD OF GENERATING
BEVEL GEARS

Fig. 7. Bevel-gear cutting.

motion in the process of cutting. The process is especially adapted to
cutting large teeth, which would be difficult with a formed cutter,
and also to cutting bevel-gear teeth. The principle involved in a
bevel-gear planer is shown in Figure 7. The frame carrying the
reciprocating tool is guided at one end by a roller acting against a
templet, while the other end is pivoted at a fixed point corresponding
to the cone apex of the gear being cut. Three sets of templets are
necessary, one for the roughing cut and one for finishing each
side of the tooth space. The gear blank is held stationary during

the process and is moved only when indexed. This method of cutting produces an accurately formed tooth having the proper taper. Machines of this type are used only for planing teeth of very large straight bevel gears. Most bevel gears are cut by various generating processes.

Cutter-Gear Generating Process

The *cutter-gear* generating process for cutting involute gears is based on the fact that any two involute gears of the same pitch will mesh together. Hence, if one gear is made to act as a cutter and is given a reciprocating motion, as in a shaper, it will be capable of cutting into a gear blank and generating conjugate tooth forms. A gear-shaper cutter of this description is shown in Figure 8, and Figure 9 shows how it is mounted in a Fellows gear shaper. In operation, both the cutter and the blank

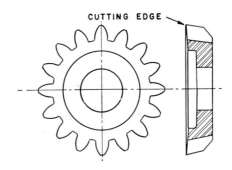

Fig. 8. Gear-shaper cutter.

rotate at the same pitch line velocity and, in addition, a reciprocating motion is given to the cutter. The rotary feed mechanism is so

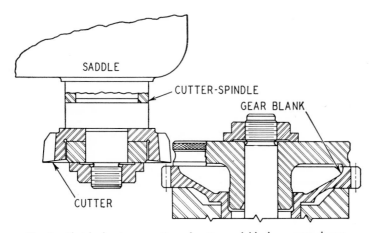

Fig. 9. Sketch showing mounting of cutter and blank on gear shaper.

arranged that the cutter can be automatically fed to the desired depth while both cutter and work are rotating. The cutter feed takes place at the end of the stroke, at which time the work is withdrawn from

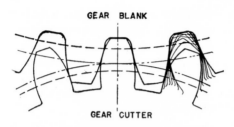

GEAR BLANK

GEAR CUTTER

Fig. 10. Generating action of Fellows gear-shaper cutter.

the cutter by cam action. The generating action of the cutter and the blank is shown in Figure 10, the fine lines indicating the amounts of metal removed by each cut in a given tooth space. The usual practice is to have the cut take place on the down stroke, although in some cases the cutting action is of necessity on the up stroke. A complete view of a gear shaper is shown in Figure 11.

Fig. 11. Gear shaper setup for cutting spur gears. (Courtesy The Fellows Gear Shaper Company.)

The cutter-gear method of generating gears is not limited to involute spur gears but has many other applications. By using a spiral cutter and giving it a twisting motion on the cutting stroke, spiral or helical gears may be generated. Worm threads may be cut in a similar fashion. Figure 12 illustrates the application of this process in the cutting of internal gears. In addition, this process may be used in cutting sprocket wheels, splines, gear-type clutches, cams, ratchet wheels, and many other straight and curved forms.

Fig. 12. Shaping an internal gear. (Courtesy The Fellows Gear Shaper Company.)

A gear-shaper machine, known as a *rotary gear shaper,* has been designed for high production jobs. This machine, with its ten complete gear-generating units, is mounted to rotate on a single base. Each unit operates independently of the others and is timed to complete a gear in one revolution of the machine. In other words, nine gears are being cut simultaneously while at one station unloading and loading is taking place. The machine has a production rate greater than ten single-spindle machines and requires much less floor space.

Another interesting application of the cutter-gear generator principle is the Sykes gear-generating machine, well known for its ability to cut continuous herringbone teeth. One of these machines is illustrated in Figure 13. This machine employs two cutter gears mounted in a horizontal position, as shown in Figure 14. In the cutting of

Fig. 13. Sykes gear-generating machine for continuous-tooth herringbone gears. (Courtesy Farrel-Birmingham Company.)

Fig. 14. View of the cutter gears on Sykes gear-generating machine. (Courtesy Farrel-Birmingham Company.)

herringbone gears the cutters are given a reciprocating motion, one cutting in one direction up to the center of the gear blank and the other cutting to the same point when the motion is reversed. The cutters not only reciprocate but also are given a twisting motion according to the helix angle. Both the gear blank and cutters slowly revolve, generating the teeth in the same fashion as the Fellows shaper does. Machines of this type are built in various sizes up to those capable of cutting gears 22 feet in diameter.

An important feature of the cutter-gear process is its ability to cut double and single helical gears, internal gears, spur gears, worms, racks, pump rotors, and a large variety of special forms. Two members of a cluster gear may be cut simultaneously, even though they are not the same type of gear nor of the same pitch. The machine generates tooth contours of true involute shape, with teeth uniformly spaced and smoothly finished.

Bevel Gear Generators

Straight bevel gears can be produced by two different types of generators—the *two-tool generator,* with two reciprocating tools, and the *completing generator* with two multiblade rotating cutters. The principle involved is based on the fact that any bevel gear will mesh with a crown gear of the same pitch whose center coincides with the pitch cone apex of the gear. In the lower right hand corner of Figure 7, the two cutting tools represent the sides of adjacent teeth of a crown gear. These tools are mounted on a cradle which rotates about the axis of the crown gear. At the same time the tools are given a reciprocating motion. The gear blank is also rotated about its axis at the rate it would have were it meshing with the crown gear. As the tools are simulating the respective positions taken by the crown gear, the correct form of tooth is cut. Both sides of a single tooth are cut on a single generating roll of the cradle, and at the end of the generating roll the blank is withdrawn and indexed while the cradle returns to the starting position for the next cut. This cycle is repeated until all the teeth in the gear are cut. In general, the tooth spaces are roughed out in a separate operation, so that only a small amount of metal is removed by the reciprocating tools when finishing.

A straight-bevel-gear generating machine using two multiblade, disk-type cutters is shown in Figure 15. In this generating process the two cutters simulate a tooth of a mating gear. The action is as though the gear blank being cut were in mesh and rolling with a mating generating gear, of which the cutters represent a tooth. At the start the cutter head is fed into the blank for rough cutting just short of the whole depth. The cradle, on which the cutters are mounted, and the work then roll down to the bottom of the generating roll, rough shaping the tooth. The work is next fed to full depth, and a fast up-roll finish generates the tooth space. The blank is then indexed and the motion repeated until all teeth are cut. The entire operation of the machine is automatic.

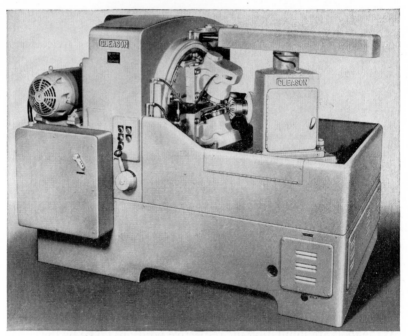

Fig. 15. Straight-bevel-gear generator using two multiblade disk-type cutters. (Courtesy Gleason **Works.**)

An advantage of this process is that a previous roughing out is unnecessary, thus saving one handling of the blank. Cutter life is longer, gear quality is improved, and less time is required for setup. Both processes will produce a localized tooth bearing in straight bevel gears. A slight crowning on the tooth surface localizes the tooth bearing in the center three quarters and eliminates load concentrations on the ends of the teeth.

The method of cutting spiral-bevel gears also uses the generating principle, but the cutter in this case is circular and rotates as a face milling cutter. The cutter is similar to the one in Figure 16, which is shown cutting a hypoid pinion. The spiral teeth on gears cut by this process are curved on the arc of a circle, the radius being equal to the radius of the cutter. The blades of the cutter have straight cutting profiles to correspond with the tooth profile of a crown gear.

The revolving cutters move through the same space as would be occupied by a crown gear tooth. As in the previous method, the teeth are first roughed out before the true shape is generated. The rotating cutters may be designed to cut only one or both sides of the tooth space, the latter-type cutter having the advantage of more rapid production. Spiral-bevel gears have an advantage over straight-bevel gears in that the teeth engage with one another gradually, eliminating any shock or noise in their operation.

Fig. 16. Close-up of a hypoid gear-generating machine cutting a pinion. (Courtesy Gleason Works.)

A special type of gear, known as a hypoid gear, can be cut in the machine just described. The hypoid gear, widely used in drives for automobiles, streetcars, motorcycles, and similar vehicles, has the axis of the pinion offset and does not intersect the axis of the gear. Such a gear is shown in Figure 4. As the cutter rotates (see Figure 16), it is fed into the gear blank and then withdrawn. There is an accompanying rolling generating movement of the cutter cradle and gear blank to produce the correct tooth profile. The rolling motion corresponds to the meshing action between the gear and a crown gear of which the cutter represents a tooth. This operation is repeated until all teeth are cut. Heat-treated spiral-bevel, zerol, and hypoid gears may be ground by using a cup wheel and employing the principles just described.

Generating Gears with a Hob Cutter

Any involute gear of a given pitch will mesh with a rack of the same pitch. One form of cutting gears utilizes a rack as a cutter. If it is given a reciprocating motion, similar to cutting on a Fellows shaper, involute teeth will be generated on the gear as it rotates in-

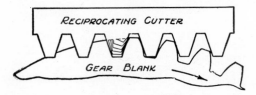

Fig. 17. Rack-type cutter generating teeth of spur gear.

termittently in mesh with the rack cutter. This method is shown diagrammatically in Figure 17. Such machines require a long rack cutter in order to cut all the teeth on the circumference of a large gear, and for this reason they are little used.

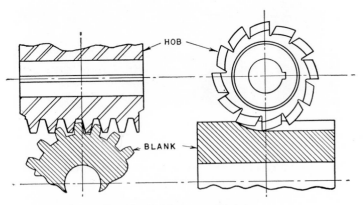

Fig. 18. Cutting gear with hob.

The hobbing system of generating gears is somewhat similar to the principle just described. A rack is developed into a cylinder, the teeth forming threads and having a lead as in a large screw. Flutes are cut across the threads, forming rack-shaped cutting teeth. These cutting teeth are given relief, and if the job is viewed from one end, it looks the same as the ordinary form gear cutter. This cutting tool, known as a *hob*, may be briefly described as a fluted steel worm. In Figure 18 is shown a hob in section and end view, as it appears when cutting a gear blank.

Fig. 19. Cutting a spur gear in single-spindle hobbing machine. (Courtesy Barber-Coleman Company.)

Hobbing, then, may be defined as a generating process consisting of rotating and advancing a fluted steel worm cutter past a revolving blank. This action is clearly illustrated in Figure 19, where the teeth on a spur gear are being cut to full depth by a rotating hob. In this process all motions are rotary, there being no reciprocating or indexing movements. In the actual process of cutting, the gear and hob rotate together as in mesh. The speed ratio of the two depends upon the number of teeth on the gear and on whether the hob is single-threaded or multithreaded.

At the start of operations, the gear blank is moved in toward the rotating hob until the proper depth is reached, the pitch-line velocity of the gear being the same as the lead velocity of the hob. The action is the same as if the gear were meshing with a rack. As soon as the depth is reached, the hob cutter is fed across the face of the gear until the teeth are complete, both gear and cutter rotating during the entire process.

Fig. 20. Hobbing machine setup for cutting three helical gears. (Courtesy Gould and Eberhardt.)

Inasmuch as the hob teeth have a certain amount of lead, the axis of the hob cannot be at right angles to the axis of the gear when cutting spur gears but must be moved an amount equal to the lead angle. For helical gears, the hob must be moved around an additional angle equal to the helix angle of the gears. Worm gears may be cut with the axis of the hob at right angles to the gear and the hob fed tangentially as the gear rotates.

In Figure 20 is shown a hobbing machine set up for cutting three helical gears. This is a universal machine and can be used for the production of spur gears, single- or double-helical gears, worm gears, worms, sprockets, or splines.

It is interesting to note that gear hobs based on the rack principle will cut gears of any diameter. This eliminates the need for a variety of hobs for gears having the same pitch but varying in diameter. Special hobs, such as those used for cutting splines, will cut only the one part.

Finishing Operations Used on Gears

The object of any finishing operation on a gear is to eliminate slight inaccuracies in the tooth profile, spacing, and concentricity so that the gears will have conjugate tooth forms and give quiet operation at high speeds. These inaccuracies are very small dimensionally, frequently not exceeding 0.0005 inch, but even this amount is sufficient to increase wear and set up undesirable noises at high speeds. In spite of the accuracy of various gear-forming and gear-generating processes, slight errors enter into gears as a result of wear in machine bearings, lead screws, or gear trains; faulty mounting of cutter on work; use of improper material; heat treatment; and the like.

To remedy these errors in gears that are not heat-treated, such operations as *shaving* or *burnishing* are used. Burnishing is a cold-working operation accomplished by rolling the gear in contact and under pressure with three hardened burnishing gears. Although the gears may be made accurate in tooth form, the disadvantage of this process is that the surface of the tooth is covered with amorphous or "smear" metal rather than metal having true crystalline structure, which is desirable from a long-life standpoint. More accurate results may be obtained by a shaving process which removes only a few thousandths of an inch of metal. This process is strictly a cutting and not a cold-working process.

Rolling the gear in contact with a rack cutter and using a rotary cutter are two methods of shaving. Either will produce accurately formed teeth. Both external and internal spur and helical gears can be finished by this process.

In Figure 21 is shown a *rack-type gear finisher*, the insert above showing a close-up view of the rack shaving cutter, finishing a spur gear. The generating rack consists of straight, replaceable blades, each tooth having a number of small vertical grooves separated by lands which form the parallel cutting edges. It is mounted on the table of the machine, which reciprocates similarly to a planer table. The gear to be finished is mounted above the rack on live centers

Finishing a spur gear with a rack shaving cutter.

Rack-type gear finisher. (Both photos Courtesy Michigan Tool Company.)

Fig. 21.

and is driven by contact with the cutting rack. The gear shaving or finishing is accomplished by the gear rolling on the rack cutter and at the same time being reciprocated back and forth across the face of the cutter. At each stroke the gear is fed down into the rack cutter until the correct tooth depth is obtained. Spur gears are shaved with racks having blades at a slight angle, whereas gears having helix angles up to 30 degrees are shared with straight-bladed racks. Only one rack is required for gears of the same pitch.

A close-up view of the *rotary crossed-axis gear finisher* in operation is shown in Figure 22. The rotary cutter is a gearlike tool having a plurality of cutting edges on the teeth, which in turn are conjugate to

Fig. 22. Rotary shaving cutter finishing transmission gears. (Courtesy Michigan Tool Company.)

the teeth to be produced on the gear in the machine. On the surfaces of the rotary cutters are small cutting edges similar to those used on rack-type cutters. Improved cutting action is obtained by having the axis of the gears and cutter at some angle ranging from 3 to 15 degrees. The cutter is the driver, and at the same time there is an axial movement of the cutter so as to finish the full width of the gear. Both types of gear-finishing machines may be arranged for curve shaving, a process that produces teeth slightly thicker at the center to eliminate load concentrations on the ends of the teeth. This operation is commonly known as *crowning*.

The time required for gear shaving is very short, and many thousand gears may be cut before the cutter must be resharpened. Rack cutters are more expensive than rotary cutters, but the tool cost per gear is much lower by reason of the increased life of the cutter.

Rotary finishing machines, being less expensive, are economical for finishing varieties of gears in relatively smaller quantities. Also, if the gears are extremely large, or if there is close interference (as in cluster gears), rotary shaving is economical. The process of gear shaving is widely used in accurately finishing gears for transmissions, reduction units, machine tools, pumps, and numerous other high-speed applications.

Heat-treated gears can be finished either by *grinding* or by *lapping*. Grinding may be done either by the forming or the generating process. In the forming process the grinding wheel conforms to the tooth space to be ground. Three diamonds are mounted on the machine and controlled by templates through a pantograph mechanism to give the correct contour to the wheel. The generating process, as shown in Figure 23, uses a flat-faced grinding wheel which corresponds to the face of an imaginary rack meshing with the gear. One side of a tooth is ground at a time, the gear rolling on its pitch circle past the revolving wheel as if meshing with a rack. Another machine, operating on the same principle, will grind both surfaces of a tooth simultaneously. The disadvantage of gear grinding is that considerable time is consumed in the process. Also the surfaces of the teeth have small scratches or ridges which increase both wear and noise. To eliminate the latter defect, ground gears are frequently lapped a short time.

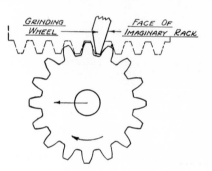

Fig. 23. Grinding involute gears.

Gear lapping is accomplished by having the gear in contact with one or more cast-iron lap gears of true shape. A two-lap gear finishing machine, operating on the cross-axis principle similar to the rotary gear shaver, is shown in Figure 24. The work is mounted between centers and is slowly driven by the rear lap. It in turn drives the front lap, and at the same time both laps are rapidly reciprocated across the gear face. Each lap has individual adjustment and pressure control. A fine abrasive is used with kerosene or a light oil to assist in the cutting action.

The machines may be adjusted to provide an automatic lapping cycle of 4 seconds to 20 minutes, operating first in one direction and then reversing for the same length of time in the opposite direction

By adjusting the axis of the laps it is possible to crown the tooth slightly so that the major bearing is at the center.

The entire operation of lapping is essentially a corrective and finishing one, and very little material is removed in the process. The

Fig. 24. Gear-lapping machine using two laps. (Courtesy Michigan Tool Company.)

time consumed for average-sized gears is ½ to 2 minutes per side of gear teeth. The results of lapping are demonstrated by longer-wearing and quieter-operating gears.

Gear-Testing Equipment

Although modern gear-cutting and gear-generating machines are capable of producing correctly formed gears, it is advisable to subject gears required for high-speed and accurate machinery to some tests before their assembly. These tests vary but include factors such as concentricity, size, noise, tooth bearing, and spacing. All tests should be made with accurate and rigid equipment and in the shortest possible time. The best method of testing and inspection is that which most nearly simulates the actual working conditions of the gears.

Numerous inspecting and testing devices have been developed for checking such factors as the pitch diameter, tooth form, eccentricity, tooth spacing, and helix angle. Minor defects, such as those caused by distortions during heat treatment, can be detected readily by these measuring devices. Similar equipment is available for checking gear hobs and cutters of other types. Although individual tests are necessary to locate some specific error, the final test of whether a gear is satisfactory or not is to run it under conditions as near the actual service operation as possible.

REVIEW QUESTIONS

1. What is the difference between a 14½-degree and a 20-degree involute gear?

2. What is the base circle on a gear and how is its diameter determined?

3. Distinguish between zerol, hypoid, and miter gears.

4. Define diametral and circular pitch, and state the relationship that exists between the two.

5. What is the profile of an involute gear tooth?

6. A spur gear is cut with a 6-pitch cutter (diametral pitch). Determine the outside diameter if the gear has 42 teeth.

7. A 14½-degree standard involute gear has a pitch diameter of 4 inches and is to be cut with a 16-pitch cutter. How many teeth will the gear have and what is its addendum height?

8. List the various processes used in making gears.

9. The circular pitch of a gear is 0.314 inches, and the pitch diameter is 5 inches. What standard gear cutter should be used?

10. What are the two methods used for generating bevel gears?

11. Describe the operation of a Fellows gear shaper.

12. How are gears cut on a shear-speed shaper?

13. What is a hob, and how can it be used for cutting gears?

14. What is the object of gear-finishing, and what methods are used?

15. How is gear shaving accomplished?

16. How are gears lapped?

17. What are important items to check in gear inspection?

18. How may heat-treated gears be ground?

REFERENCES

American Machinist's Handbook, McGraw-Hill Book Company, 1955.

Buckingham, Earle, *Spur Gears,* McGraw-Hill Book Company, 1928.

Colvin, F. H., and F. A. Stanley, *Gear Cutting Practice,* McGraw-Hill Book Company, 1937.

Gears—Cutting, Finishing, Checking, Michigan Tool Company, 1945.

Kent's Mechanical Engineers' Handbook, 12th edition, John Wiley and Sons, 1950.

Machinery Handbook, 13th edition, Industrial Press, 1948.

Staub, C. R., and M. R. Anderson, "Shaving and Lapping Gears," *Tool Engineer,* December 1940.

Strauchen, D., "Producing Precision Gears in a Machine Tool Plant," *Machinery,* September 1939.

The Practical Art of Generating, Fellows Gear Shaper Company.

Tool Engineers Handbook, McGraw-Hill Book Company, 1949.

Trautschold, R., *Standard Gear Book,* McGraw-Hill Book Company, 1935.

Wildhaber, Ernest, (a) "Precision Gears Cut Quickly," *American Machinist,* June 7, 1945. (b) "Basic Relationships of Bevel Gears," *American Machinist,* September 27, 1945. (c) "Special Analysis of Gear Mesh Clarifies Curvature Conditions," *American Machinist,* October 25, 1945.

Young, Gardner, "Modern Methods in Gear Manufacture," *Machinery,* October 1940.

CHAPTER 23

METAL SAWING

An important operation in any shop is the sawing of materials and bar stock for subsequent machining operations. Although most machine tools can do cutting-off operations to a limited extent, special machines are necessary for mass-production work and for miscellaneous work which requires a wide variety of shapes and sizes. Metal sawing is similar to wood sawing, except that the saw has teeth specially designed for metal work, with the proper spacing and angles for efficient cutting.

Hand sawing, used on many simple jobs and in situations where the work cannot be brought to a power saw, is done with a thin flexible blade, usually 8 to 12 inches in length, held in a hacksaw frame which is provided with a suitable hand grip. The tooth pitch will vary from 14 to 32 teeth per inch. Although coarse-tooth saws allow more chip space, the spacing will vary according to the thickness and kind of material being cut. An average pitch for handsaws is around 18 teeth per inch, but for thin materials and tubing a finer pitch is advisable.

Metal saws for power machines are made in *circular, straight,* or *continuous* shapes, depending on the type of machine with which they are to be used. The various types of power sawing machines are listed in the following classification:

Metal-Sawing Machines

1. Reciprocating saw
   (a) Horizontal hacksaw machine
   (b) Vertical sawing and filing machine
2. Circular saw
   (a) Metal saw

   (b) Steel friction disk
   (c) Abrasive disk

3. Band saw
   (a) Saw blade
   (b) Friction blade

Reciprocating Sawing Machines

The reciprocating hacksaw, which may vary in design from light-duty crank-driven saws to large heavy-duty machines hydraulically driven, has long been a favorite because of its simplicity in design and low operating cost. It consists of a saw frame, a means for reciprocating the saw and frame, a work table and vise, a supporting base, and a source of power. Machines of this type vary in the manner in which the saw is fed into the work and the type of drive used.

The simplest type of feed is the *gravity feed,* in which the saw blade is forced into the work by the weight of the saw and frame. Uniform pressure is exerted in the work during the stroke, but some provision is usually made to control the depth of feed for a given stroke. Some machines of this type have weights clamped on the frame to give additional control to the cutting pressure. This may also be accomplished by means of springs with suitable adjustment. Positive-acting screw feeds, with some provision for overloads, provide a means of obtaining a definite depth of cut for each cutting stroke. Hydraulic feeds are now widely used, since they afford excellent control of the cutting pressures. Several machines with this type of feed are discussed in subsequent paragraphs of this chapter.

In general, methods of feeding can be classified as either *positive* or *definite pressure* feeds. A positive feed has an exact depth of cut for each stroke, and the pressure on the blade will vary directly with the number of teeth in contact with the work. Therefore, in cutting a round bar the pressure is light at the start and maximum at the center. A disadvantage of this method is that the saw is prevented from cutting fast at the start and the finish where the contact stroke is short. With definite pressure feeds, the pressure is uniform at all times, regardless of the number of teeth in contact. This condition prevails in gravity or friction feeds. Here the depth of cut varies inversely

with the number of teeth in contact, so that the maximum pressure
that can be used depends on the maximum load that a single tooth
can stand.   Many machines of recent design have incorporated both
these systems into their design with automatic control.   In all cases
the pressure is released on the return stroke to eliminate wear on the
saw blade.

Fig. I. Hydraulic heavy-duty metal-cutting machine. (Courtesy Racine Tool &
Machine Company.)

The simplest drive for the saw frame is that with a crank rotating
at a uniform speed.   With this arrangement the cutting action is taking place only 50% of the time, since the time of the return stroke
equals that of the cutting stroke.   An improvement of this design
provides a link mechanism which gives a quick-return action.   Several
such link mechanisms are used, including the Whitworth mechanism
found on some shapers.   These designs reduce the idle time to about
one third of the total and result in faster cutting than the crank saws
without increasing the cutting speed.

Figure 1 shows a hydraulic, shear-cut production saw.   The term
"shear cut" describes a cutting action, whereby the cutting edge of
a metal saw is fed progressively and uniformly to give the most

effective cutting. The feed is hydraulically operated and is equipped with valve control to give either a positive progressive feed or a flexible constant-pressure feed. The positive feed is recommended for production runs in the sawing of tough steels, such as stainless steel, die blocks, and numerous other alloys. The flexible constant-pressure feed is used for automatically increasing or decreasing the

Fig. 2. Automatic bar-feed hacksaw machine. (Courtesy Armstrong-Blum Manufacturing Company.)

feed in accordance with the area, shape, or density of the material being cut. In both cases the hydraulic-feed pressure is applied progressively during the cut, and each tooth produces a long curling chip. This machine can be provided with an automatic stock feed with which a single bar, or a bundle, can be cut to the desired lengths, leaving the operator free to do other work. The entire cycle is hydraulically controlled and positive in its action.

Another reciprocating saw, equipped with automatic bar feed and discharge tracks, is shown in Figure 2. Bars to be cut are loaded on a rolling dolly and vise, and are either manually or automatically moved forward by a chain arrangement. The usual cycle for automatic feed after the gage has been set is as follows: the bars move forward through an open vise the desired distance, the vise is clamped, pieces are cut off by the saw, the saw is raised to the original position, the vise is opened, and so on, until the length of bar has been cut up.

Hacksaw blades. Power hacksaw blades are similar to those used for hand sawing. High-speed steel blades vary from 12 to 36 inches in length and are made in thicknesses from 0.050 to 0.125

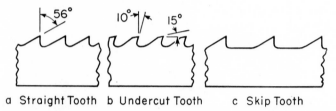

a Straight Tooth   b Undercut Tooth   c Skip Tooth

Fig. 3. Tooth construction for metal saw blades.

inch. The pitch is coarser than for hand sawing, ranging from 2½ to 14 teeth per inch, since the material being cut is usually much larger. The tooth construction of most hacksaw blades is indicated in Figure 3, (a) and (b). The most common type in the *straight tooth* design having zero rake. The undercut tooth, which resembles a milling cutter tooth, is used for the larger blades. For efficient cutting of ordinary steel and cast iron, as coarse a pitch as possible should be used to provide ample chip space between teeth. However, two or more teeth should always be in contact with the stock being cut.

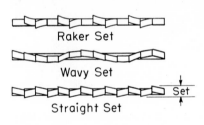

Fig. 4. Types of set for metal saw blades.

High-carbon and alloy steels require a medium-pitch blade, whereas thin metal, tubing, and brass require a fine pitch. To provide ample clearance for the blade while cutting, the teeth are set to cut a slot or *kerf* slightly wider than the thickness of the blade. This is done by bending certain teeth slightly to the right or left as may be seen in Figure 4. *Set* refers to the type of tooth construction on a saw. A *straight-tooth saw* has one tooth set to the right and the next tooth to the left. This type of saw is used for brass, copper, and plastics. On the *raker-tooth saw* one straight tooth alternates with two teeth set in opposite directions. This tooth construction is used for most steel and iron cutting. A *wave set* consists of an alternate arrangement of several teeth set to the right and several teeth set to the left. This design is used in cutting tubes and light sheets of metal.

A lubricant is recommended for all power-hacksaw cutting to lubricate the tool and to wash away the small chips accumulating between the teeth. Since there is little heat generated in most sawing operations the problem is one of lubricating rather than cooling and the cutting fluid should be chosen accordingly. Hacksaw machines cut between 40 and 160 strokes per minute according to the machinability of the metal being cut. Surface speed in feet per minute is seldom specified as it is not uniform throughout the stroke length.

Circular Sawing Machines

Machines using circular saws are commonly known as *cold sawing machines*. The saws are fairly large in diameter and operate at low rotational speeds. The cutting action is the same as that obtained with a milling cutter. The machine consists of a rotating saw, means for feeding the saw into the work, a vise for clamping the part to be cut, and a supporting frame.

In Figure 5 is shown a hydraulic-feed cold sawing machine capable of sawing round stock up to 10 inches in diameter. Nine changes of speed in geometric progression are provided for the saw blade. This affords a wide selection of cutting speeds, ranging from 18 fpm for hard materials to 134 fpm for softer materials. The feed for the saw carriage is hydraulically operated and provides a "stepless" variable feed as well as a quick return. The feed pressure may be set at a point that will protect the saw, regardless of the rate for which the feed is set. Hence, if the saw encounters a change in section or hardness of material which overloads the blade, the rate of feed is automatically decreased until the overload is eliminated.

Circular metal saws. Saws for rotating cutter machines are similar to the metal-slitting saws used with milling machines. However, metal-slitting saws are made only in diameters up to 8 inches, which is not sufficient for large-size work. Some solid blades, with diameters not exceeding 16 inches, are used in circular sawing machines. Their use is limited because of cost and the fact that broken or worn teeth cannot be replaced. Most large cutters have either replaceable inserted teeth or segmental-type blades. In the latter type the segments, each having about four teeth, are grooved to fit over a tongue on the disk and are riveted in place. Both inserted teeth and segmental-type blades are economical from the standpoint of cutter-

material cost and have the additional advantage that worn teeth can
be replaced.

Fig. 5. Cold sawing machine. (Courtesy The Motch & Merryweather Company.)

In Figure 6 is shown the type of teeth found on most circular
metal saws. The teeth are alternately ground so that one half of

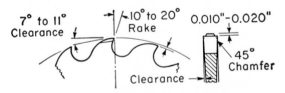

Fig. 6. Tooth construction for circular saws.

them are 0.010 to 0.020 inch higher than the rest. The high teeth
are for rough cutting and have a 45-degree chamfer on each side;
the others are ground square across and are the finishing teeth for
cleaning up both corners. A clearance angle of around 7 degrees is
used for most steels and cast iron; and, if nonferrous metals are to

be cut, this angle should be increased to 11 degrees. Rake angles vary from 10 to 20 degrees, the smaller angles being for the harder materials.

Cutting speeds of circular blades range from 25 to 80 fpm for ferrous metals. For nonferrous metals the speeds are much higher, the range being from 200 to 4000 fpm. Best saw life is obtained if the peripheral speed is not too high. The use of a lubricating fluid is recommended for all circular sawing work.

Steel friction disks. Steel disks operating at high peripheral speeds provide a rapid means of cutting through structural-steel members and other steel sections. When the disk is rotating at rim speeds from 18,000 to 25,000 fpm, the heat of friction quickly melts a path through the part being cut. About one-half minute is required to cut through a 24-inch I beam. Disks, ranging in diameter from 24 to 60 inches, are used in this work. They are usually furnished with small indentations on the circumference, about $\frac{3}{32}$ inch deep. The disks are ground slightly hollow to provide side clearance in cutting through a large member. Water cooling is recommended.

Friction cutting is not limited by the hardness of the material. Stainless steel and high carbon steel can be cut more easily than low carbon steel. Cutting ability seems to depend more upon the structure of the metal and its melting characteristics than upon metal hardness. In cutting, the tensile strength of the steel is rapidly lowered as the temperature increases. The heated steel is finally weakened to the extent that the friction disk pulls it away from the colder metal. The temperature at which this occurs is below the melting point of steel. Nonferrous metals cannot be cut satisfactorily by friction sawing since the metal tends to adhere to the disk and does not break away readily as a result of the disk action.

Abrasive disks. An abrasive wheel machine adapted for either wet or dry cutting is shown in Figure 7. This machine will cut solids up to 2 inches in diameter or tubing up to $3\frac{1}{2}$ inches. For dry cutting, resinoid-bonded wheels should be used, operating at speeds around 16,000 sfpm. High wheel speed cuts more efficiently than low because the metal is rapidly heated to the extent that it becomes soft and can be easily removed. For wet grinding, rubber-bonded wheels operating around 8000 sfpm are used. The surface speed is limited to this figure in order to retain sufficient coolant on the wheel to prevent overheating. Cutting action in this case depends entirely upon the abrasive grains in the wheel and is not influenced by any softening of the metal.

Although most work done on abrasive-disk machines is less than

2 inches in diameter, sizes up to 6 inches can be cut on automatic machines, with the wheel reciprocating across the work. Abrasive cutting can be used for almost all metals as well as many other materials. The finish and accuracy is much better than that obtained from using steel friction blades.

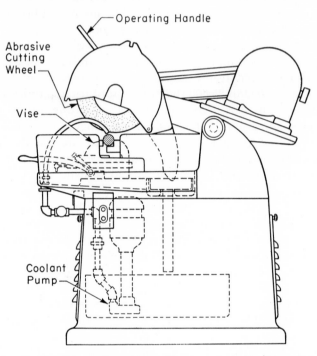

Fig. 7. Abrasive-disk cutoff machine. (Courtesy A. P. De Sanno & Son.)

Band-Sawing Machines

Band sawing. The sawing machines described thus far are designed for taking straight cuts and are used primarily for cutting-off purposes. Cutting saws of the *band type* can also be used for this work but, in addition, can cut irregular curves in metal. This widens the field of usefulness for the band saw, since it enables the machine to do a great variety of work that formerly had to be done with other machine tools. Contour sawing of dies, jigs, cams, templets, and numerous other parts that formerly had to be made entirely on other machine tools, or by hand at much greater expense, is now done with band saws. In recent years suitable and accurate arrangements for continuous filing and polishing, both necessary operations in contour finishing, have been accomplished by the use of band saws.

Band-sawing machines for metals are similar in appearance to those used for wood but differ in the saw-cutting speed and type of saw. Most machines are designed with the saw running in a vertical position, the work being supported on a horizontal table having a tilting adjustment for cutting angles. Another type is quite similar in design to the ordinary hacksaw machine. The work is held in a vise while a small band saw operates above the work in nearly a horizontal position. Both types are widely used for cutting off stock in the same way that such work is done on circular and reciprocating sawing machines.

Band-saw blades. An important step in precision sawing is the selection of the proper saw for each job. The width is determined by the feed that is to be used and by the curvature to be cut. It is a good rule always to use the widest blade possible. The tooth construction of band-saw blades is about the same as that used for hacksaw blades. The two common types are illustrated in Figures 3, (a) and (c). The *skip-tooth* blade shown at (c) is adaptable for nonferrous and nonmetallic materials. It is also used for sawing thick sections of ferrous metals where coarse-pitch saws should be used. The number of teeth per inch is a function of the material being worked on. This factor does not vary directly with the hardness of the material but is determined from actual cutting experience; manufacturers' recommendations should be followed in this respect. Modern band-sawing machines have 50 to 1500 fpm speeds available to accommodate a wide range of materials.

Band-friction cutting. High-speed band-sawing machines, designed for friction cutting, have a surface speed range of 3000 to 15,000 sfpm. Saws for these machines must be selected with care since the teeth should be properly spaced according to the material's thickness. The pitch varies from 10, for thick materials, to 18, for thin materials. This type of cutting is limited to relatively thin ferrous metals and some thermoplastic materials. Figure 8 shows the operation of band-saw friction cutting and illustrates the fact that material hardness is not a limiting factor in this process.

Band filing. When the machine is to be used for filing work, the saw band is removed and a file band is put in its place. The file band is made up of 26 files mounted on a flexible Swedish steel band. A snap joint, shown in Figure 9, is provided for quick fastening and

Fig. 8.   Friction-sawing hardened steel.   (Courtesy The DoAll Company.)

Fig. 9.   Setting up file band for internal filing.   (Courtesy The DoAll Company.)

unfastening for internal filing. A light-to-medium pressure is used on contour filing, and the filing speeds range from 50 to 200 fpm. An advantage of this type of filing is that it is accomplished with a continuous downward stroke. The absence of a backstroke greatly lengthens the life of the file and helps in holding the work onto the table.

Files used on this machine have the same shapes and styles found on standard commercial files. *Single cut, double cut,* and *rasp cut* are the terms used in describing the cut of the file. Rasp cut differs from the other two in that the teeth are disconnected from each other, each tooth being made by a single punch. The coarseness of the teeth is described by the terms *rough, coarse, bastard, double cut,* and *smooth.* File cross sections are indicated by such terms as *flat, oval, half round,* and *mill.*

Band polishing. A third function of band machines is polishing. This work calls for an endless band of emery cloth which is mounted in the same way as the band saws. At the point of work the cloth band is backed up by a rigid plate. The band is made of the same kind of emery cloth and in the same grits that are conventionally used in hand-polishing work.

REVIEW QUESTIONS

1. Prepare a list of the various kinds of power saw machines.

2. What factors should be considered in the selection of the pitch for a hacksaw blade?

3. What methods of feeding the saw into the metal are used on reciprocating saws?

4. Describe the operation of a bar-feed carrier on a power hacksaw.

5. What are the advantages and disadvantages of positive feed on a hacksaw?

6. Explain the meaning of the term *kerf.*

7. What three types of saws are used on a cold sawing machine?

8. What kinds of disks are used in abrasive cut-off machines? At what surface speeds are they operated?

9. Discuss the various types of work that can be done on a metal band saw.

10. In band-saw work what determines the width of the saw, the number of teeth per inch, and the set?

11. How are files used on a band-sawing machine?

12. Why is a cutting fluid recommended for most sawing work?

13. For what type of cutting is a skip-tooth blade used?

14. Describe the action of friction cutting.

15. What is the difference between straight set, raker set and wave set as applied to saw blades?

REFERENCES

American Machinist's Handbook, McGraw-Hill Book Company, 1955.

Holloway, R. C., "Friction Sawing," *American Machinist,* June 7, 1945.

Tool Engineers Handbook, American Society of Tool Engineers, McGraw-Hill Book Company, 1949.

Wiese, R. R., "Cutting with Abrasives," *American Machinist,* February 19, 1941.

CHAPTER 24

BROACHING MACHINES
AND TOOLS

Broaching is the operation of removing metal by means of an elongated tool having a number of successive teeth of increasing size which cut in a fixed path. A part is completed in one stroke of the machine, the last teeth on the cutting tool conforming to the desired shape of the finished surface. In most machines the broach is moved past the work, but equally effective results are obtained if the tool is stationary and the work is moved. Although the process of broaching has been known for many years, it has not been used extensively in production work until recently. The first developments of broaching were confined principally to internal operations, such as the broaching of holes and keyways. Many cuts, both external and internal, can be made on recently designed machines at a high rate of production and with satisfactory accuracy and finish.

Types of Broaching Machines

A broaching machine consists of a work-holding fixture, a broaching tool, a drive mechanism, and a suitable supporting frame. Although the component parts are few, several variations in design are possible. A brief classification of broaching according to method of operation is as follows:

1. Pull broaching. The broaching tool moves and the work is stationary.

2. Push broaching. The broaching tool moves and the work is stationary.

3. Surface broaching. Either the work or the broaching tool moves across the other.

4. Continuous broaching. The work is moved continuously against stationary broaches. The path of movement may be either straight or circular.

According to actual construction, most broaching machines are of horizontal- or vertical-type design. The decision of which design to use is dependent on such factors as size of part, size of broach, quantity, and type of broaching to be done. In general, vertical machines are well adapted for surface broaching with the tool supported on a suitable slide, although both pull- and push-type internal broaching machines are made in this design. Horizontal machines pull the broach and are often used on internal broaching of small and medium-sized work. They too have many surface broaching applications.

Another variation in broaching machines is the method of drive. Because a large force is required, most modern machines are hydraulically driven. Such a drive is smooth-acting, economical, and readily adjustable for both speed and length of stroke. Other drive systems are operated by means of gears, power screws, chains, or link mechanisms. The chain type of drive is especially adapted to the continuous broaching machine. On all intermittent-type machines, a quick-return feature is incorporated in the drive. The return stroke is two to five times the speed of the cutting stroke.

Advantages and Limitations of Broaching

Broaching is a metal cutting operation which has been adopted for mass-production work because of the following outstanding features and advantages:

1. Both roughing and finishing cuts are completed with one pass of the tool.

2. Rate of production is high as the actual cutting time is a matter of seconds. Rapid loading and unloading of fixtures keep the total production time to a minimum.

3. The process can be used for either internal or external surface finishing.

4. Any form that can be reproduced on a broaching tool can be machined.

5. Tolerances can be maintained which are suitable to interchangeable manufacture.

6. Finishes comparable to those achieved in milling work can be obtained, and in some cases burnishing shells are incorporated on the broach to improve the surface finish.

In spite of all the advantages listed broaching is not without the following limitations:

1. High tool cost. This is particularly true for large or irregular-shaped broaches.

2. Short-run jobs are not advisable because of high tooling cost.

3. Parts to be broached must be capable of being rigidly supported and must be able to withstand the broaching forces set up.

4. The surface to be broached cannot have an obstruction.

5. Broaching is not recommended for the removal of a large amount of stock.

Broaching Machines

Vertical single-slide surface machine. The surface broaching operation being performed on the vertical machine shown in Figure 1 is both simple and quick. Most machines of this type are provided with a receding table so that the fixture may be unloaded and loaded while the broach is returning to its original position. In most cases the cycle is automatic and continuous except for the loading operation; but, if conditions warrant it, even this can be made automatic. As a machining operation, broaching can be adapted readily to an automated line.

Vertical double-slide surface machine. A broaching machine of this type (Figure 2) is shown finishing the sides and ends of connecting-rod bolt bosses at the rate of 600 per hour. This machine differs from the single-slide machine in that it has two slides which operate opposite one another. The work is held on shuttle tables which move out during the unloading and loading opera-

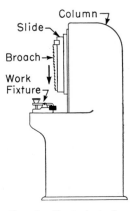

Fig. 1. Vertical single-slide surface broaching machine.

tions while the ram returns to its starting position. While this is going on, the other ram is at work. Single-slide machines are usually equipped with a quick return, but the return and cutting strokes on these machines are the same. This machine is well suited for subse-

Fig. 2. Finish sides and ends of connecting-rod bolt bosses on double-slide vertical broaching machine. (Courtesy The Detroit Broach & Machine Company.)

quent operations on connecting rods such as cutting the cap from the rod, and finishing bearing and joint faces. It is adapted to quantity production of flat and contour surfaces, slots, and cutting-off operations.

Vertical push broaching. The operation of push-broaching the internal diameter of gears at the rate of 450 per hour is shown in

Figure 3. This production speed is facilitated by the use of an index-ing-type fixture which makes possible rapid loading of the gears away from the operation. As soon as the broach returns to starting posi-tion, the fixture is indexed, and the previously broached piece drops below to a tote box. Push broaching requires comparatively short

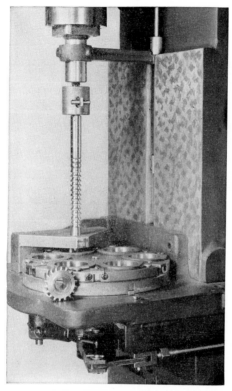

Fig. 3. Illustrating use of indexing fixture in push-broaching internal diameter of gears. (Courtesy Colonial Broach Company.)

broaches of sufficient cross section so that there is no column action due to the load imposed on it during the operation. Push broaching can be done on simple utility presses.

Vertical pull-down broaching machines. Vertical pull-down machines are adapted to internal broaching, as shown in Figure 4. Parts to be broached in this manner are placed in a fixture on the work table, the pulling mechanism being in the base of the machine. Broaching tools are suspended above by an upper carriage. As the operation starts, the broaches are lowered through the holes to be broached and are automatically engaged by the mechanism which pulls them through the part. Upon removal of the work, the tools rise, are engaged by the upper holders, and return to their starting

Fig. 4. Broach bolt holes in two caps on vertical pull-down broaching machine. (Courtesy The Detroit Broach & Machine Company.)

position. Machines of this type have the advantage over pull-up machines in that the positioning of the part is easier and large parts are handled without difficulty.

Vertical pull-up broaching machines. These machines are also adapted to internal broaching and are frequently preferred for small parts. In many machines there are four or more broaching tools involved. Although the general cycle of operation is similar to the pull-down machine, it is reversed. At the starting position the parts to be broached are placed over the shanks of the broaches then being held by the lower mechanism. As the broaches rise, they engage the upper pulling mechanism, and the parts are then held against the lower side of the work table. At the completion of the operation the parts fall and are deflected into a container. In this and most other broaching machines the operator has only to load the machine.

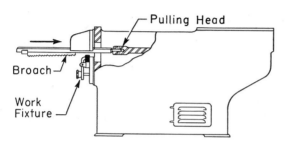

Fig. 5. Horizontal broaching machine.

Horizontal broaching machine. Although horizontal broaching machines have many surface-broaching applications, they are generally used for internal broaching of large and medium-sized parts. A diagrammatic sketch of a horizontal broaching machine, adapted for surface broaching, is shown in Figure 5. In this case the broach is pulled over the top surface of the workpiece held in the fixture. The hydraulic cylinder, which pulls the slide and broach, is housed in the right end of the machine. These machines operate at cutting speeds of 10 to 40 fpm and have return speeds around 100 fpm. For broaching internal work, the shank of the broach is manually threaded through each workpiece.

An example of surface broaching on a horizontal machine is shown in Figure 6. In this case a number of teeth having a depth of $\frac{3}{16}$ inch are cut on a segment gear at a production rate of 180 pieces per hour. In order to eliminate manual handling of the heavy broaching tool, the tool slide extends past the face plate that holds the work fixture.

An interesting development in horizontal broaching[1] is the cutting of helical grooves or splines by pulling a broach through the part and, at the same time, either rotating the part or broaching tool ac-

[1] T. A. Swindle, "Rifling Gun Barrels by Broaching," *American Machinist*, October 14, 1943.

Fig. 6. Broaching teeth of gear segment on a horizontal broaching machine. (Courtesy Colonial Broach Company.)

cording to the helix desired. This procedure has been adopted by many gun manufacturers in rifling small-caliber and light-cannon-gun barrels. Horizontal machines are used, equipped with either single or six-station-type fixtures. Both arrangements pull the broaches through the barrels, and a positive lead is usually provided which will turn either the barrel or the broach. Two passes are used in the single-fixture machines, one for roughing and one for finishing. In the multiple-type fixture having six stations, one is used for loading and five for reaming, broaching, and finishing the bore. Rifling produced by broaching is more economical and more rapid than by the old hook-cutter method, and the rejections are much fewer.

Rotary-broaching machines. Rotary broaching consists in mounting the work in fixtures supported on a revolving table which moves past stationary broaches. These broaches are made in short sections so that they can be easily adjusted and sharpened. Rotary-broaching machines limited to small parts, are used for squaring distributor shafts, slotting, straddle milling, form milling, and the facing of small parts.

Continuous broaching machine. Continuous broaching machines are adapted only for surface broaching. This type of broaching machine consists of a frame and driving unit with several work-holding fixtures, mounted on an endless chain which carries the work in a straight line past the stationary broaches. A view of a continuous machine equipped with a motor-driven conveyor for removing work from the machine is shown in Figure 7. Loading is done by an operator who drops the parts in the fixtures as they pass the loading station. The work is automatically clamped before it passes into the fixture tunnel in which the broaches are held. After the fixtures pass through the broach cut, they are automatically released by a cam, and at the unloading position the work falls out of the fixtures into the work chute. Production is high, since the operator handles only the work in the loading position; the output of the machine varies with the ability of the operator to keep the machine loaded.

Fig. 7. Continuous-surface-broaching machine equipped with motor-drive conveyor used in removing work from machine. (Courtesy The Foote-Burt Company.)

The design of this machine permits the use of long broaches, and each tooth has only a small amount of metal to remove. The first teeth are roughers and remove the major portion of the metal; the last teeth do the final finishing and sizing. Broaches are made up in short sections to facilitate replacement. A variable cutting speed of 20 to 40 fpm is provided by a gear drive.

Examples of surface-broaching operations are shown in Figure 8. Where there are several surfaces to be broached, such as on a hexagonal section, an indexing fixture can be used, with three pairs of broaches mounted in the broach holder and spaced so that the fixture can be indexed between each pair of broaches.

Some large tunnel broaches are designed for finish-broaching the tops of engine cylinders and cylinder heads. The part to be broached is held in a fixture which is pushed under the stationary broaches by a hydraulic ram. A wire cable then pulls the finished part onto

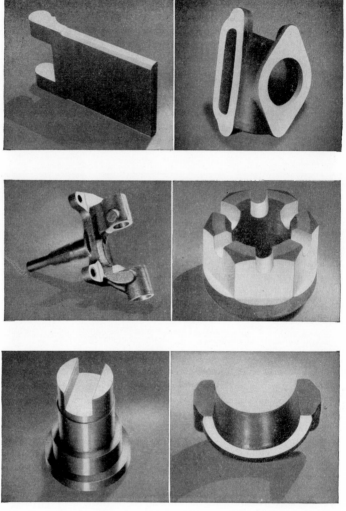

Fig. 8.   Examples of surface broaching.   (Courtesy The Foote-Burt Company.)

an exit conveyor while the fixture returns to starting position. Six-cylinder blocks can be surfaced in this manner at the rate of 120 per hour.

Broaching Tools

Broaching tools differ from most other production tools in that they are usually adapted to a single operation. The feed of the tool must be predetermined, and, once a broach is made, the feed remains a

constant. These facts necessitate having complete information concerning the job, the material, and the machine to be used before a
broach can be made. A few types of flat or regular section broaches
can be made up in advance, but those that finish unusual surfaces and
shapes are specially designed. In designing and constructing a
broach, the following information must be known:

1. Kind of material to be broached.
2. Size and shape of cut.
3. Quality of finish required.
4. Hardness of material.
5. Tolerance to be maintained.
6. Number of parts to be made.
7. Type of machine to be used.
8. Method of holding broach.
9. Pressure that the part will stand without breakage.

Fixtures are frequently designed simultaneously with the broaching
tools in order to work out the best arrangement. A fixture for broaching serves the same purpose as for milling operations; that is, it
merely holds the workpiece in proper relation to the cutter and does
not in any way guide the cutting tool. All broaching fixtures should
be as quick acting as possible and must support the work rigidly
against the heavy forces imposed on it during the operation. Reference to most of the previous figures will show various fixtures in use.

A common example of broaching is the finishing of round holes
which is more rapid than reaming or boring and at the same time
can be held to accurate limits. The life of the tool is long, since the
broach has a great number of cutting teeth, with each taking only
a very small cut. Two round broaches, one *push-type* and one *pull-
type,* are shown in Figure 9. Finished holes can be made from holes
previously drilled, reamed, bored, punched, or cored. At least $\frac{1}{64}$
inch of stock should be allowed for the finish when broaching holes
that have been previously machined.

In some cases holes are sized and the finish improved by *burnishing.* This can be done with a burnishing broach or a regular broach
which has several burnishing shells following the finishing teeth. The
amount of stock left for burnishing should not exceed 0.001 inch,
but for ordinary steel 0.0005 inch is sufficient. This amount should
be distributed over three or four burnishing shells. The operation
is one of cold working, which produces a hard smooth surface.

Square, hexagonal, and other uniformly shaped holes usually start
from round holes. The first teeth of such broaches conform to the

original hole, but gradually the broach changes in section according
to the final shape of hole desired.   If the starting-hole diameter for
a square hole can be slightly larger than the finished side, a more
economical broach can be made.

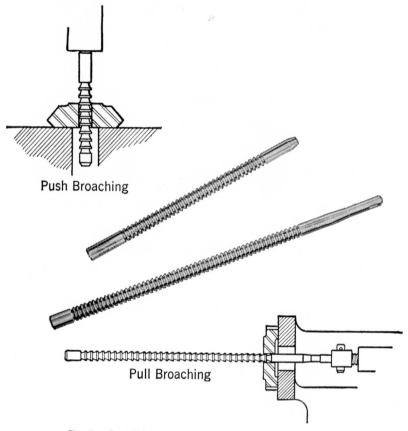

Fig. 9.   Round broaches for push-and-pull-type machines.

The broaching of internal keyways is one of the oldest uses of this
process.   A keyway broach and its adapter are shown in Figure 10.
The adapter guides the broach and also assists in holding and locating the work.   Broaching tools for this purpose are extremely simple
and can be obtained for general-purpose use.   If multiple keyways of
splines are to be cut, a single broach can be used with the work, the
proper amount being indexed after each cut.   This procedure is used
only for large splines or in jobs where the production is small, since
spline broaches can be obtained for any number of keys desired.

Internal-gear broaches are similar to spline broaches except for the involute contours on the sides of the teeth. They can be made to cut any number of teeth and are used for broaching as small as 48-diametral pitch. This method of gear cutting is known as the form-tooth process, and the accuracy of the teeth is entirely dependent on the accuracy of the form cutter. External-gear teeth may also be broached, but external-gear cutting is usually limited to cutting teeth on sector gears where only a few teeth are involvd.

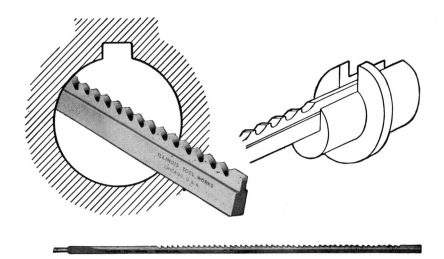

Fig. 10. Keyway broaching. (Courtesy Illinois Tool Works.)

Surface broaching has rapidly become an important means of surface finishing. The simplest broaches, designed for flat surfaces, can be made up with either straight or angular teeth, but the latter produce a smoother cutting action. Since the entire length of such broaches is supported on a slide, it is possible to make them up in short sections. Heavy-duty broaches frequently have inserted teeth to reduce the initial cost and facilitate replacements. Many irregular or intricate shapes can be broached, but the tools must be specially designed for each job.

The method of holding broaches in the machine depends on the type of broach as well as on its size and shape. One requirement of all types of puller ends is that they must permit rapid insertion and removal of the broach. The attachment of surface-type broaches presents no difficult problem since their entire length is supported on the slides of the machines.

Broaching terms and angles.   Reference to Figure 11, showing a pull-type broach, will illustrate some of the terms usually applied to broaches.   Starting at the puller end, that portion of the tool up to the first teeth is known as the *shank*.   It is made up of the *keyed* or

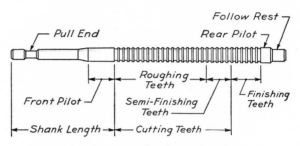

Fig. 11.   Internal pull-type broach.

pull end and the *front pilot,* which is a short section next to the teeth. The first teeth of the broach are the *cutting teeth;* the last few are called the *finishing teeth*.   The distance from a point on one tooth to the corresponding point on an adjacent tooth is the *pitch*.   This

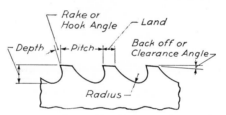

Fig. 12.   Tooth form on broach with principal terms and angles indicated.

depends on the length of broach, chip thickness, and the kind of material being broached.   The short end next to the finish teeth is the *rear pilot*.

The shapes or angles used on broaching tools are not necessarily the same throughout the length of the broaching tools.   Figure 12 shows an enlarged tooth form with terms and angles indicated.   The top portion of a tooth is called the *land* and in most cases is ground to give a slight clearance.   This angle, called *backoff* or *clearance angle,* is usually $1\frac{1}{2}$ to 4 degrees on the cutting teeth.   Finish teeth have a smaller angle, ranging from 0 to $1\frac{1}{2}$ degrees.   There should be no regrinding on the lands of most broaching tools, because this changes the size of the broach.   Sharpening is done by grinding the face or front edge of the teeth.   The angle to which this surface is ground corresponds to the rake angle on a lathe tool and is called the *face angle, hook angle, undercut angle,* or *rake angle.* The last term is probably the best, as it is the term used for this angle on other cutting tools. The rake angle varies according to the material being cut and, in general, increases as the ductility increases. Values of this angle range from 0 to 20 degrees, but for most steels a value of 12 to 15 degrees is recommended. This angle has considerable effect on the force required to make the cut and the finish. A large angle might give excellent results, but from the standpoint of lengthening tool life a smaller angle would be used. Frequently the first cutting teeth are rugged in shape and have a small rake angle, while the finish teeth are given a larger rake angle to improve the finish. Side-rake angles of 10 to 30 degrees are widely used on surface broaching to improve the finish of the cut.

REVIEW QUESTIONS

1. Define broaching, and state how it is done.
2. What are the advantages and limitations of the broaching process?
3. Classify broaching machines according to method of operation.
4. What is meant by surface broaching?
5. What types of broaches and presses are used in push-broaching?
6. Describe the operation of a pull-down broaching machine.
7. What type of work is done on a horizontal broaching machine?
8. How is rifling put in gun barrels?
9. What type of work is done on a rotary-broaching machine?
10. What type of broaching machine do you recommend for broaching the following parts: keyway in gear, involute teeth on gear segment, top of engine cylinder, splines in gears, and cutting cap from connecting rod?
11. What is meant by burnishing, and how is it done on a broaching machine?
12. Describe the operation of a continuous broaching machine.
13. What is a broaching fixture?
14. What information must be known in order to purchase or design a broach?
15. Sketch a tooth on a broach, and indicate rake angle, clearance angle, pitch, and land.

REFERENCES

American Machinist's Handbook, McGraw-Hill Book Company, 1955.
Baumbeck, W., "Development of Broach Rifling at Rock Island Arsenal," *Mechanical Engineering,* June 1943.
Bolz, R. W., *Production Processes,* Vol. 1, Penton Publishing Company, 1949.
Broaches and Broaching, Broaching Tool Institute, 1944.

Cady, E. L., "Broaching of Machine Gun Barrels," *Metals & Alloys*, February 1943.

Einstein, S., and M. Romaine, (*a*) "Surface Broaching in High Production Industries," *Mechanical Engineering*, May 1937. (*b*) "Recent Developments in Broaching Automatic Parts," *Machinery*, February 1940. (*c*) "Rifle Parts Broached," *American Machinist*, November 1940.

Gotberg, H. H., "Simplified Tools Designed for Broaching Spline Forms," *American Machinist*, October 25, 1945.

Liebert, Hugo W., "Broached Blades for Navy Turbines," *American Machinist*, August 5, 1943.

Metal Cutting Tool Handbook, Metal Cutting Tool Institute, 1949.

Romaine, M., "Broaching Cylinder Blocks and Heads in the Latest Engine Plant," *Machinery*, April 1938.

Tool Engineers Handbook, American Society of Tool Engineers, McGraw-Hill Book Company, 1949.

CHAPTER 25

ABRASIVES,
GRINDING WHEELS,
AND
GRINDING MACHINES

Grinding

To grind means "to abrade, to wear away by friction, or to sharpen." As applied to machine-shop practice, it refers to the removal of metal by means of a rotating abrasive wheel. The action of a grinding wheel is very similar to that of a milling cutter. The wheel is made up of many small abrasive grains bonded together, each one acting as a small cutting tool. Definite elongated metal chips may be seen clearly by examining the material removed under a microscope.

The grinding process is one of extreme importance in production work. It possesses certain advantages that are not found in other cutting processes:

1. It is the only method of cutting such materials as hardened steel. Parts requiring hard surfaces are first machined to shape while the metal is in an annealed state, only a small amount of excess material being necessary for the grinding operation. The amount of this allowance depends on the size, shape, and tendency of the part to

warp during the heat-treating operation. The sharpening of hand cutting tools is an important use of this process.

2. It produces finishes that are extremely smooth and, hence, very desirable at contact and bearing surfaces. This is due to the many small cutting edges on the wheel. As the wheel has considerable width, there are no marks as a result of feeding it across the work.

3. Grinding can finish work to very accurate dimensions in a short time. Since only a small amount of material is removed, the grinding machines require a close regulation of the wheel, and it is possible to hold work to a fraction of a thousandth of an inch with considerable ease.

4. Very little pressure is required in this process, thus permitting its use on very light work that would otherwise tend to spring away from the tool. This characteristic permits the use of magnetic chucks for holding the work in many grinding operations.

Abrasives

An *abrasive* is a hard material which can be used to cut or wear away other materials. Theoretically, any material can act as an abrasive to other materials that are softer. A brief classification of the common abrasive materials used for grinding wheels is given here:

Abrasives for Grinding Wheels

1. Natural
   (*a*) Sandstone or solid quartz
   (*b*) Emery, 50–60% crystalline Al_2O_3 plus iron oxide
   (*c*) Corundum, 75–90% crystalline Al_2O_3 plus iron oxide
   (*d*) Diamonds
   (*e*) Garnet
2. Manufactured
   (*a*) Silicon carbide, SiC
   (*b*) Aluminum oxide, Al_2O_3
   (*c*) Boron carbide

For many years it was necessary to rely on natural abrasives in the manufacture of grinding wheels. *Sandstone* wheels are still used to some extent for hand-operated grindstones. Although they are cut from high-grade quartz or sandstone, they have the disadvantage that they frequently do not wear evenly in use because of the variations in the natural bond. Most wheels of this type are made in Ohio, where suitable deposits of sandstone are found.

Corundum and *emery* have long been used for grinding purposes. Both are made up of crystalline aluminum oxide in combination with iron oxide and other impurities. In the United States corundum is found in Tennessee, Georgia, and South Carolina. Emery first came from Greece and Asia Minor but is now mined in New York and Massachusetts. Like sandstone these minerals lack a uniform bond and, consequently, are not suitable for high-speed grinding work. Before the discovery of manufactured abrasives, these abrasives were crushed and bonded with various materials in the manufacture of grinding wheels. The best results were obtained by using the vitrified process. Although they were a great improvement over natural stones, the wheels still lacked uniform structure because of the impurities associated with the emery and corundum.

Diamond wheels, made with a resinoid bond, are especially useful in sharpening cemented-carbide tools. In spite of high initial cost, they have proved economical because of their rapid cutting ability, slow wear, and free cutting action. Very little heat is generated with their use, which is an added advantage in tool grinding.

Manufactured or electric-furnace abrasives were not known until the latter part of the 19th century. *Silicon carbide* was first discovered by E. G. Acheson of Monongahela City, Pennsylvania, in 1891, while he was attempting to manufacture precious gems in an electric furnace. The hardness of this material, according to Mohs' scale,[1] is slightly over 9.5, which approaches the hardness of a diamond. Realizing the possibilities of this hard crystalline material as an abrasive, the Carborundum Company developed the process on a commercial scale. The raw materials now used are silica sand, petroleum coke, sawdust, and salt. The furnace employed (see Figure 1) is quite long and of the resistance type. The raw materials are piled around the carbon electrode and walled up on each side with loose brick. The purpose of the sawdust is to give porosity to the mixture and to permit the escape of the carbon monoxide gas. The furnace is heated to around 4200 F and held there for a considerable period of time. The product consists of a mass of crystals surrounded by partially unconverted raw material. After cooling, the material is broken up, graded, and then crushed to grain size. Silicon carbide crystals are very sharp and extremely hard, but their use as an abrasive is limited because of brittleness.

The development of *aluminum oxide* occurred a few years after the discovery of silicon carbide through experiments made by C. B. Jacobs of the Ampere Electro-Chemical Company of Ampere, New Jersey. The raw material for this process is the claylike mineral

[1] Mohs' scale of hardness: (1) Talc, (2) gypsum, (3) calc spar, (4) fluorspar, (5) apatite, (6) feldspar, (7) quartz, (8) topaz, (9) sapphire, (10) diamond.

bauxite (mined in Arkansas), which is the main source of the metal aluminum. Bauxite consists principally of aluminum oxide in combination with water and various impurities. In brief, the process consists in first driving off the excess moisture by heating the ore, adding small amounts of coke and iron filings to the ore to act as

Fig. I. Silicon carbide furnace charged with coke, sand, and sawdust under operating conditions. Note inflammable gases escaping at the sides. ("Lecture Course on Coated Abrasives," Behr-Manning.)

reducing and purifying agents, and then putting it into the electric furnace of the arc type. The furnace consists of an unlined conical shell which is placed on a carbon base. Two carbon electrodes hang down inside the shell, and the bauxite is charged from above, filling the space around the electrodes. The current arcs pass from one electrode to the mass and then into the other electrode, producing intense heat which melts the mass and eliminates the impurities. The finished product is a large pig, weighing several tons, which is broken up and graded. The purest material is at the center of the mass. Aluminum oxide is slightly softer than silicon carbide, but it is much tougher. Most manufactured wheels are made of aluminum oxide.

Manufacture of Grinding Wheels

The process of making a grinding wheel is the same for both the aluminum oxide and silicon carbide materials. In brief, the procedure is:

1. The material is first reduced to small sizes by being run through roll and jaw crushers. Between crushing operations the fines are removed by passing the material over screens.
2. All material is passed through magnetic separators to remove iron compounds.
3. A washing process removes all dust and foreign material.
4. The grains are graded by being passed over vibrating standard screens. (A standard 30-mesh screen has 30 meshes per inch or 900 openings per square inch. No. 30-size material is that which passes through a no. 30 screen and is retained on the next finer size, which in this case is no. 36.)
5. Grains are mixed with bonding material, molded or cut to proper shape, and heated. The heating or burning procedure varies considerably, according to the type of bond used.
6. The wheels are bushed, trued, tested, and given a final inspection.

Bonding Processes

1. Vitrified process. The abrasive grains are mixed with clay-like ingredients which are changed to glass upon being burned at a high temperature. In the puddling process sufficient water is added to form a thick smooth mixture. It is then poured into a steel mold and allowed to dry for several days in a room with controlled temperature. The dry-press process requires the addition of little water. In this case the wheels are shaped in metal molds under a hydraulic press. Wheels made this way are dense and are accurately shaped. The time for burning varies with the wheel size, being anywhere from 2 to 14 days. The process is similar to burning tile or pottery.

Vitrified wheels are porous, strong, and unaffected by water, acids, oils, and climatic or temperature conditions. About 75% of all wheels are made by the vitrified process. The recommended speed for these wheels is 5500 fpm with a maximum speed of 6500 fpm.

2. Silicate process. In this process silicate of soda is mixed with the abrasive grains, and the mixture is tamped in metal molds. After drying several hours, the wheels are baked at 500 F from one to three days.

Silicate wheels are milder acting than those made by other processes and wear away more rapidly. They are suitable for grinding edge tools where the heat must be kept to a minimum. This process is also to be recommended for very large wheels since they have little tendency to crack or warp in the baking process. The hardness of the wheel is controlled by the amount of silicate of soda used and the amount of tamping given the material in the mold.

3. Shellac process. The abrasive grains are first coated with shellac by being mixed in a steam-heated mixer. The material is then placed in heated steel molds and rolled or pressed. Finally, the wheels are baked a few hours at a temperature around 300 F.

This bond is adapted to thin wheels, as it is very strong and has some elasticity. Shellac-bonded wheels are also used for grinding camshafts and other parts where a high polish is desired. Other uses are sharpening large saws, cutting-off operations, and finishing large rolls.

4. Rubber process. Pure rubber with sulfur as a vulcanizing agent is mixed with the abrasive by running the material between heated mixing rolls. After it is finally rolled to thickness, the wheels are cut out with proper-shaped dies and then vulcanized under pressure. Very thin wheels can be made by this process because of the elasticity of material. Wheels having this bond are used for high-speed grinding (9000–16,000 fpm), since they afford rapid removal of the stock. They are used a great deal as snagging wheels in foundries and also for cutting-off wheels.

5. Bakelite or resinoid process. The abrasive grains in this process are mixed with a synthetic-resin powder and a liquid solvent. This plastic mixture is then molded to proper shape and baked in an electric oven at 312 F one-half to three days. This bond is very hard and strong, and wheels made by this process can be operated at speeds around 9500 to 16,000 fpm. They are used for general-purpose grinding and are widely used in foundries and billet shops for snagging purposes because of their ability to remove metal rapidly.

Grinding-Wheel Selection

The proper selection of a grinding wheel for a definite purpose is important. There is a great variation in the wheels from which one may choose, and the selection is somewhat difficult because of the many factors involved. The factors to be considered in ordering a wheel are:

1. Size and shape of wheel. The principal grinding wheel shapes have been standardized by the United States Department of Commerce and the Grinding Wheel Manufacturers Association. *Standard*

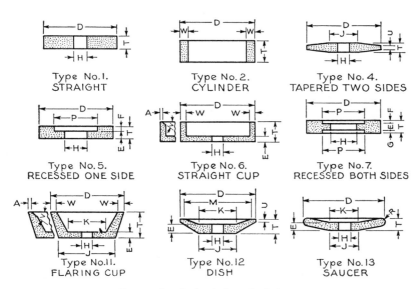

Fig. 2. Standard grinding-wheel shapes.

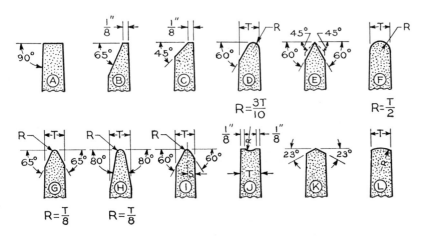

Fig. 3. Standard grinding-wheel faces.

shapes which are available are shown in Figure 2, each having its own type number. These may be obtained from any wheel manufacturer. Grinding wheels of the straight wheel type have been standardized according to *wheel face* as shown in Figure 3. These wheels are used for grinding special contours and sharpening saws.

2. Kind of abrasive. A decision as to whether to use silicon carbide or aluminum oxide is largely dependent on the physical properties of the material to be ground. Silicon carbide wheels are recommended for materials of low tensile strength, such as cast iron, brass, stone, rubber, leather, and cemented carbides. The aluminum oxide wheels are best used on materials of high tensile strength like hardened steel, high-speed steel, alloy steel, and malleable iron.

3. Grain size of abrasive particles. In general, coarse wheels are used for fast removal of materials. Fine-grained wheels are used where finish is an important consideration. Coarse wheels may be used for soft materials, but generally a fine grain should be used for hard and brittle materials. Grain size is specified according to standard screen sizes. The Norton Company classes abrasives from no. 6 to no. 24, coarse, no. 30 to no. 60 medium, no. 70 to no. 120 fine, and no. 150 to no. 240 very fine. Flour sizes run as high as no. 600 mesh.

4. Grade or strength of bond. The grade depends on the kind and hardness of the bonding material used. If the bond is very strong and capable of holding the abrasive grains against the force tending to pry them loose, it is said to be hard. If only a small force is needed to release the grains, the wheel is said to be soft. Most companies indicate the grade of the wheel by a letter. Although company standards differ, in general, the grade letters increase in hardness from D to Z. Hard wheels are recommended for soft materials, and soft wheels for hard materials.

5. Structure or grain spacing. The structure refers to the number of cutting edges per unit area of wheel face as well as to the number and size of void spaces between grains. The structure to use depends principally on the physical properties of the material to be ground and the type of finish desired. Soft, ductile materials require a wide spacing. A fine finish requires a wheel with a close spacing of the abrasive particles.

6. Kind of bond material. The vitrified bond is most commonly used; but, where thin wheels are required or high operating speed or high finish is necessary, other bonds are more advantageous.

7. Function of grinding wheel.[2] The use or purpose for which a grinding wheel is to be employed is the defining factor in wheel selection. The following are basic functions of grinding wheels:

[2] *Grinding Facts*, Carborundum Company, 1944,

(a) Generation of size or grinding to close tolerance.

(b) Generation of surface finishes or effects which may or may not involve close tolerances.

(c) Removal of a large amount of stocks, as in snagging.

(d) Cutting-off operations.

(e) Production of sharp edges or points as in knife grinding.

(f) Reduction of material to particle form.

8. Other factors that must be given some consideration are the wheel speed, speed of work, materials to be ground, and general condition of the machine. Table 18 lists recommended grinding-wheel speeds.

TABLE 18. Recommended Grinding-Wheel Speeds

Type of Grinding	Wheel Speed, Surface Feet per Minute
Internal	2000–6000
Hemming cylinders	2100–5000*
Machine knives	3500–4500
Surface	4000–5000
Cutlery—large wheels offhand	4000–5000
Wet tool	5000–6000
Cylindrical	5500–6500
Snagging—vitrified bond	5000–6000
Snagging—resinoid and rubber bond	7000–9500
Cut-off—rubber, resinoid, and shellac bond	9000–16,000*

* Recommended only where bearings, protection devices, and machine rigidity are adequate (Abrasive Company).

A standard system[3] of marking grinding wheels, recently adopted by the American Standards Association, is shown in the accompanying chart. Although the standard greatly facilitates ordering, from the standpoint of uniform marking of all wheels, there is no assurance that competitors' wheels marked alike will cut the same. Provision for each manufacturer to incorporate into the system such symbols as further describe the wheel and qualify the standard markings are stated in the first and last symbols of the identification marking.

[3] American Standard B5.17–1949.

STANDARD MARKING SYSTEM CHART

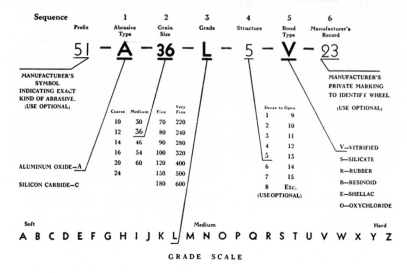

Grinding Machines

Grinding machines are designed principally to finish parts having cylindrical, flat, or internal surfaces. The kind of surface machined largely determines the type of grinding machine thus, a machine grinding cylindrical surfaces is called a cylindrical grinder. Machines designed for some special function such as tool grinding or cutting off, are designated according to the type of operation they perform.

A classification of grinding machines according to type of surface generated or work done is as follows:

Classification of Grinding Machines

1. Cylindrical grinder
    (a) Work between centers
    (b) Centerless
    (c) Tool post
    (d) Crankshaft and other special applications
2. Internal grinder
    (a) Work rotated in chuck
    (b) Work rotated and held by rolls
    (c) Work stationary
3. Surface grinder
    (a) Planer type (reciprocating table)
        (1) Horizontal spindle
        (2) Vertical spindle

   (b) Rotating table
    (1) Horizontal spindle
    (2) Vertical spindle
  4. Tool grinder
   (a) Universal
   (b) Special
    (1) Drill
    (2) Tool bit
    (3) Cutter
    (4) Pedestal, etc.
  5. Special grinding machines
   (a) Swinging frame—snagging
   (b) Cutting off—sawing
   (c) Portable—offhand grinding
   (d) Honing and lapping—accurate finishing
   (e) Superfinishing
   (f) Flexible shaft—general purpose
  6. Surface finishing
   (a) Disk
   (b) Flexible band
   (c) Two-wheel polishing or buffing machine

Cylindrical Grinders

  As the name implies, this machine is used primarily for grinding cylindrical surfaces, although tapered and simple formed surfaces

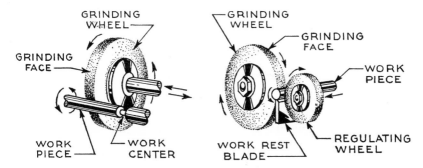

Fig. 4. Illustrating the methods of supporting work in the center and the centerless types of cylindrical grinding.

may also be ground. This type of machine may be further classified according to the method of supporting the work. Schematic diagrams illustrating the essential difference in supporting the work between the center and the centerless grinders are shown in Figure 4. In the centerless type, the work is supported by the arrangement of the work rest, a regulating wheel, and the grinding wheel itself.

Both types use plain grinding wheels with the grinding face as the outside diameter.

An illustration of a hydraulic center-type cylindrical grinding machine is shown in Figure 5. Three movements are incorporated that are necessary in the operation of cylindrical grinding.

Fig. 5. Hydraulic cylindrical grinding machine, 14 × 96. (Courtesy Landis Tool Company.)

1. Rapid rotation of the grinding wheel at the proper grinding speed, usually 5500 to 6500 sfpm.

2. Slow rotation of the work against the grinding wheel at a speed to give best performance (this varies from 60 to 100 sfpm in the grinding of steel cylinders).

3. Horizontal traverse of the work back and forth along the grinding wheel so as to grind the entire surface of a long piece.

In some machines the work remains stationary except for its rotation, and the wheel is slowly fed back and forth across the work. The narrower the face of the wheel, the slower must be the traverse and the faster should be the work revolution. For most cases the work should be traversed nearly the entire width of the wheel during each revolution of the work. In finishing, the traverse may be reduced to one half the width of the wheel.

The depth of the cut is controlled by feeding the wheel into the work. Roughing cuts around 0.002 inch may be made, but for finishing, the feed should be reduced to about 0.00025 inch. In selecting the amount of infeed, consideration must be given to the size, rigidity of the work, the finish desired and to whether or not a coolant is used.

Where the face of the wheel is wider than the part to be ground, it is not necessary to traverse the work. This is known as "plunge-cut" grinding and is common practice in the grinding of crankshafts. Cuts up to 9 inches wide may be made in this manner if the work is properly supported. Grinders for crankshaft work are usually built especially for that purpose, owing to the special features necessary for supporting and driving the crankshaft. Another special machine of this general type is the camshaft grinder. In order for the cams to be ground to proper shape, the movement of the work to and away from the wheel is controlled by master cams at the end of the shaft.

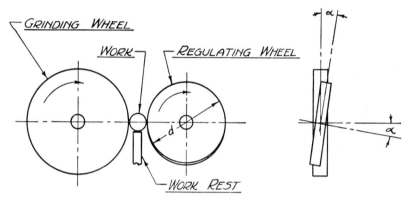

Fig. 6. Sketch illustrating the principle of centerless grinding.

The *tool-post grinder* is used for miscellaneous and small grinding work on a lathe. It is held on the tool post and fed across the work, the regular longitudinal or compound rest feed being used. A common application of this grinder is the truing up of lathe centers.

Centerless grinders are designed so that they support and feed the work by using two wheels and a work rest, as illustrated diagrammatically in Figure 6. The large wheel is the grinding wheel; and the smaller one, the pressure or regulating wheel. The regulating wheel is a rubber-bonded abrasive wheel having the frictional characteristics to rotate the work at its own rotational speed. The speed of this wheel may be controlled and varies from 50 to 200 sfpm. Both wheels are rotated in the same direction. The slide assists in supporting the work while it is being ground and is extended on both sides to direct the work travel to and from the wheels.

The axial movement of the work past the grinding wheel is obtained by tilting the wheel at a slight angle from horizontal. An angular adjustment of 0 to 8 or 10 degrees is provided in the machine for this purpose. The actual feed can be calculated by this formula:

$$F = \pi dN \sin \alpha$$

where F = feed in inches per minute

              N = revolutions per minute

              d = diameter of regulating wheel in inches

              α = angle of inclination of wheel

The formula assumes no slippage, and, in actual practice, the error is slight. Centerless grinding may be applied to any cylindrical parts of one diameter, as shown in Figure 7. In production work on

Fig. 7. Tube grinding in centerless grinder. (Courtesy Cincinnati Milling & Grinding Machines.)

such parts as piston pins, a magazine feed is arranged, and the parts may go through several machines before completion, each grinder removing from 0.0005- to 0.002-inch stock.

Where parts are not uniformly of the same diameter, or where they require form grinding as a ball bearing (see Figure 8), the *infeed* type of centerless grinding must be used. The method of operation corresponds to the plunge-cut form of grinding, and the length of the section to be ground is limited to the width of the grinding wheel. The part is placed on the work rest and is moved against the grinding wheel with the regulating wheel. Upon completion, the gap between the wheels is increased either manually or automatically and the work is ejected from between the wheels.

This type of grinding is also illustrated in Figure 9, in the grinding of a textile spindle of several diameters. In this case the loading and unloading of the spindle is done by a holding cradle and elevator

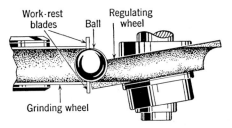

Fig. 8. Centerless grinding of ball bearings. (Courtesy The Carborundum Company.)

Fig. 9. Centerless grinding of long shaft using work handling device. (Courtesy Cincinnati Grinders.)

mechanism which is operated by and synchronized with the infeed mechanism.

A third type of centerless grinding called *end feed* has been devised for use only on short taper work. Both wheels are dressed to the correct taper, and the work is automatically fed in from one side to a fixed stop.

The advantages of centerless grinding are:

1. Less skill is required in the operation of the machine.

2. No chucking or mounting of the work on mandrels or other holding devices is required.

3. The work is rigidly supported, and there is no tendency for chatter or deflection of the work.

4. The process is rapid and especially adapted for production work. Idle machine time is negligible.

5. The size of the work is easily controlled.

6. As a true floating condition exists during the grinding process, less grinding stock is required.

Some disadvantages are:

1. Work with flats and keyways cannot be ground.

2. In hollow work there is no assurance that the outside diameter will be concentric with the inside diameter.

3. Work having several diameters is not easily handled in this type of machine.

Internal Grinders

The work done on an internal grinder is diagrammatically shown in Figure 10. Tapered holes, or those having more than one

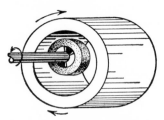

Fig. 10. Sizing to close tolerance by internal grinding.

diameter, may be accurately finished in this manner. Although especially adapted for heat-treated parts, internal grinding is frequently used on production parts that have not been heat-treated to save on reamer cost and maintenance.

According to general construction there are several types of internal grinders.

1. The wheel is rotated in a fixed position while the work is slowly rotated and traversed back and forth.

2. The wheel is rotated and at the same time reciprocated back and forth through the length of the hole. The work is rotated slowly but otherwise has no movement. The usual setup for this type of work is shown in Figure 11. The bearing is fastened to the slowly rotating chuck while the grinder wheel is rotated at high speed against one side of the hole.

Fig. 11. Internal grinding. (Courtesy Landis Tool Company.)

3. The work remains stationary, and the rotating wheel spindle is given an eccentric motion, according to the diameter of hole to be ground. This type of grinder is frequently called the planetary type, and it is used for work that is difficult to rotate. In actual construction the wheel spindle is adjusted eccentrically in a larger one that rotates about a fixed axis. The wheel spindle is driven at high speed and at the same time rotates about the axis of the large spindle.

4. In another type of grinder which embodies the principle of centerless grinding, the work is rotated on the outside diameter by driven rolls, thus making it possible to grind the bore absolutely concentric with the outside diameter. This arrangement lends itself to production work since loading is simplified and magazine feed may be used.

A diagrammatic sketch of a centerless internal grinder is shown in Figure 12. Three rolls are used to support and drive the work, a regulating roll, a supporting roll, and a pressure roll. Centerless grinders of this type can be arranged for automatic loading and unloading by swinging the pressure roller out of the way at the end of the cycle. Advantages of centerless grinding include the elimination of work-holding fixtures and the ability of the machine to grind both straight and tapered holes.

Since internal-grinding wheels are small in diameter, the spindle speed is much higher than for cylindrical grinding in order to attain surface speeds up to 6000 fpm. Most toolroom grinding is done

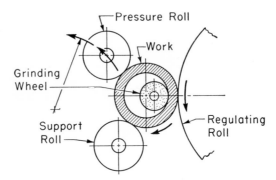

Fig. 12. Schematic sketch of centerless internal grinding.

dry, but common practice on production work is to grind steel wet and to grind bronze, brass, and cast iron dry. The amount of metal to be allowed for internal grinding depends on the size of the hole to be ground; in most cases this allowance is around 0.010 inch.

Surface Grinding

The grinding of flat or plane surfaces is known as *surface grinding*. Two general types of machines have been developed for this purpose, those of the planer type with a reciprocating table and those having a rotating work table. Each type of machine has the possible variation of having the grinding-wheel spindle in either a horizontal or a vertical position. The four possibilities of construction are diagrammatically illustrated in Figure 13.

A large surface grinder with a horizontal spindle and reciprocating table is shown in Figure 14. Straight or recessed wheels (type 1, 5, and 7), grinding on the outside face or circumference, are used. This grinder has hydraulic control of the table movement with possible speeds up to 100 fpm. Likewise, a hydraulic cross-feed is used which may be varied up to width of wheel face. This type of grinder is well adapted for reconditioning dies, as the large-diameter wheels permit this operation without the guide pins being removed. Other applications include the grinding of grooves, ways on machine tools, and other long surfaces.

𝓅 F 𝒩

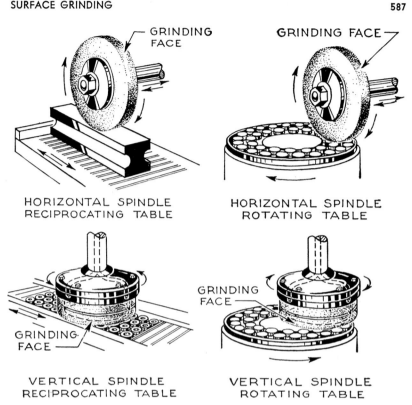

HORIZONTAL SPINDLE
RECIPROCATING TABLE

HORIZONTAL SPINDLE
ROTATING TABLE

VERTICAL SPINDLE
RECIPROCATING TABLE

VERTICAL SPINDLE
ROTATING TABLE

Fig. 13. Types of surface-grinding machines.

Fig. 14. Precision surface grinder with horizontal spindle. (Courtesy Mattison Machine Works.)

Another type of construction for planer-table grinders is the vertical spindle design, the grinding being done by a large-diameter ring-shaped wheel. This machine is similar in appearance to the one shown in Figure 14 but has the grinding wheel spindle held in a vertical position. Vertical and crosswise adjustments for the wheel are incorporated in the head assembly.

Fig. 15. Rotary surface grinder. (Courtesy Arter Grinding Machine Company.)

A rotary-table surface grinder having the grinding wheel spindle in a horizontal position is shown in Figure 15. Work is held on a magnetic chuck and is rotated slowly under the grinding wheel which, in turn, is given a reciprocating motion during the grinding operation. This type of surface grinder is adapted to circular work such as milling cutters, saws, piston rings, and valves. By tilting the table, concave surfaces or short run tapers may be ground.

Both types of vertical spindle surface grinders use wheels like those shown in Figure 16. The wheel is a hollow cylinder which cuts on its end and can be made up as a *plain cylindrical* wheel, a *sectored* wheel, or a *segment* wheel. All three of these wheels are illustrated in this figure. The cylinder and sectored wheels are set

Fig. 16. A sectored wheel, a plain cylindrical wheel, and a segment wheel, used in vertical-spindle surface grinding. (Courtesy The Blanchard Machine Company.)

Fig. 17. Double-spindle surface grinder with feed-through fixture for grinding bearing races. (Courtesy Gardner Machine Company.)

with sulfur into a cast-iron ring which fastens to the face plate of the spindle. The segment wheel uses a chuck secured to the face plate in which the segment blocks are clamped. Because of the large area of work in contact with these wheels, they are especially adapted to grinding large surfaces.

Several modifications of standard-type surface grinders are available for various production uses. Shown in Figure 17, is a specially designed machine for the simultaneous grinding of both sides of bearing races. In this double-spindle machine, parts are fed through the opposed wheels in a constant stream. The push-through-type fixture is actuated by rubber feed rollers.

Magnetic chucks. Work can be held on surface grinders and other machine tools by means of magnetic chucks, this method of holding having the advantage of being both simple and rapid. Parts to be held are placed on the chuck, which is energized by the turning of a switch.

The two types of chucks used are the *permanent-magnet* and those magnetized by means of *direct-current.* The direct-current chucks, made in both rectangular and circular shapes, have a pulling power of around 125 psi. The rectangular style is suitable for use on reciprocating grinders or for light milling machine work. Rotary chucks, designed for lathes and rotating table grinders, are shown in Figure 18. The problem of getting the current to these chucks is overcome by the use of collector rings and a brush unit mounted at the back end of the chuck or spindle. The pulling power varies according to the type of winding used and may be as high as 165 psi. The equipment for furnishing the direct current consists of a motor-generator set and demagnetizing switch.

All parts held on a magnetic chuck should be demagnetized after the work is finished. Several types of demagnetizers are available, operating on either alternating or direct current, which successfully remove the residual magnetism from knives, bearing races, blades, and many other parts.

Permanent-magnet chucks do not require any electric equipment, and work can be held on these chucks without damage to work or chuck. The operation of this chuck is by means of a lever on one side. Figure 19 shows what takes place when the operating lever is shifted. In the "off" position the conductor bars and separator are shifted in such a way that the magnetic flux passes through the top plate and is short-circuited from the work. When the handle is turned to the "on" position, the conductor bars and nonmagnetic separators line up so that magnetic flux, in following the line of least resistance, goes through the work in completing the circuit. The holding power, obtained by the magnetic flux passing through,

Fig. 18. Concentric-gap and radial-pole rotary chucks. (Courtesy O. S. Walker Company.)

is sufficient to withstand the action of grinding wheels and other light machining operations. This chuck and the d-c chucks may both be used for either wet or dry operations.

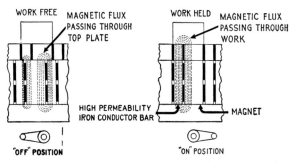

Fig. 19. Diagrammatic sketch showing how work is held on permanent-magnet chuck. (Courtesy Brown & Sharpe Manufacturing Company.)

Tool and Cutter Grinders

In grinding tools by hand (known as offhand grinding) a bench- or pedestal-type grinder is used. The tool is held by hand and moved across the face of the wheel continually to avoid excessive grinding in one spot. This type of grinding is used to a large extent on single-point tools and is dependent on the skill of the operator for good results.

In large production plants much of this type of grinding is done on special single-purpose grinders. Special drill or tool-bit grinders are justified by the large amount of grinding work necessary to keep production tools in proper cutting condition. In addition, tools can be ground uniformly and with accurate cutting angles.

Fig. 20. Tool and cutter grinder. (Courtesy Cincinnati Milling Machine Company.)

For the sharpening of miscellaneous cutters a universal-type grinder as shown in Figure 20 is used. It is equipped with a universal head, vise, headstock and tailstock, and numerous other attachments for holding tools and cutters. Although essentially designed for cutter sharpening, it can also be used for cylindrical, taper, internal, and surface grinding.

Honing

Honing is a grinding or abrading process in which very little material is removed. This process is used primarily to remove the grinding or tool marks left on the surface by previous operations. The cutting action is obtained from abrasive sticks (aluminum oxide and silicon carbide) mounted in a mandrel or fixture. A floating action between the work and tool prevails so that any pressure exerted in the tool is transmitted equally to all sides. The honing tool is given a slow reciprocating motion as it rotates, having resultant honing speeds ranging from 50 to 200 sfpm. This action results in rapid removal of stock and at the same time the generation of a straight and round surface. Defects such as a slight eccentricity, a wavy surface, or a slight taper, caused by previous operations, can be corrected by this process. Parts honed for finish remove only 0.001 inch or less; however, where certain inaccuracies must be corrected, amounts up to 0.020 inch represent usual practice. Coolants are essential to the operation of this process to flush away small chips and to keep temperatures uniform. Sulfurized mineral-base or lard oil mixed with kerosene is generally used.

A portable-type hone, used in connection with electric or pneumatic hand tools, is shown in Figure 21. Such hones are used in repair and salvage work, as well as on small-lot production jobs. External honing may also be done by rotating the work and moving the honing stones back and forth as they are held in a suitable fixture.

Semiautomatic honing machines used in the finishing of automobile cylinder bores are vertical-type machines. Both single and multi-spindle machines are used for this operation. Horizontal machines are used only for honing long gun barrels and similar work. Manually operated machines hold the work in a horizontal position, and the rotational movement only is supplied by the machine.

All honing gives a smooth finish with a characteristic cross-hatch appearance. The depth of these hone marks can be controlled by variations in pressure, speed, and type of abrasive used. Accurate dimensions can be maintained by the use of automatic size-control devices in connection with the hone.

Lapping

The purpose of lapping is to produce geometrically true surfaces, correct minor surface imperfections, improve dimensional accuracy, or provide a very close fit between two contact surfaces. Although it is a material-removing operation, it is not an economical one. The amount of material removed is usually less than 0.001 inch. Lapping is used on flat, cylindrical, spherical, or specially formed surfaces.

The actual operation consists of having the work surfaces in contact with a *lap,* the two having motion with one another in such a way that fresh contacts are constantly being made. Loose abrasive, carried in some vehicle such as oil, grease, or water, is used between the lap and work to do the necessary abrading. In some cases the abrasive is in the form of a bonded wheel, and the lapping operation is similar to that of centerless and vertical spindle surface grinding. Metal laps used must be softer than the work and for machine lap-

Fig. 21. Portable hone. (Courtesy Sunnen Products Company.)

Fig. 22. Vertical lapping machine for cylindrical and flat lapping operations. (Courtesy Hauser Machine Tool Corporation.)

ping are usually made of close-grained gray iron. Other materials like steel, copper, lead, and wood are used in special cases where cast iron is not suitable. By having the lap softer than the work, the abrasive particles (usually boron carbide, silicon carbide, aluminum oxide in fine-screened sizes, or flour) become embedded in the lap and cause the greatest wear to occur on the hard surface being worked on. In the lapping of carbide tools and jewels, diamond particles permanently embedded in copper laps are most successful.

Vertical lapping machines, similar to the one shown in Figure 22, are used for both flat and cylindrical lapping. These machines have two laps, a lower one which supports the work and rotates at relatively slow speeds and a stationary upper lap. The upper lap floats on the work and supplies pressure for the abrading action. Cylindri-

cal work is loosely held and guided in a plate-type holder so that
it travels on an off-radial axis, the work propelling the holder from
motion received from the lower-lap. A similar holder is used in the
lapping of flat surfaces, where the holder propels the work. Either it
is provided with drive pins which impart to it a rotary and gyratory
motion, or it is given a planetary motion. In either case the work is
brought in contact with the entire surface of the lap in an ever-
changing path. Commercial accuracy can be held to 0.000024 inch
readily and to even closer limits if needed. Products commonly
finished by this process include gages, piston pins, valves, gears, roller
bearings, thrust washers, and optical parts.

Superfinishing

All machining operations as well as the usual grinding processes
leave a surface coated with fragmented, noncrystalline, or smear metal
which though easily removed by sliding contact results in excessive

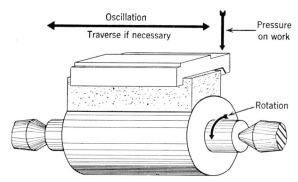

Fig. 23. Motions employed between abrasive stone and work in cylindrical superfinishing. (Courtesy Gisholt Machine Company.)

wear, increased clearances, noisy operation, and lubrication difficulties. Superfinishing is a surface-improving process which removes this
undesirable fragmentation metal, leaving a base of solid crystalline
metal. It is somewhat similar to honing since both processes use an
abrasive stone, but differ in the type of motions given to the stone.
Superfinishing is largely confined to exterior regular surfaces, both
flat and curved. This process, which is essentially a finishing process
and not a dimensional one, can be superimposed on other commercial
finishing operations.

In cylindrical superfinishing (see Figure 23), a bonded-form abrasive stone, having a width about two thirds the diameter of the part
to be finished and the same length, is operated at low speed and

pressure. The motion given to the stone is an oscillating one ($\frac{1}{16}$ to $\frac{1}{4}$ inch amplitude) of about 450 cycles per minute. If the part is of greater length than the stone, an additional longitudinal movement of either stone or work is necessary. The work is rotated at a speed of around 50 sfpm and during the operation is flooded with a light oil which carries away the minute particles abraded from the surface by the short oscillating stone strokes. The stone action is

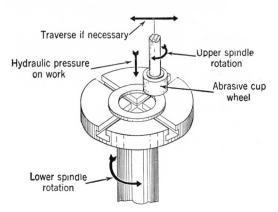

Traverse if necessary

Hydraulic pressure on work

Upper spindle rotation

Abrasive cup wheel

Lower spindle rotation

Fig. 24. Basic features of flat superfinishing. (Courtesy Gisholt Machine Company.)

similar to a scrubbing movement and removes all excess and defective metal on the surface with low abrasive stone pressures of 3 to 40 psi.

The superfinishing of flat surfaces is illustrated in Figure 24. A rotating, cup-shaped abrasive stone is used, with the work resting on a circular table carried by a rotating spindle. An additional oscillating movement can be given to the stone; but, since both it and the work are rotating, this action is not so important in developing a continually changing path of the abrasive particles. The superfinishing of spherical surfaces is similar to that used for flat surfaces except that the formed cup spindle is at an angle to the work spindle, and no oscillating motion can be used.

It is interesting to note that, when a surface has been made smooth by this process, any further stone action has little or no effect, owing to the supporting oil film between the stone and the work. With proper equipment it takes only 5 to 30 seconds to finish a single bearing area. Surfaces may be processed to a mirror finish or may be given a slight cross-hatch pattern, desirable in certain bearing surfaces. A special superfinishing machine, designed for finishing the bearings of a crankshaft, is shown in Figure 25. The time for completing the operation varies from 15 to 50 seconds, depending on the initial con-

Fig. 25.   Crankshaft superfinisher.   (Courtesy Gisholt Machine Company.)

dition of the surface.   Numerous other variations of the superfinishing process have been worked out for the many other bearing surfaces found in high-speed machinery.

Coated Abrasives

When abrasive particles are glued to paper or other flexible backings, as illustrated in Figure 26, they are known as coated abrasives. Any of the abrasives used in wheel manufacture may be applied in this way.   The most common type is the ordinary "sandpaper," which name is frequently applied to this entire group.   The abrasive in this case is a flint quartz, which is mined in large lumps and then crushed to size and graded.   Another important natural abrasive is the red mineral garnet.   Of the several kinds of garnet known, the one called almandite is the best for abrasive coatings.   It is much harder and sharper than flint and, when broken down, breaks into crystals with many cutting edges.   The best garnet comes from the Adirondack Mountains in New York State.   Other natural abrasives are emery and corundum.   The two manufactured abrasives that have wide application are silicon carbide and aluminum oxide. Figure 27 is a photomicrograph of three natural abrasive grains compared with common sea sand, showing outstanding differences in shape and structure.

The three types of backing used are paper, cloth, and a combination of the two. Paper-coated abrasives are cheapest but lack flexibility. For applications requiring both strength and flexibility, a cloth backing is preferred. Combination backings are used where

Fig. 26. Various types of metal-working coated abrasives. (Courtesy The Carborundum Company.)

a backing stronger than paper but not with the extreme flexibility of cloth is needed.

An important phase in the manufacture of coated abrasives is the application of the abrasive particles on the backing material. The abrasive grains must be securely held in a manner to give the best cutting action for the type of work to be done. For severe service, closed coating is recommended, the grains completely covering the surface of the backing. Where increased flexibility is required, with no tendency for the particles to become loaded or clogged, an open coating is used. Particles are separated at predetermined distances, leaving the base surface of the backing exposed. A method of coating, known as the electrocoating process, is illustrated in Figure 28. This method is based upon the scientific fact that particles oppositely charged attract one another. Referring to the figure, we see the

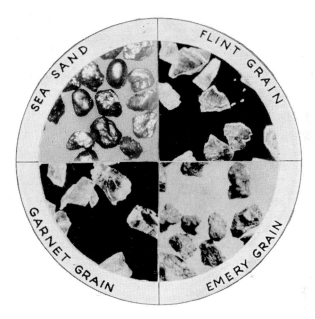

Fig. 27. Photomicrographs of three natural abrasive grains. ("Lecture Course on Coated Abrasives," Behr-Manning.)

abrasive particles being carried between the two electrodes, across which is built up a high electrostatic field. As the particles enter the field, they first stand on end, aligning themselves in the direction of the flow of the electric force, and are then attracted to the glue-covered backing which is traveling in the same direction as the other belt. The abrasive grains are imbedded on end and are equally spaced on the backing. By this process the spacing of abrasive particles is controlled.

Machines for using coated abrasives are usually of the disk- or belt-type. On the disk machines, parts to be finished are supported on a work table and manually moved back and forth while being pressed against the disk. Belt machines have backing rollers or plates against which pressure is exerted. Both types of machines can be used for either wet or dry grinding. Dimensional accuracy of this form of grinding is not very close, and the process is used primarily as one to prepare surfaces for further treatment. The quality of surface finish is governed by the fineness of the abrasive grains on the cloth.

All forms of woodwork, such as mill work, patterns, floors, and furniture, are finished in this manner. Leather goods, felt hats,

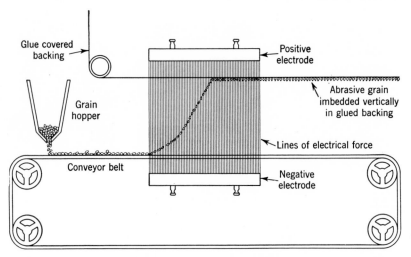

Fig. 28. Electrocoating method of applying abrasive grains to glue-covered backing. (Courtesy Behr-Manning Company.)

metallurgical specimens, and many metal parts also rely on coated abrasives in manufacturing operations. The selection of the proper coated abrasive for a given job depends on the finish desired, amount of stock to be removed, speed and pressure used by the sanding equipment, and the kind of surface to be sanded. These factors should be considered for each application, as they influence the selection of the grit number, type of abrasive, the abrasive spacing, and the backing material. Unfortunately, not all coated abrasives are graded in the same manner. Flint paper and emery cloth have their own systems, while garnet and manufactured abrasives are graded by another system. Table 19 will be of assistance in the selection of the proper grades to use.

TABLE 19. Grading Chart for Coated Abrasives*

Garnet Silicon Carbide Aluminum Oxide	Flint Paper	Emery Cloth	Description
500			
400 or 10/0			
360			
320 or 9/0			
280 or 8/0			Very fine
240 or 7/0	5/0		
220 or 6/0	4/0		
	3/0		
180 or 5/0		3/0	
150 or 4/0		2/0	Fine
	2/0		
120 or 3/0			
	0	0	
100 or 2/0			
	½	½	
80 or 0		1	
	1	1½	Medium
60 or ½			
		2	
50 or 1	1½		
40 or 1½	2	2½	
	2½		Coarse
36 or 2			
30 or 2½	3	3	
24 or 3	3½		
20 or 3½			
16 or 4			Very coarse
12 or 4½			

* Table prepared by Behr-Manning Company.

REVIEW QUESTIONS

1. What advantage does the grinding process have over other cutting processes?
2. List the abrasives used for grinding wheels.
3. Why are natural abrasives inferior to manufactured abrasives?
4. How is silicon carbide made?
5. State briefly how vitrified wheels are made.
6. What bonding materials are used in wheel manufacture?
7. In purchasing a wheel for a specific purpose, what factors must be considered?

8. What are the basic functions of a grinding wheel?

9. What type of wheel is best adapted for grinding hardened steel?

10. What three movements are necessary in the operation of cylindrical grinding?

11. Describe the operation of a centerless grinder.

12. What are the advantages and limitations of centerless grinding?

13. What is meant by "plunge-cut" grinding?

14. List and describe the several types of surface grinders.

15. What are the four types of design used in internal grinders?

16. Describe the type of wheel used on a vertical spindle surface grinder.

17. For what type of work is honing used, and how much metal is usually removed in this operation?

18. What is the purpose of lapping?

19. What abrasives are used in lapping, and how are they applied?

20. Briefly describe the superfinishing process.

21. How does superfinishing differ from honing?

22. What type of work is done with coated abrasives?

REFERENCES

American Machinist's Handbook, McGraw-Hill Book Company, 1955.

Bolz, R. W., *Production Processes,* Vol. 1, Penton Publishing Company, 1949.

Boston, O. W., *Metal Processing,* Chapter XV, John Wiley and Sons, 1951.

Burghardt, H. D., *Machine Tool Operation,* Part II, McGraw-Hill Book Company, 1922.

Colvin, F. H., and F. A. Stanley, *Grinding Practice,* 3rd edition, McGraw-Hill Book Company, 1950.

Heywood, J., *Grinding Wheels and Their Uses,* Penton Publishing Company, 2d edition, 1942.

Hine, C. R., *Machine Tools for Engineers,* McGraw-Hill Book Company, 1950.

Kline, J. E., "Desired Characteristics of Surface Finishes," *Mechanical Engineering,* Vol. 57, no. 12, 1935.

Principles of Tool Room Grinding, Carborundum Company, 1944.

Rose, Kenneth, "Ultra-Fine Surfaces on Metals," *Metals & Alloys,* July 1945.

Shoemaker, S. S., "Selecting the Correct Speeds and Feeds for Cylindrical Grinding," *Machinery,* February 1945.

Swigert, A. M., *The Story of Superfinish,* Lynn Publishing Company, 1940.

Tool Engineers Handbook, American Society of Tool Engineers, McGraw-Hill Book Company, 1949.

Trowbridge, T., "Use of Coated Abrasives in Woodworking Industries," *Mechanical Engineering,* June 1945.

INDEX